Absolutely Every *

BED & BREAKFAST

*Almost

WASHINGTON

12-25-99

Brian & Amy

May you dream of owning
a Bed & Breakfast come true
one day. Hopefully this
book will help guide your
ideas. Your Friends Always
Tony &
Alisha

Absolutely Every*

BED & BREAKFAST

*Almost

WASHINGTON

EDITED BY CARL HANSON

SASQUATCH BOOKS
SEATTLE

Printed in the United States of America.
Distributed in Canada by Raincoast Books Ltd.
03 02 01 00 99   5 4 3 2 1

Cover design: Jane Jeszeck
Cover illustration: Christopher Irion/The Image Bank
Interior design and compostion: Alan Bernhard
Editor: Carl Hanson
Copy editors: Diane Sepanski, Christine Clifton-Thornton

ISSN 1522-3914
ISBN 1-57061-190-4

Sasquatch Books
615 Second Avenue
Seattle, Washington 98104
206) 467-4300
·oks@SasquatchBooks.com
ͻ://www.SasquatchBooks.com

CONTENTS

ABSOLUTELY EVERY BED & BREAKFAST SERIES

Welcome to *Absolutely Every* Bed & Breakfast: Washington (*Almost)*, a comprehensive guide to virtually every bed and breakfast establishment in Washington. We've done the work for you: Everything you need to know in choosing a bed and breakfast is included on these pages, from architectural style to atmosphere, from price range to breakfast variety. Listings are in alphabetical order by town, so locating the perfect stay at your destination is a snap, and the simple format makes comparing accommodations as easy as turning the page. So whether you're looking for an elegant country inn, a stunning mountain chalet, or a cozy seaside cottage, *Absolutely Every* Bed & Breakfast: Washington (*Almost)* will help you find it.

In addition to Washington, the *Absolutely Every* series covers Arizona, Colorado, New Mexico, northern California, southern California, Oregon, and Texas; look for the latest edition of each in your local bookstore. The guides list small- and medium-sized inns, hotels, and host homes that include breakfast in the price of the room. The lists of B&B establishments are compiled from a variety of sources, including directories, chambers of commerce, tourism bureaus, and the World Wide Web. After gathering a complete list, the editors send each innkeeper a survey, asking for basic lodging information and for those special details that set them apart. The completed surveys are then examined and fact-checked for accuracy before inclusion in the book. The **Almost* in the series title reflects the fact that a small number of innkeepers may choose not to be listed, may neglect to respond to the survey and follow-up phone calls, or are not listed because of negative reports received by the editors.

The editors rely on the honesty of the innkeepers in completing the surveys and on feedback from readers to keep the *Absolutely Every Bed & Breakfast* series accurate and up-to-date. (*Note:* While innkeepers are responsible for providing survey information, none are financially connected to the series, nor do they pay any fees to be included in the book.) Please write to us about your experience at any of the bed and breakfasts listed in the series; we'd love to hear from you.

Enjoy your bed and breakfast experience!

—The editors, *Absolutely Every Bed & Breakfast*

How to Use This Book

Absolutely Every Bed & Breakfast: Washington is organized alphabetically by town and by establishment name, and includes a comprehensive index. The concise, at-a-glance format of the complete bed and breakfast listings covers fifteen categories of information to help you select just the right bed and breakfast accommodation for your needs. This edition offers you a choice of establishments in cities, towns, and outlying areas.

THE BED & BREAKFAST LISTINGS

Note that although specifics of each establishment have been confirmed by the editors, details such as amenities, decor, and breakfast menus have been provided by the innkeepers. Listings in this guide are subject to change; call to confirm all aspects of your stay, including price, availability, and restrictions, before you go. Some bed and breakfast listings offer only selected information due to lack of response or by request of the innkeeper; complete listings include the following information.

Establishment name

Address: Note that street addresses often vary from actual mailing addresses; confirm the mailing address before sending a reservation payment.

Telephone numbers: Includes any toll-free or fax numbers.

Innkeepers' languages: Languages spoken other than English.

Location: Directions from the nearest town, highway, or landmark.

Open: Notice of any seasonal or other closures.

Description: Overview of architecture, furnishings, landscaping, etc.

Rooms: Number of rooms with private bathrooms vs. shared baths; availability of suites and/or additional guesthouses; and the innkeeper's favorite room.

Rates: Range of room prices, which vary based on private or shared bathroom, season, and individual room amenities. Also noted here are any minimum stay requirements and cancellation policies (usually two weeks' notice is required for a full refund).

Breakfast: Description of breakfast served (full, continental, continental plus, or stocked kitchen).

Credit cards: Indicates which, if any, credit cards are accepted. Note that credit cards may be listed for reservation confirmation purposes only; be prepared to pay by check or cash.

Amenities: Details any special amenities that are included.

Restrictions: Lists any restrictions regarding smoking, children, and pets. Also listed here are any resident pets or livestock.

Awards: Any significant hospitality or historic preservation awards received.

Reviewed: Publications in which the B&B has been reviewed.

Rated: Indicates whether the B&B has been rated by institutions such as the American Automobile Association (AAA), American Bed & Breakfast Association (ABBA), or the Mobil Travel Association.

Member: Indicates membership in any professional hospitality associations or organizations.

Kudos/Comments: Comments from guests who have stayed in the establishment.

ABERDEEN

With the timber industry in decline, this old lumber town is in transition, as it has been since the sawmilling and shipping glory days of the early 1900s. The Grays Harbor Historical Seaport, on the east side of Aberdeen, provides tours of a splendid replica of Captain Robert Gray's Lady Washington, a 105-foot floating museum.

ABERDEEN MANSION INN BED & BREAKFAST

807 North M Street, Aberdeen, WA 98520　　　　　　　360-533-7079

KUDOS/COMMENTS　　"Excellent architecture."

ANCHOR HOUSE BED & BOOK

102 West 11th Street, Aberdeen, WA 98520　　　　　360-532-2099

COONEY MANSION BED & BREAKFAST

1705 Fifth Street, Cosmopolis, WA 98537　　　　　360-533-0602
Jim & Judi Lohr, Innkeepers　　　　　　　　　　800-977-7823
EMAIL cooney@techline.com　　*WEBSITE www.come.to/cooneymansion*

LOCATION	Enter Cosmopolis (next to Aberdeen) on Highway 101. Look for large state signs for Cooney Mansion; turn on C Street and go to Fifth, then turn left and go to top of the hill.
OPEN	All year
DESCRIPTION	A 1908 four-story Arts and Crafts inn listed on both the National and State Historic Registers. The mansion was built by lumber baron Neil Cooney to showcase his mill's timber. It is the largest home in the county and has been restored to its original condition.
NO. OF ROOMS	Five rooms with private bathrooms and three rooms share two bathrooms. Judi and Jim recommend the Cooney Suite.
RATES	April through December, rates are $65-165 for a single or double with a private bathroom, $70 for a single or double with a shared bathroom, $165 for the Cooney Suite, and $800 for the entire B&B. January through March, a single or double with a private bathroom is $70-80, the Cooney Suite is $165, and the entire B&B

Cooney Mansion Bed & Breakfast, Cosmopolis

rents for $800. There is no minimum stay and cancellation requires five days' notice plus a $20 fee.

CREDIT CARDS	Carte Blanche, Diners Club, Discover, MasterCard, Visa
BREAKFAST	Full "lumber baron" breakfast is served in the dining room. "You won't need lunch!" Dinners and lunches for groups are also available.
AMENITIES	Golf, tennis, spa, sauna, exercise room, shower room, library, video collection, player piano, rose garden, short walk to a park with a lake and waterfall, robes in rooms, afternoon refreshments, kayaking available, ballroom for meeting, deck overlooking golf courses, sun room.
RESTRICTIONS	No smoking, no pets, children over 12 are welcome. Well-behaved children under 12 by prior arrangement. The pets, a Welsh terrier named Mali and an "airhead pound puppy" named Pookie, are restricted to the owners' office and the outdoors.
REVIEWED	*Northwest Best Places; Hidden Pacific Northwest; Recommended Romantic Inns; The Official Guide to American Historic Inns; Country Inns of the Far West; Grays Harbor Passport; Northwest Travel; Country Pleasures*
MEMBER	American Bed & Breakfast Association, Washington State Bed & Breakfast Guild, National Bed & Breakfast Association, Professional Association of International Innkeepers, Olympic Peninsula Travel Association, Innkeepers of Grays Harbor, Washington State Hotel Association
RATED	AAA 3 Diamonds, ABBA 2 Crowns
AWARDS	1996 National finalist in the Jones Dairy B&B Recipe Contest; 1997 Merit Award, American Bed & Breakfast Association

A HARBOR VIEW BED & BREAKFAST

113 West 11th Street, Aberdeen, WA 98520　　　　360-533-7996
Cindy & Bill Lonn, Resident Innkeepers　　　　877-868-6273
Spanish spoken　　　　FAX 360-533-0433
EMAIL *harborview@olynet.com*
WEBSITE *www.olynet.com/users/harborview*

LOCATION	From downtown Aberdeen, go north on Broadway 12 blocks (one mile) to 11th Street. Go west on 11th Street to the second house on the left side.
OPEN	All year
DESCRIPTION	A 1905 four-story colonial revival inn with Victorian decor overlooking Grays Harbor.
NO. OF ROOMS	Two rooms with private bathrooms and two rooms with one shared bathroom. The Lonns recommend the Windsor Room.
RATES	May 1 through September 30, rates are $95 for a single or double with a private bathroom, $65-75 for a single or double with a shared bathroom, and $120 for a suite. October 1 through April 30, rates are $85 for a single or double with a private bathroom, $55-65 for a single or double with a shared bathroom, and $95 for a suite. There is no minimum stay and cancellation requires three days' notice with a $15 charge.
CREDIT CARDS	American Express, MasterCard, Visa
BREAKFAST	Full breakfast is served in the dining room or sun room.
AMENITIES	Afternoon snacks, historic homes walking tour, phones, TV/VCR, meeting room, deck with view, robes in room, candy in room, dessert and sodas available.
RESTRICTIONS	No smoking, no pets, children over eight are welcome.
MEMBER	Olympic Peninsula Bed & Breakfast Association
RATED	AAA 3 Diamonds

ANACORTES

The gateway to the San Juans, Anacortes is itself on an island: Fidalgo Island. Though most travelers rush through here on their way to the ferry, this town, adorned with colorful, life-size cutouts of early pioneers, is quietly becoming a place worth slowing down for. Washington Park is less than a mile west of the ferry terminal. Here you'll find scenic picnic areas and a paved 2.5-mile trail looping through an old-growth forest with great views of the San Juans.

A BURROWS BAY BED & BREAKFAST

4911 MacBeth Drive, Anacortes, WA 98221   360-293-4792
Bev & Win Stocker, Resident Owners

ALBATROSS BED & BREAKFAST

5708 Kingsway West, Anacortes, WA 98221   360-293-0677
Barbie & Ken Arasim, Resident Owners   800-622-8864
                                               FAX 360-293-0677

BLUE ROSE BED & BREAKFAST

1811 9th Street, Anacortes, WA 98221   360-293-5175
"Creamy" Wilkins, Resident Owner

CHANNEL HOUSE BED & BREAKFAST

2902 Oakes Avenue, Anacortes, WA 98221   360-293-9382
Dennis & Patricia McIntyre, Resident Owners 800-238-4353
                                               FAX 360-299-9208

KUDOS/COMMENTS   "Charmingly restored home with great views of Guemes Channel,
                   warm hosts, beautiful beds, lovely and thoughtful amenities,
                   delicious fruit bowl, nice breakfast." (1996)

Hasty Pudding House Bed & Breakfast

1312 8th Street, Anacortes, WA 98221   360-293-5773
Mike & Melinda Hasty, Resident Owners   800-368-5588
EMAIL hasty@mail1.halcyon.com   FAX 360-293-5773 (call first)
WEBSITE www.hastypudding.net/hasty/

LOCATION	Take exit 230 from I-5. Go west on Highway 20 and follow the signs into Anacortes. On Commercial Avenue go north to 8th Street and turn left. Go three-and-a-half blocks.
OPEN	All year
DESCRIPTION	A 1913 two-story Craftsman with original paneling, unique window seats, Victorian antiques, and collectibles.
NO. OF ROOMS	Four rooms with private bathrooms. Try the Queen Anne's Lace Room.
RATES	Year-round rates are $75-109 for a single or double. There is no minimum stay and cancellation requires seven days' notice.
CREDIT CARDS	American Express, Discover, MasterCard, Visa
BREAKFAST	Full breakfast is served in the dining room and includes fresh fruit and juice and an entrée such as hazelnut pancakes, stuffed cream cheese French toast, or Mexican strata.
AMENITIES	Flowers, robes, bedside chocolates, TV/VCR and movies, coffee service in two rooms, hot spiced cider in common room, picnic breakfast "to go" for those catching an early ferry.
RESTRICTIONS	No smoking, no pets, children over six are welcome.
MEMBER	Washington Bed & Breakfast Guild, Tulip Valley Bed & Breakfast Guild, Fidalgo Island Bed & Breakfast Guild
KUDOS/COMMENTS	"Truly warm and inviting, a place to pamper oneself, gracious hosts, wonderful amenities." "Romantic, quiet setting with very comfortable guestrooms. Great hosts." "Delightful innkeepers, attractive table decorations, and comfortable home."

Lowman House Bed & Breakfast

701 K Avenue, Anacortes, WA 98221   360-293-0590
Richard Storwick, Resident Owner

Majestic Inn, Anacortes

MAJESTIC INN

419 Commercial Avenue, Anacortes, WA 98221   360-293-3355
J. R. Wetmore, Innkeeper   800-588-4780
WEBSITE *www.majesticinn.com*   FAX 360-293-5214

LOCATION	Take exit 230 off I-5 and drive approximately 17 miles on Highway 20 to Anacortes. Take a right on Commercial to the corner of 5th.
OPEN	All year
DESCRIPTION	An 1889 four-story Victorian inn with Victorian interior.
NO. OF ROOMS	Twenty-three rooms with private bathrooms. Try room 405.
RATES	Year-round rates are $98-198 for a single or double. There is no minimum stay and cancellation requires seven days' notice.
CREDIT CARDS	American Express, Discover, MasterCard, Visa
BREAKFAST	Continental plus is served on the mezzanine and includes a selection of cold cereals, fresh-baked croissants, two kinds of muffins, seasonal fruit, orange juice, English muffins and bagels, cream cheese and jam, plus coffee, teas, hot cocoa, and cider.
AMENITIES	All rooms with English antiques, some have oversize tubs with overhead skylights, some with decks, others with VCRs; majority have irons, ironing boards, and hair dryers; several areas for meetings; free parking; handicapped access.
RESTRICTIONS	No pets

REVIEWED   Northwest Best Places; Fodor's Pacific Northwest; America's
                 Wonderful Little Hotels & Inns; Recommended Country Inns; Best
                 Places to Kiss in the Northwest; Hidden Pacific Northwest; Grand
                 Old Hotels

MEMBER   Washington State Hotel & Motel Association

NANTUCKET INN BED & BREAKFAST

3402 Commercial Avenue, Anacortes, WA 98221   360-293-6007
                                                           888-293-6007
                                                       FAX 360-299-4339

OLD BROOK INN

7270 Old Brook Lane, Anacortes, WA 98221   360-293-4768
Richard M. Ash, Resident Owner   800-503-4768
WEBSITE www.oldbrookinn.com/   FAX 360-299-9720

LOCATION   From Anacortes, go south on Commercial Avenue past 34th Street.
                 Take a left on the Highway 20 spur and go 2.8 miles. Take a right at
                 a sign that says "Oak Harbor, Highway 20 west" and go 0.2 mile to
                 Old Brook Lane. Take a right and go 0.25 mile to inn.

OPEN   All year

DESCRIPTION   A 1982 two-story Cape Cod host home on ten wooded acres.

Old Brook Inn, Anacortes

NO. OF ROOMS	Two rooms with private bathrooms. Richard recommends the upstairs room.
RATES	Year-round rates are $80-90 for a single or double. The entire B&B rents for $200. There is no minimum stay and cancellation requires seven days' notice.
CREDIT CARDS	MasterCard, Visa
BREAKFAST	Continental breakfast is served in the dining room and includes seasonal fruit (blackberries, raspberries, apples from the orchard), pecan muffins, and baked eggs.
AMENITIES	Trout fishing, bird-watching, and hiking.
RESTRICTIONS	No smoking
MEMBER	Washington Bed & Breakfast Guild, Anacortes Bed & Breakfast Guild, Tulip Valley Bed & Breakfast Association

SHANNON HOUSE

2615 D Avenue, Anacortes, WA 98221   360-299-3876
Cathy & Al Holiday, Innkeepers   800-828-1474
EMAIL *shannon@pacificrim.net*   FAX 360-299-8352
WEBSITE *www.anacortes-city.com/shannon*

LOCATION	Upon entering Anacortes, turn right onto Commercial Avenue, turn left onto 32nd Street, and right onto D Avenue. The B&B is three blocks down on the east side of the street.
OPEN	All year
DESCRIPTION	A restored 1915 two-story farmhouse with an eclectic interior, some antiques, and luxurious linens.
NO. OF ROOMS	Two rooms with private bathrooms and two rooms with one shared bathroom. Try the master bedroom.
RATES	Year-round rates are $110 for a single or double with a private bathroom and $80-90 for a single or double with a shared bathroom. There is no minimum stay and cancellation requires 72 hours' notice.
CREDIT CARDS	MasterCard, Visa
BREAKFAST	Full breakfast is served in the dining room and includes fresh-baked muffins or bread, seasonal fruit, a baked egg dish or French toast, and juice, tea, or coffee.
AMENITIES	Robes for guests in rooms with a shared bathroom, cable TV in the library.

SUNSET BEACH BED & BREAKFAST

100 Sunset Beach, Anacortes, WA 98221   360-293-5428
WEBSITE *www.whidbey.com/sunsetbeach/*   800-359-3448

ANDERSON ISLAND

A well-kept secret that lies a short ferry ride from Steilacoom. This is isolated country for when you really want to get away.

ANDERSON HOUSE ON ORO BAY

12024 Eckenstam Road, Anderson Island, WA 98303   253-884-4088
Randy & B. Anderson, Innkeepers   800-750-4088
Danish, Spanish, and German spoken   FAX 253-884-9449
EMAIL *ahouse@ptinet.net*   WEBSITE *www.non.com/anderson*

LOCATION	Take I-5 to exit 119 (Dupont-Steilacoom). Follow signs to Steilacoom Dock (about seven miles west). Take the 20-minute ferry ride to Anderson Island. Upon arriving, drive directly up the hill to Eckenstam-Johnson Road (just past the community church). Bear left and continue south for approximately three miles. Anderson House is the big gray house with the big red barn at the head of Oro Bay.
OPEN	All year
DESCRIPTION	This 1920s four-story Scandinavian farmhouse with country decor is surrounded by 200 acres of timber and wetlands. A vintage fishing log cabin is also available.
NO. OF ROOMS	Two rooms with private bathrooms and five rooms with two shared bathrooms.
RATES	Year-round rates are $98 for a single or double with a private bathroom and $55-83 for a single or double with a shared bathroom. The guesthouse rents for $240 per night or $260 on

holidays. The entire B&B rents for $575 per night. There is a minimum stay on holidays, and cancellation requires 14 days' notice for the main house and 30 days for the beach house.

CREDIT CARDS	American Express, MasterCard, Visa
BREAKFAST	Full breakfast is served in the dining room or in the living room in front of the fireplace. Breakfast includes Danish breads and fresh pastries, gourmet egg dishes, smoked salmon, sausage, juices, fresh berries, fruit from the orchard and garden, and vegetarian choices. Lunch, dinner, and special meals also available.
AMENITIES	Meeting facilities; gift shop; lake swimming; golf; outstanding private beachcombing; boat and seaplane moorage; copier, fax, and email; fresh flowers; front porch with view of Mount Rainier.
RESTRICTIONS	No smoking, no pets, children over 14 are welcome in the main house. All ages welcome in the beach house.
REVIEWED	*Northwest Best Places; Romantic Weekend Getaways*
AWARDS	1995, One of the 10 Best Coastal Inns in Washington, *Washington* magazine

THE INN AT BURG'S LANDING

8808 Villa Beach Road, Anderson Island, WA 98011   253-884-9185
Ken & Annie Burg, Resident Owners   800-431-5622
EMAIL *innatburgslanding@mailexcite.com*

LOCATION	Take the Dupont/Steilacoom exit (119) off I-5 south of Tacoma. The inn is located on Villa Beach Road, 100 yards east of the ferry landing on Anderson Island.

The Inn at Burg's Landing, Anderson Island

OPEN	All year
DESCRIPTION	A 1987 three-story log host home with contemporary and country decor.
NO. OF ROOMS	Two rooms with private bathrooms and two rooms with one shared bathroom.
RATES	Call for rates.
CREDIT CARDS	MasterCard, Visa
BREAKFAST	Full gourmet breakfast is served.
AMENITIES	Cookies, hot tub, beach, fire pit, gazebo, covered decks, golf, tennis, swimming.
RESTRICTIONS	No smoking inside, children are welcome. Buddy the dog and Cali the calico are the resident critters.
REVIEWED	*Romantic Weekend Getaways*
MEMBER	American Bed & Breakfast Association
RATED	ABBA 3 Crowns

ARLINGTON

MT. HIGGINS HOUSE

29805 SR 530 NE, Arlington, WA 98223
Renee Ottersen, Innkeeper
EMAIL *mthigginshouse@juno.com*

360-435-8703
888-296-3777
FAX *360-435-9757*

ASHFORD

The gateway to Paradise, Ashford is a great place to stop on the way to Mount Rainier. From Ashford, explore ancient forests, dozens of massive glaciers, waterfalls, and alpine meadows lush with wildflowers during the brief summer season.

ALEXANDER'S COUNTRY INN

37515 SR 706 E, Ashford, WA 98304

360-569-2323
800-654-7615

THE CHALET

37615 SR 706 E, Ashford, WA 98304

360-569-2300
800-654-7615

THE FOREST HOUSE

37615 SR 706 E, Ashford, WA 98304

360-569-2323
800-654-7615

GROWLY BEAR BED & BREAKFAST

37311 SR 706 E, Ashford, WA 98304
Susan Jenny Johnson, Resident Owner

360-569-2339
800-700-2339

LOCATION	Approximately four miles east of Ashford on Highway 706 toward Mount Rainier National Park. The B&B is the next left after the Goat Creek Bridge, just past milepost 12.
OPEN	All year
DESCRIPTION	An early 1890s-era two-story mountain farmhouse decorated with comfortable farmhouse furnishings with a lodge-type appearance, hand-split cedar shake roof, enclosed front porch, and two decks.
NO. OF ROOMS	Two rooms with private bathrooms and two rooms with one shared bathroom. Susan suggests the Mesler Room.
RATES	Year-round rates are $110 for a single or double with a private bathroom and $80 for a single or double with a shared bathroom. There is no minimum stay and cancellation requires seven days' notice.
CREDIT CARDS	American Express, MasterCard, Visa
BREAKFAST	Full breakfast is served in the dining room and includes fruit beverages, fresh fruit plate with yogurt, hot entrée, assorted fresh pastries, and hot beverages. A packed trail lunch is also available.
AMENITIES	Basket with fresh fruit, crackers, and candy in rooms; fresh flowers; cookies and beverages in the common room.
RESTRICTIONS	No smoking
REVIEWED	*Hot Showers, Soft Beds, and Dayhikes in the Central Cascades*
MEMBER	Washington Bed & Breakfast Guild

JASMER'S BED & BREAKFAST & CABINS

30005 SR 706 E, Ashford, WA 98304   360-569-2682

MOUNTAIN MEADOWS INN BED & BREAKFAST

28912 SR 706 E, Ashford, WA 98304   360-569-2788

AUBURN

Situated midway between Seattle and Tacoma in the Green River Valley, Auburn features access to both metropolitan areas, as well as to numerous outdoor amenities, Emerald Downs Race Track, and the Muckleshoot Indian Casino.

ROSE ARBOR INN
BED & BREAKFAST & MASSAGE

514 A Street NE, Auburn, WA 98002   253-931-8564
Rae Boggs, Resident Owner

LOCATION	From I-5, take the Auburn exit (North Bend/Highway 18) into Auburn Valley. Take the second Auburn exit (Auburn Way/ Enumclaw) and turn right onto Auburn Way. Go one mile north, turn left onto 7th Street, go two blocks, and turn left onto A Street.
OPEN	All year
DESCRIPTION	A 1950s-era two-story inn with casual country interior.
NO. OF ROOMS	One room with a private bathroom and three rooms with one shared bathroom. Try the Rose Room.
RATES	Year-round rates are $90 for a single or double with a private bathroom and $60-70 for a single or double with a shared bathroom. The entire B&B rents for $260. There is no minimum stay and cancellation requires seven days' notice.
CREDIT CARDS	MasterCard, Visa

BREAKFAST	Full breakfast is served in the dining room and includes homemade granola, individual cereals, fruit parfait, fresh bread or muffins, homemade cinnamon rolls (Saturday only), coffee, tea, juice, or milk. Sundays feature pancakes with strawberry sauce and whipped cream. Vegan diets are accommodated and eggs are available on request.
AMENITIES	Swedish massage available; fresh flowers, robes, fresh chocolate chip cookies, and ice water in rooms; fresh fruit basket; juice and soda available.
RESTRICTIONS	No smoking inside, no pets, children over 12 are welcome.
MEMBER	Greater Tacoma Bed & Breakfast Association

BAINBRIDGE ISLAND

Once a major logging center, Bainbridge Island is now a semirural, semisuburban haven for city professionals (who don't mind the half-hour commute via ferry to downtown Seattle), writers, artists, and people seeking simpler lives. It makes a pleasant tour by car or bike, during which you can see small pastoral farms, enviable waterfront homes, and spectacular cityscapes (especially from Fay Bainbridge State Park, on the northeast corner of the island). The wooded and waterfront trails in Fort Ward State Park, on the south end of the island, make for a nice afternoon stroll (good picnic spots, too). Bloedel Reserve, open by reservation only, encompasses 150 acres of lush, tranquil gardens, woods, meadows, and ponds; plants from all over the world make these grounds interesting all year long.

AGATE PASS WATERFRONT BED & BREAKFAST

16045 Highway 305, Bainbridge Island, WA 98110   *206-842-1632*
Mike & Penny McLaughlin, Innkeepers   *800-869-1632*
French and German spoken   *FAX 800-411-2660*
EMAIL *beds@agatepass.com*   WEBSITE *www.agatepass.com*

LOCATION	From the Bainbridge Island ferry landing, drive north six miles up Highway 305. Cross the Agate Pass Bridge and at the traffic light, take an immediate left into the driveway, bearing right at the mailbox, and wind about 0.33 mile through the trees. The only house you'll see, the B&B, is at the end of the road past the lighthouse.
OPEN	All year
DESCRIPTION	A 1953 one-story rambler host home with contemporary furnishings and antiques.

NO. OF ROOMS	Three rooms with private bathrooms. Mike and Penny recommend the Water Room.
RATES	Year-round rates are $75-125 for a single or double. There is no minimum stay and cancellation requires two weeks' notice.
CREDIT CARDS	MasterCard, Visa
BREAKFAST	Breakfast is served in the guestrooms. Each room's kitchen is stocked with guest-selected ingredients, as well as comestibles from apple juice to lox.
AMENITIES	Air conditioning; privacy and peace amidst breathtaking scenery; beach walks; close to shopping, fine dining, sailing, kayaking, mountain climbing, trail biking.
RESTRICTIONS	No smoking, no pets. Baby and Sandy are the resident long-haired Chihuahuas; Heather is the West Highland terrier; and there are several cats that are "VERY territorial and possessive, making other animals' presence somewhat disruptive."

BEACH COTTAGE HIDEAWAYS BED & BREAKFAST

5831 Ward Avenue NE, Bainbridge Island, WA 98110   206-842-6081
Eileen Young, Resident Owner   FAX 206-842-6544

THE BUCHANAN INN

8494 NE Oddfellows Road, Bainbridge Island, WA 98110   206-780-9258
Ron & Judy Gibbs, Innkeepers   FAX 206-842-9258
Some Spanish spoken
EMAIL jgibbs@buchananinn.com
WEBSITE www.buchananinn.com

LOCATION	Four miles south of the Bainbridge ferry terminal near Fort Ward State Park and Pheasant Beach.
OPEN	All year
DESCRIPTION	A restored 1912 three-story New England-style barnhouse with traditional and casually elegant decor situated on 1.5 acres of landscaped gardens.
NO. OF ROOMS	Four rooms with private bathrooms. The Gibbs recommend the Bilberry Suite.

The Buchanan Inn, Bainbridge Island

RATES	Year-round rates are $99-149 for a single or double and $600 for the entire B&B. There is no minimum stay and cancellation requires seven days' notice.
CREDIT CARDS	American Express, Discover, MasterCard, Visa
BREAKFAST	Full breakfast is served in the dining room and includes gourmet entrées with a spicy southwestern flavor, plus fresh fruit from the garden, juices, egg dishes, waffles, and breakfast meat.
AMENITIES	CD players with a selection of CDs, in-room coffee-makers, hair dryers, mini-refrigerators stocked with complimentary beverages, silky robes, wine and hors d'oeuvres, hot tub in private cedar cottage, gas fireplaces, and the finest Egyptian cotton linens.
RESTRICTIONS	No smoking inside, no pets, children over 16 are welcome. Nikki and Thurston are the resident springer spaniels.
MEMBER	Washington Bed & Breakfast Guild, Professional Association of Innkeepers International
RATED	AAA 3 Diamonds

THE CAPTAIN'S HOUSE

234 Parfitt Way, Bainbridge Island, WA 98110   *206-842-3557*

CEDAR MEADOW BED & BREAKFAST

10411 NE Old Creosote Hill Road,   206-842-5291
Bainbridge Island, WA 98110
John & Karen Yearsley, Innkeepers

LOCATION	From the ferry terminal, turn left onto Winslow Way. Go to the four-way stop and turn right onto Madison. Continue to the next four-way stop and go left on Wyatt Way. Go 0.5 mile. After the road turns sharply left and goes down a steep hill, get in the left lane and follow the sign to Eagledale. Go two miles and turn right on Taylor Avenue. Then take the first left onto Creosote and go to the second driveway on the right.
OPEN	All year
DESCRIPTION	A 1972 three-story contemporary Northwest host home on 6 acres, with cedar cathedral ceilings upstairs, hardwood floors, and area rugs. There are two living rooms with grand pianos and a large basement with a play area for children.
NO. OF ROOMS	Four rooms share two bathrooms.
RATES	Year-round rates for a single or double are $50-80.
CREDIT CARDS	No
BREAKFAST	Full breakfast is served in the dining room and includes fresh fruit salad, orange juice (fresh-squeezed in season), homemade waffles with maple syrup, coffee, bacon, or ham and eggs if desired. Menu varies and can include crepes, hot cakes, or soufflés. Low-fat or special diets can be accommodated.
AMENITIES	Flowers; robes; use of laundry and kitchen facilities; cable TV/VCR, and phone in King Room; apple, berry, and vegetable picking in gardens; bird- and deer-watching; croquet; badminton; sandbox; crib and baby furniture available.
RESTRICTIONS	No smoking, no pets, children of all ages are welcome. Other guests are not booked at the same time as families with small children. Wildlife includes pheasants, deer, racoons, squirrels, and 18 species of birds.
REVIEWED	*The Berkeley Guide; The Budget Traveler's Handbook: Pacific Northwest and Alaska on the Loose*

FROG ROCK INN

15576 Washington Avenue NE
Bainbridge Island, WA 98110
Bob & Ellen Green, Resident Owners

206-842-2761
FAX 206-842-8621

ISLAND COUNTRY INN

920 Hilderbrand Way NE, Bainbridge Island, WA 98110   206-842-6861

MARY'S FARMHOUSE BED & BREAKFAST

5129 McDonald Avenue NE, Bainbridge Island, WA 98110 206-842-4952

OUR COUNTRY HAUS BED & BREAKFAST

13718 Ellingsen Road NE, Bainbridge Island, WA 98110   206-842-8425

ROBIN'S NEST BED & BREAKFAST

10756 Sunrise Drive NE, Bainbridge Island, WA 98110   206-842-4034

ROCKAWAY BEACH GUEST HOUSE

5032 Rockaway Beach Road NE
Bainbridge Island, WA 98110

206-780-9427
FAX 206-780-0439

SUMMER HILL FARM BED & BREAKFAST

Summerhill Lane, Bainbridge Island, WA 98110   206-842-0640

WINSLOW INN

366 Morrill Place NE, Bainbridge Island, WA 98110   *206-842-9604*

THE WOODSMAN

7700 Spring Ridge Road NE   *206-842-7386*
Bainbridge Island, WA 98110
Joyce & Bill Ostling, Innkeepers

LOCATION	From the Bainbridge ferry dock, take Highway 305 to the second stoplight. Turn left on High School Road and take it to the end, then turn right on Fletcher Bay Road. At the Texaco station, turn left on Fletcher Bay Road. Take the first left on Spring Ridge Road. Go to the top of the hill.
OPEN	All year
DESCRIPTION	A 1975 two-story Dutch colonial host home with a traditional interior and antiques, on 5 acres surrounded by tall trees and beautiful gardens.
NO. OF ROOMS	One room with a private bathroom.
RATES	May through October, the rate is $75 for a single or double. November through April, the rate is $70. There is no minimum stay and cancellation requires one weeks' notice.
CREDIT CARDS	No
BREAKFAST	Full breakfast is served on china and crystal in the formal dining room or sun room, or outside on the patio during warm weather. Breakfast includes fresh-baked breads and pastries, fresh fruit, a hot dish, and coffee, tea, and juice.
AMENITIES	Flowers, cozy robes, cold drinks, soaps, shampoo, hot tub in the sun room.
RESTRICTIONS	No smoking, no pets. One child under 12 is permitted. Tinker Bell is the resident Samoyed.
REVIEWED	*Washington State Bed & Breakfast Cookbook*

BEAVER

Located at the far northwestern reach of Highway 101 on the Olympic Peninsula, where the road begins to turn back to the south. Get a glimpse into the region's past at the Timber Museum, just a few minutes to the south in Forks. Spectacular, pristine beaches are a short drive southwest on Highway 101.

EAGLE POINT INN

384 Storman Norman Lane, Beaver, WA 98305   *360-327-3236*
Chris Christensen, Resident Owner

LOCATION	At mile1 post 202 on Highway 101, turn onto Storman Norman Lane and go 0.3 mile on the private road.
OPEN	All year
DESCRIPTION	A 1994 two-story log lodge with hardwood floors and decorated with antiques, located in a temperate rainforest on 5 secluded acres along the Soleduck River.
NO. OF ROOMS	Three rooms with private bathrooms. Chris recommends the River Room.
RATES	May through September, the rate is $85 for a single or double. October through April, the rate is $75. There is no minimum stay.
CREDIT CARDS	No
BREAKFAST	Full breakfast is served in the dining room.
RESTRICTIONS	No smoking, children over 12 are welcome. Tiger Woods is the resident "larger than life" Lab mix, Daisy is the "slightly cranky" cocker, and Moana is the "aptly named" cat.
REVIEWED	*Northwest Best Places; The Best Places to Kiss in the Northwest, Frommer's*
RATED	Northwest Best Places 2 Stars
KUDOS/COMMENTS	"Perfect hosts."

BELFAIR

At the tip of the Hood Canal's "fishhook," Belfair provides easy access to popular Belfair State Park. Three acclaimed golf courses are within a dozen miles. Area celebrations include the Belfair Summerfest in June and the Shelton Oysterfest in October.

COUNTRY GARDEN INN

NE 2790 Old Belfair Highway, Belfair, WA 98528　　　　　360-275-3683
Pat & Tina Matijevich, Resident Owners

LOCATION	In Bremerton follow Highway 304 to Highway 3 and go south to Belfair. Take the first right in Belfair and drive to the stop sign, take a right onto Old Belfair Highway, and drive three miles north.
OPEN	All year
DESCRIPTION	A 1990 two-story gambrel log inn with open-beam construction, Laura Ashley prints, and antique decor. Situated on a working farm.
NO. OF ROOMS	Three rooms with private bathrooms.
RATES	Year-round rates are $75 and up for a single or double. There is no minimum stay and "common sense prevails" regarding the cancellation policy: $25 is nonrefundable.
CREDIT CARDS	MasterCard, Visa
BREAKFAST	Full breakfast is served in the dining room or guestrooms, or on the deck and includes pancakes, waffles, French toast, or omelets served with bacon, sausage, or ham; fresh fruit from the farm; and beverages. Special meals are available upon request—"So dream up a wild, believable excuse for us," says Pat.
AMENITIES	Hors d'oeuvres and refreshments, secluded hot tub, robes, fireplaces in all guestrooms, wood-burning stove in sitting room, assortment of toiletries provided, microwave, refrigerator, stereo. Owners reside in a separate building.
RESTRICTIONS	No smoking, children over 13 and infants are welcome. Pets are considered on a case-by-case basis. The resident beasts are Rocket the greyhound, Hellen the mutt, and Roscoe the cat.

Selah Inn

130 NE Dulalip Landing, Belfair, WA 98528 360-275-0916
Bonnie & Pat McCullough, Resident Owners FAX 360-277-3187
EMAIL esa@hctc.com *WEBSITE www.selahinn.com*

LOCATION	Sixty miles west of Seattle. From the I-5 Tacoma exit, take Highway 16 north to Gorst (about 30 minutes). Exit west to Belfair. Go about 12 miles and exit to Highway 300 west. Go four miles to Belfair State Park. Take the next left—Beck Road—past the park and go to Dulalip Landing (about 0.25 mile).
OPEN	All year
DESCRIPTION	A 1996 two-story Northwest lodge-style country inn and guesthouses located on the Hood Canal.
NO. OF ROOMS	Four rooms with private bathrooms. The owners recommend the King Suite.
RATES	Year-round rates are $80-120 for a single or double, $125-145 for a suite, and $150-200 per night or $700-1,200 per week for the guesthouses. The entire B&B rents for $400-455 per night. There is a two-night minimum stay in the guesthouses and cancellation requires 10 days' notice with a $10 processing fee.
CREDIT CARDS	MasterCard, Visa
BREAKFAST	Full breakfast is served in the dining room or the sun room and includes fresh-baked breads, fruit parfait, egg entrée, breakfast meats, juice, coffee, and tea. Lunch, dinner, high tea, Sunday brunch, and other special meals are available.
AMENITIES	Flowers and chocolates in rooms; robes; hot tub on deck overlooking the water; library; Great Room with river-rock fireplace and carved mantel; beach access; kayak, canoe, sailboat, paddleboat, and raft available; clam and oyster digging and crab trapping; seminar/conference rooms; modem hookups; stereo system.
RESTRICTIONS	No smoking, no pets. Children welcome in guesthouses adjacent to the inn. Goldie is the resident yellow Lab who chairs the inn's welcoming committee. Goldie will fetch oysters on the beach and swim with you to the raft.
REVIEWED	*The Best Places to Kiss in the Northwest; The Romantic Pacific Northwest*
MEMBER	Professional Association of Innkeepers International, Washington Bed & Breakfast Guild

BELLEVUE

This erstwhile hamlet, which can now rightfully be called Seattle's sister city, boasts its own downtown skyline, a growing population, and more shop-till-you-drop options than you'd care to shake a credit card at. Bellevue is the heart of the "Eastside"—the former suburbs of Seattle, east of Lake Washington, that now stand on their own. The quiet neighborhoods that ring downtown are a large part of what makes Bellevue such a livable city. The neighborhood surrounding Bridle Trails State Park on the Kirkland border looks like a condensed version of Virginia equestrian country, with backyards full of horses and stables. The park features miles of riding and hiking trails through vast stands of Douglas fir. Day hikers can head east toward Issaquah to explore Cougar Mountain, the forested, western-most hill of an ancient mountain range that stretches from Lake Washington to the younger present-day Cascades.

BELLEVUE BED & BREAKFAST

830 100th Avenue SE, Bellevue, WA 98004   425-453-1048
Cyrus & Carol Garnett, Innkeepers   888-453-1048
WEBSITE *www.bellevuebandb.com*

LOCATION	Call for directions.
OPEN	All year
DESCRIPTION	A two-story Northwest contemporary host home overlooking the city of Bellevue.
NO. OF ROOMS	Two rooms with private bathrooms. The owners recommend the North Room.
RATES	Year-round rates are $70-80 for a single or double and $150 for the suite. The fifth day is free. There is a two-night minimum stay.
CREDIT CARDS	MasterCard, Visa
BREAKFAST	Full breakfast is served, including bacon and eggs, waffles, cereal, and fruit. Dinner is also available.
AMENITIES	Cable TV, radios, telephones, laundry facilities.
RESTRICTIONS	No smoking, no pets
REVIEWED	*Bed & Breakfasts of the Northwest; Seattle Best Places*
MEMBER	Washington Bed & Breakfast Guild, Bed & Breakfast Association of Suburban Seattle

A CASCADE VIEW BED & BREAKFAST

13425 NE 27th Street, Bellevue, WA 98005   425-883-7078
Marianne & Bill Bundren, Innkeepers   888-883-7078
EMAIL cascadev@wolfenet.com   FAX 425-702-9326
WEBSITE www.acascadeview.com

LOCATION	Half a mile northeast of the intersection of Highways 405 and 520 in Bellevue.
OPEN	All year
DESCRIPTION	A 1984 three-story Northwest contemporary guesthouse with eclectic decor and panoramic views of the Cascade Mountains.
NO. OF ROOMS	Two rooms with private bathrooms. Marianne and Bill suggest the Garden Room.
RATES	Year-round rates are $90-110 for a single or double. There is a two-night minimum stay from June through September and cancellation requires 14 days' notice.
CREDIT CARDS	American Express, MasterCard, Visa
BREAKFAST	Full breakfast is served in the kitchen and includes juice, an entrée, homemade breads or muffins, coffee, a variety of teas, and seasonal fruit.
AMENITIES	Air conditioning, roses from the garden, gas log fireplace and TV/VCR in Garden Room, grand piano, patios with garden access.
RESTRICTIONS	No smoking, no pets. Blue Wolf is the resident collie, and Goldie and Gandolf are the cockatiels.
REVIEWED	Best of the West
MEMBER	Bed & Breakfast Association of Suburban Seattle

PETERSEN BED & BREAKFAST

10228 SE 8th Street, Bellevue, WA 98004   425-454-9334

BELLINGHAM

Full of fine old houses, stately streets, and lovely parks, Bellingham has been enjoying a period of rediscovery lately. From Bellingham, many travelers begin the long journey up the coast and through Alaska's famed Inside Passage. Lake Whatcom Railway, located not on Lake Whatcom but on Highway 9 at Wickersham, makes scenic runs on Saturdays in July and August using an old Northern Pacific engine. During Memorial Day weekend, the annual Ski to Sea Race attracts teams from all over the world. The Bellingham Music Festival has quickly become an institution, featuring more than two weeks of orchestral, chamber, and jazz performances, beginning the third week of August.

A SECRET GARDEN

1807 Lakeway Drive, Bellingham, WA 98226   *360-671-5327*
Susan Neuman, Resident Innkeeper

ANDERSON CREEK LODGE

5602 Mission Road, Bellingham, WA 98226   *360-966-2126*
Bob & Bernie Bell, Innkeepers   *FAX 360-966-2126 (call first)*
EMAIL *andersoncreek@compuserve.com*
WEBSITE *www.andersoncreek.com*

LOCATION	From I-5, take exit 255 (Sunset Drive, Mount Baker Highway) and drive east 0.7 mile. Turn left on Hannigan Road and drive 3.9 miles, then right on Smith Road and drive four miles. Turn left on Mission Road. The lodge is on the right side.
OPEN	All year
DESCRIPTION	A 1986 two-story timber-frame lodge with an elegant Northwest-style interior of white oak, cedar, and maple; an open-beam ceiling; and a massive stone fireplace.
NO. OF ROOMS	Three rooms with private bathrooms. The best is the Cascade Room.
RATES	Year-round rate is $85 for a single or double. There is no minimum stay and cancellation requires 72 hours' notice.
CREDIT CARDS	MasterCard, Visa
BREAKFAST	Full breakfast is served in the dining room and begins with sweet bread, juice, and fruit, followed by an entrée such as blackberry pancakes, orange French toast, or egg tortilla wraps, plus a

breakfast meat. Special meals are also available. Breakfast for business conferences can be accommodated in the conference room.

AMENITIES   Recreation room with Ping-Pong table, TV/VCR, hot tub on the veranda, all-day beverage and snack bar, trails for walking (with or without llamas) through the fields down to Anderson Creek.

RESTRICTIONS   Smoking outside only. Duke is the resident outdoor golden retriever and Donavon is the miniature horse. There are 35 llamas roaming the premises, all of which are trained for various jobs: some are backpacking llamas, some are cart-pulling llamas, and the three studs compete in national shows.

REVIEWED   *Northwest Best Places; Fodor's*

BELLINGHAM'S DECANN HOUSE BED & BREAKFAST

2610 Eldridge Avenue, Bellingham, WA 98225   360-734-9172
Van & Barbara Hudson, Resident Owners
EMAIL *hudson@pacificrim.net*   WEBSITE *www.pacificrim.net/~hudson*

LOCATION   Take exit 253 and turn west, following the arterial for 2.3 miles. Lakeway Drive will become Holly and then turn into Eldridge Avenue.

OPEN   All year

Bellingham's DeCann House Bed & Breakfast, Bellingham

DESCRIPTION	A 1902 two-story Victorian inn close to downtown, the waterfront, and the university, with a Victorian interior and family heirlooms. Listed on the National Historic Register.
NO. OF ROOMS	Two rooms with private bathrooms. Try the South View Room.
RATES	Year-round rates are $59-74 for a single or double.
CREDIT CARDS	No
BREAKFAST	Full breakfast is served in the dining room and includes special omelets, fruit, toast, homemade jam or fruit blintzes, sausage, granola, tea, coffee, and juice.
AMENITIES	Rooms with robes and radios; common area with games, puzzles, books, and pool table.
RESTRICTIONS	No smoking, no pets, children over eight are welcome. Missy is the resident cat.
REVIEWED	*Washington State Travelers: Affordable Accommodations*
MEMBER	Whatcom Bed & Breakfast Guild

BIG TREES BED & BREAKFAST

4840 Fremont Street, Bellingham, WA 98226　　　　*360-647-2850*
Jan Simmons, Resident Owner　　　　　　　　　　　*800-647-2850*
EMAIL *bigtrees@nas.com*
WEBSITE *www.nas.com/~bigtrees*

LOCATION	Approximately three miles east of the center of town. Take the Lakeway exit (253) off I-5. Take Lakeway east (away from the city center) and turn right on the first street after the baseball field on the right. Go to the stop sign and turn left on Fremont.
OPEN	All year
DESCRIPTION	A 1907 two-story Craftsman with eclectic decor, surrounded by giant trees and overlooking Lake Whatcom.
NO. OF ROOMS	Two rooms with private bathrooms.
RATES	Year-round rates are $95-115 for a double with a private bathroom. There is no minimum stay and cancellation requires 14 days' notice.
CREDIT CARDS	MasterCard, Visa
BREAKFAST	Full breakfast is served in the dining room and includes juice, coffee, or tea; fruit; muffins or scones; and an entrée.
AMENITIES	Flowers, robes, TV, feather beds, lake view, gardens, old-growth trees, homemade jams and preserves, unforgettable chocolate chip cookies.

RESTRICTIONS	No smoking, no pets. Children are welcome with advance notice and approval. Two dogs and two cats share the premises.
REVIEWED	*Northwest Best Places; The Best Places to Kiss in the Northwest*
MEMBER	Bed & Breakfast Guild of Whatcom County
KUDOS/COMMENTS	"Comfortable Craftsman home near Lake Whatcom with a wonderfully gracious and warm innkeeper."

THE CASTLE BED & BREAKFAST

1103 15th Street, Bellingham, WA 98225   360-676-0974
Gloria & Larry Harriman

LOCATION	Exit 250 off I-5 on Old Fairhaven Parkway. Go toward Fairhaven for one mile, turn right on 14th, and right again on Knox. The B&B is on the corner of 15th and Knox.
OPEN	All year
DESCRIPTION	An 1889 three-story host home above the historic Fairhaven neighborhood of Bellingham. The 21-room mansion is furnished with antiques from European castles.
NO. OF ROOMS	Two rooms with private bathrooms and two rooms share one bathroom.
RATES	Year-round rates for a single or double with a private bathroom are $85-125, and $45-85 for a single or double with a shared bathroom. Cancellation requires one weeks' notice or a $25 fee is charged.
CREDIT CARDS	No
BREAKFAST	Continental breakfast includes yogurt, fresh fruit, muffins or toast, cereals, coffee, teas, and orange juice.
AMENITIES	Fireplace; meeting room; walking distance to shopping, restaurants, and ferries. Guests are invited to tour the mansion.
RESTRICTIONS	No smoking, no pets, children over 12 are welcome.
REVIEWED	*Historic Inns; Northwest Best Places*
MEMBER	Northwest Bed & Breakfast Association
AWARDS	1986, Mayor's Award for Restoration

North Garden Inn, Bellingham

NORTH GARDEN INN

1014 North Garden Street, Bellingham, WA 98225   360-671-7828
Frank & Barbara Defreytas, Innkeepers   800-922-6414
Some French spoken
EMAIL *NGI@northgardeninn.com*
WEBSITE *www.northgardeninn.com/ngi*

LOCATION	On I-5 take exit 253, then Lakeway NW to Holly to North Garden Street. Go south on Garden for two-and-a-half blocks.
OPEN	All year
DESCRIPTION	An 1897 four-story Queen Anne Victorian with traditional interior decor and wonderful views of Bellingham Bay. Listed on the National and State Historic Registers.
NO. OF ROOMS	Eight rooms with two private bathrooms and two rooms with one shared bathroom. Try the Overture Room.
RATES	Year-round rates are $79-99 for a single or double with a private bathroom and $50 for a single or double with a shared bathroom.

There is no minimum stay and cancellation requires 24 hours' notice.

CREDIT CARDS	Discover, MasterCard, Visa
BREAKFAST	Full breakfast is served in the dining room and includes a hot entrée, baked breads or muffins, fruit, juice, and cereal.
AMENITIES	Afternoon tea; picnic tables in the yard; Victorian garden swing with a view of the bay; musical entertainment in evenings; fresh flowers; umbrellas; local maps; first-floor sitting room with grand piano; second-floor sitting room with wing chairs, oriental carpet, and a library.
RESTRICTIONS	No smoking, no pets. Frostina is the resident cat.
REVIEWED	*Northwest Best Places; Recommended Country Inns*
MEMBER	Professional Association of Innkeepers International, Bed & Breakfasts of Whatcom County
RATED	AAA 3 Diamonds
AWARDS	Third Place in Northwest Chowder Challenge

SCHNAUZER CROSSING BED & BREAKFAST INN

4421 Lakeway Drive, Bellingham, WA 98226   360-733-0055
Donna & Monte McAllister, Resident Owners   800-562-2808
EMAIL *schnauzerx@aol.com*   FAX 360-734-2808
WEBSITE *www.schnauzercrossing.com*

LOCATION	Three miles east of Bellingham; take exit 253 off I-5 and travel east on Lakeway Drive for 2.8 miles to the intersection. Turn left onto the secondary road (also Lakeway) and drive 0.5 mile.
OPEN	All year
DESCRIPTION	A remodeled 1934 two-story contemporary Northwest inn with traditional and Asian-inspired decor, located above Lake Whatcom and surrounded by gardens and woods.
NO. OF ROOMS	Three rooms with private bathrooms. Try the cottage.
RATES	Year-round rates are $120-200 for a single or double, $180 for a suite, and $200 for the cottage. There is a two-night minimum stay on weekends and holidays, and cancellation requires seven days' notice.
CREDIT CARDS	Discover, MasterCard, Visa
BREAKFAST	Full breakfast is served in the dining room and includes a fresh fruit starter, blueberry bran muffins or hazelnut scones, and a hot entrée such as Triple Sec French toast or individual quiches, plus Black Forest ham, inn-blend coffee, and fresh juice.

AMENITIES	Fresh flowers, terry robes, outdoor hot tub, hammock and chaise lounges in yard, tea and goodies on arrival, snack baskets with fruit and Northwest treats, "I-forgot-it" baskets in all rooms, perfumes and colognes to sample, great library, Northwest original art, video and CD library, VCRs in suite and cottage, CD players in all rooms, Jacuzzis and fireplaces in suite and cottage, handicapped access to cottage, 1.5 acres of beautiful gardens with raspberries and blueberries ("for the picking"), schnauzer slippers in all guestrooms.
RESTRICTIONS	No smoking, no pets. There are two resident schnauzers, Bärbel and Marika. They are nonallergenic and do not shed, so there is no dander for the allergy-sensitive to contend with.
REVIEWED	*Northwest Best Places; The Best Places to Kiss in the Northwest; Fodor's; Frommer's; Lonely Planet Pacific Northwest; Hidden Pacific Northwest; Ultimate Washington; Quick Escapes in the Pacific Northwest; Bed, Breakfast and Bike the Pacific Northwest; Best Places to Stay in the Pacific Northwest; Inside Out Washington; Compass Guide Washington; Short Trips in the Pacific Northwest*
MEMBER	Professional Association of Innkeepers International, Washington Bed & Breakfast Guild, Bed & Breakfast Guild of Whatcom County
RATED	AAA 3 Diamonds, *The Best Places to Kiss in the Northwest* 4 Lips, *Northwest Best Places* 3 Stars
KUDOS/COMMENTS	"Pristine setting. Donna has thought of everything to make her guests comfortable." "Luxurious room with garden and lake views. Delightful innkeeper."

STRATFORD MANOR

1416 Van Wyck Road, Bellingham, WA 98226   360-715-8441
Leslie & Jim Lohse, Innkeepers   FAX 360-671-0840
EMAIL *llohse@aol.com*   WEBSITE *www.site-works.com/stratford*

LOCATION	Take exit 255 off I-5 and go right (east) on Sunset Drive for 1.5 miles to Hannegan Road. Turn left and go north for two miles to Van Wyck Road. Turn right, go 1.3 miles to Anderson Way, turn left, and go about two blocks.
OPEN	All year
DESCRIPTION	A 1981 three-story English Tudor-style country home with traditional decor, on 30 acres with views of the countryside.
NO. OF ROOMS	Three rooms with private bathrooms. Leslie and Jim suggest the Garden Room.

RATES	Year-round rates are $125-175 for a single or double. There is no minimum stay and cancellation requires seven days' notice or one night will be charged if the room cannot be rebooked.
CREDIT CARDS	MasterCard, Visa
BREAKFAST	Full country breakfast is served in the dining room and includes juice, fruit dish, an entrée, home-baked pastries, and breads.
AMENITIES	Fresh flowers; luxurious robes; gas fireplaces; fruit basket; fresh-baked cookies; guest fridge with sodas, bottled water, and juice; jetted tubs in all bathrooms; outdoor hot tub.
RESTRICTIONS	No smoking, no pets, no children. Schatzey is the resident mini-dachshund.
REVIEWED	*The Best Places to Kiss in the Northwest; Northwest Best Places; Romantic America; Fodor's*
MEMBER	American Bed & Breakfast Association, Washington Bed & Breakfast Guild, Whatcom County Bed & Breakfast Guild, Professional Association of Innkeepers International
RATED	ABBA 4 Crowns
KUDOS/COMMENTS	"Great setting, impeccably neat, great and imaginative breakfasts, large rooms."

BENTON CITY

In southeastern Washington, nestled into the nib where the Yakima River makes its sharp bend northward, Benton City is prime orchard and vineyard country, offering access to nine wineries. Check out Benton City Daze in early September.

PALMER FARM BED & BREAKFAST

42901 North River Road, Benton City, WA 99320　　　　*509-588-4011*
William & Virginia McKenna, Innkeepers

LOCATION	Three-quarters of a mile north of Benton City.
OPEN	All year
DESCRIPTION	A 1902 two-story farmhouse, furnished in an old-fashioned style with wallpaper and lace curtains, with 2 acres of shaded lawns and a gazebo. Listed on the State Historic Register.
NO. OF ROOMS	One room with a private bathroom and three rooms with two-and-a-half shared bathrooms.

Palmer Farm Bed & Breakfast, Benton City

RATES	Year-round rates are $75 for a single or double with a private bathroom and $70 for a single or double with a shared bathroom. The entire B&B rents for $225. There is no minimum stay.
CREDIT CARDS	No
BREAKFAST	Full breakfast is served in the dining room or gazebo, or at the picnic table. Breakfast includes orange juice, seasonal fruits, ham or sausage, scones, scrambled eggs, tea, coffee, milk, vegetarian dishes, or quiche. A dinner, catered by a local company, is also available.
AMENITIES	Flowers in common rooms, air conditioning, fire pit, trail to the Yakima River, robes, clawfoot tub with bubble bath, old linens on dressers, gift shop, all queen-size beds.
RESTRICTIONS	No smoking, no pets, no children. There are over 100 quail roaming the property.

RED MOUNTAIN BED & BREAKFAST

12911 East State Road 224, Benton City, WA 99320   *509-588-1900*

BIRCH BAY

Birch Bay is just the place for 1950s teenage nostalgia. The crescent-shaped beach in far northwestern Washington draws throngs of kids. Frankie and Annette would be right at home. There's a state park and lots of sandy beach to wiggle between your toes. Off-season can be very quiet.

BIRCH BAY BED & BREAKFAST

8102 Birch Bay Drive, Birch Bay, WA 98230   *206-329-9288*
Ron & Nancy Walken, Innkeepers   *877-222-1031*
EMAIL Mr1031@aol.com   *FAX 206-325-3500*

LOCATION	Leave I-5 at exit 270, go west four miles to Harborview, and turn left to Birch Bay Drive. Take a right and go one mile.
OPEN	June to September 2
DESCRIPTION	A remodeled 1946 host home with natural wood interior, cathedral ceiling, and rattan furniture.
NO. OF ROOMS	One room with a private bathroom.
RATES	Year-round rate is $70 for a single or double. There is no minimum stay. Ask about a cancellation policy.
CREDIT CARDS	No
BREAKFAST	Continental breakfast is served in the dining room or on the porch or patio. Breakfast varies, but often features local cinnamon rolls, muffins, fresh juices, fruit, and great coffee and tea.
AMENITIES	Fresh crab in season; tandem bike, canoe, sailboard available.
RESTRICTIONS	No children

BLAINE

Any farther north and you'd be in Canada. Bellingham to the south and Vancouver to the north are within easy drives. Check out the Semiahmoo Salmon Run, Skywater Festival, Hot Air Balloon Festival, and the Northwest Washington Fair. Over Memorial Day weekend, teams from around the world compete in the Ski to Sea Race.

HARBOR HOUSE BED & BREAKFAST

5157 Drayton Harbor Road, Blaine, WA 98230 360-371-9060
Jonni Lukens, Innkeeper 888-705-9060
A little Spanish spoken FAX 360-371-2787
EMAIL *harborhouse@Harbor-House.com*
WEBSITE *www.Harbor-House.com*

LOCATION	From Seattle, head north on I-5 to exit 274. Turn left on Bell Road and go 0.9 mile, turning right on Drayton Harbor Road. Stay next to the water when the road splits. Harbor House is the fourth house on the left after the split.
OPEN	All year
DESCRIPTION	A 1900 two-story country farm with views of the water and mountains.
NO. OF ROOMS	Two rooms with private bathrooms. Jonni suggests the Drayton Harbor Suite.
RATES	Year-round rates are $65-90 for a single or double. There is no minimum stay and no charge for cancellations in most cases.
CREDIT CARDS	Discover, MasterCard, Visa
BREAKFAST	Full breakfast is served in the guestrooms and includes coffee, tea, fresh fruit, and juice, followed by a hot meal that includes fresh-baked breads, meat or seafood, and an egg entrée. Lunch, dinner, packed picnics, and family meals are available on request.
AMENITIES	Outdoor hot tub with view of water and mountains; yard full of flowers; meals include fresh fruit and vegetables from the garden; TV/VCR and video libraries in each room.
RESTRICTIONS	No smoking, children are welcome. The private suites are ideal for families. Skipper is the resident golden retriever and Gildenstern is the cat. Skipper is a great greeter and playmate, but is not intrusive. Gildenstern keeps to herself.

WATER'S EDGE BED & BREAKFAST

7379 Birch Bay Drive, Blaine, WA 98230

360-371-2043
FAX 360-371-2043

BOW

Removed from traffic and shopping malls, you'll discover orchards, oyster beds, slow-moving tractors, and fields of mustard in this neck of the woods. Chuckanut Drive, a famous stretch of road between Bellingham and Bow, used to be part of the Pacific Highway; now it is one of the prettiest drives in the state, curving along the Chuckanut Mountains and looking out over Samish Bay and its many islands. In nearby Bayview, visit the Breazeale-Padilla Bay National Estuarine Research Reserve and Interpretive Center and learn about the Padilla Bay estuary through displays, saltwater tanks, and a library.

ALICE BAY BED & BREAKFAST

982 Scott Road Sammish Island, Bow, WA 98232
Terry & Julie Rousseau, Resident Owners

360-766-6396
800-652-0223

BENSON FARMSTEAD BED & BREAKFAST

10113 Avon Allen Road, Bow, WA 98232
Jerry & Sharon Benson, Innkeepers
WEBSITE *www.bbhost.com/bensonbnb*

360-757-0578

LOCATION	One mile north of Burlington, take exit 232 off I-5 and go west on Cook Road for 2 miles, then south on Avon Allen Road for 0.5 mile.
OPEN	All year
DESCRIPTION	A 1914 three-story restored farmhouse decorated with antiques and traditional and country furnishings and surrounded by gardens.
NO. OF ROOMS	Four rooms with private bathrooms. Try the Wildflower Room.
RATES	Year-round rates are $65-75 for a single and $75-85 for a double. The entire B&B rents for $310 for up to eight guests. There is no minimum stay and cancellation requires three days' notice.
CREDIT CARDS	MasterCard, Visa

BREAKFAST	Full breakfast is served in the dining room and includes coffee; tea; orange juice; fresh fruit dish; an entrée such as French toast with applesauce and sausages, or an egg, bacon, and cheese casserole with ham; toast from homemade bread; scones; and coffeecake.
AMENITIES	Fresh flowers, mints and robes in the rooms, hot tub on the porch, homemade desserts, coffee and tea served in the evening, playground and playroom for children.
RESTRICTIONS	No smoking, no pets. Max is the resident outdoor cat.
REVIEWED	*Northwest Best Places; Hidden Places of the Pacific Northwest*
MEMBER	Tulip Valley Bed & Breakfast Association
KUDOS/COMMENTS	"Absolutely charming. The innkeepers surpass all expectations! The best berry pie, and Sharon shared the recipe!" (1996)

CHUCKANUT MANOR BED & BREAKFAST

302 Chuckanut Drive, Bow, WA 98232　　　　　　　*360-766-6191*

SAMISH POINT BY THE BAY

4465 Samish Point Road, Bow, WA 98232　　　　　*360-766-6610*
Herb & Theresa Goldston, Innkeepers　　　　　　　*800-916-6161*
EMAIL samishpoint@cnw.com　　　　　　　　　*FAX 360-766-6610*
WEBSITE www.samishpoint.com

LOCATION	Eighteen miles north of La Conner, 15 miles west of the Bow Hill exit off I-5.
OPEN	All year
DESCRIPTION	A 1994 two-story guesthouse whose architectural and interior designs are styled after the Cape Cod seaside shingle homes of the 1940s. The home is nestled among giant cedar, fir, and maple trees on spacious, parklike grounds.
NO. OF ROOMS	Three rooms with private bathrooms. Herb and Theresa recommend the King Room.
RATES	March through October, rates are $150-175 for the guesthouse. November through February, rates are $140-155. There is a minimum stay during the holiday season.
CREDIT CARDS	American Express, MasterCard, Visa
BREAKFAST	The kitchen is stocked with "country continental" breakfast items,

including coffee, tea, cocoa, juice, granola, and home-baked pastries.

AMENITIES	Complete privacy, gardens, acres of woodlands, three beaches on the point, great bird-watching, river-rock fireplace, private hot tub and deck, luxurious robes, movies and CD player.
RESTRICTIONS	No smoking, no pets, children over 12 are welcome.
REVIEWED	*Northwest Best Places; The Best Places to Kiss in the Northwest*
MEMBER	Washington Bed & Breakfast Guild, Tulip Valley Bed & Breakfast Association
RATED	AAA 3 Diamonds

BREMERTON

Bremerton and its naval station have been entwined since the early 1890s, when a young German, one William Bremer, sold close to 200 acres of bay-front property to the U.S. Navy for $9,587. Today, the Navy shipyards are still right downtown. Only the destroyer USS Turner Joy, which saw action off Vietnam, is open for self-guided tours. The Bremerton Naval Museum depicts the region's shipbuilding history back to bowsprit-and-sail days. Farther north on the Kitsap Peninsula is the Trident Nuclear Submarine Base at Bangor. Occasionally a pod of orcas can be glimpsed escorting one of the mammoth submarines through the local waters to deep-sea duty. Since 1915, Keyport has been the major U.S. site for undersea torpedo testing. Now it also is home to an extraordinary Naval Undersea Museum, housing the first Revolutionary War submarine.

HIGHLAND COTTAGE BED & BREAKFAST

622 Highland Avenue, Bremerton, WA 98337   *360-373-2235*

ILLAHEE MANOR BED & BREAKFAST INN

6680 Illahee Road NE, Bremerton, WA 98311   *360-698-7555*
Tomi & Ramon Selby, Innkeepers   *800-693-6680*
EMAIL *illaheemanor@comstation.com*   FAX *360-698-0688*

KUDOS/COMMENTS	"Exquisitely decorated, tranquil getaway." "Beautiful country property with llamas and deer. Rooms are pretty and comfortable, peaceful and private." "Wonderful, magical hideaway with Jacuzzi tubs, water views, and warm and hospitable hosts."

CAMANO ISLAND

Along with nearby Whidbey Island, Camano Island is accessible by car sans the ferry ride. Camano Island State Park, with nearly 7,000 feet of waterfront, is a must for beautiful beachside picnicking. Check out the Northwest Center for Wooden Boats. The area is also rich in Northwest pioneer history.

CAMANO ISLAND INN

1054 S West Camano Drive, Camano Island, WA 98292   *360-387-0783*
Jon & Kari Soth, Innkeepers   *888-718-0783*
EMAIL *reservations@camanoislandinn.com*   *FAX 360-387-4173*
WEBSITE *www.camanoislandinn.com*

LOCATION	From I-5, take exit 212 (aproximately 45 minutes north of Seattle). Follow Highway 532 through Stanwood and onto Camano Island. Highway 532 becomes East Camano Drive. Turn right onto Camano Hill Road and left onto West Camano Drive. Go about 0.8 mile and the inn is on the right, near the water.
OPEN	All year
DESCRIPTION	A 1900 two-story Arts and Crafts-style small hotel dedorated with the works of local artists, with exposure to the waterfront and spectacular views.
NO. OF ROOMS	Six rooms with private bathrooms. Try room 1 (with the private Jacuzzi).
RATES	Year-round rates are $100-160 for a single or double. The entire B&B rents for $700. There is no minimum stay and cancellation requires eight days' notice.
CREDIT CARDS	MasterCard, Visa
BREAKFAST	Full gourmet breakfast is served in the dining room or guestrooms and includes coffee, egg and meat dishes, fresh-baked goods, and fresh fruit dishes made with fruit from the innkeepers' orchards. Lunch and dinner are also available.
AMENITIES	Wine and hors d'oeuvres during check-in, fresh flowers daily, room service, use of kayaks, large beach area for lounging or beachcombing, meeting facilities, handicapped access, feather beds and goose-down duvets, massage available with advance reservation.
RESTRICTIONS	No smoking, no pets
MEMBER	Washington Bed & Breakfast Guild, Professional Association of Innkeepers
RATED	AAA 4 Diamonds

Inn at Barnum Point

464 South Barnum Road, Camano Island, WA 98292   360-387-2256
Caroline B. Dilorenzo, Resident Owner   800-910-2256
WEBSITE *www.whidbey.com/inn/*   FAX 360-387-2256 *(call first)*

KUDOS/COMMENTS   "Wonderful location and view. Excellent hospitality and food.
          Warm and friendly." (1996)

Log House Bed & Breakfast

800 West 650, Camano Island, WA 98292   360-387-2346

Carnation

Carnation is a lovely stretch of cow country nestled in the Snoqualmie Valley. At MacDonald Memorial Park, meandering trails and an old-fashioned suspension bridge across the Tolt River provide a great family picnic setting. The sky's the limit for your favorite fruits and vegetables at Remlinger Farms, a U-pick farm. The Strawberry Festival in mid-June starts off the season. Throughout the summer you can choose from the best in raspberries, apples, corn, and grapes. The kids, young and old alike, love tromping through the fields in search of the perfect jack-o'-lantern-to-be in October.

Alexandra's River Inn Snoqualmie Valley

4548 Tolt River Road, Carnation, WA 98014   425-333-4262
Trivia Sebile, Innkeeper
WEBSITE *www.isomedia.com/homes/riverinn*

LOCATION	One-and-a-half miles east of Carnation on Entwistle Street, which becomes Tolt River Road.
OPEN	All year
DESCRIPTION	A 1987 two-story country house with European/country decor.
NO. OF ROOMS	Five rooms with private bathrooms and two rooms with two shared bathrooms.
RATES	Year-round rates are $155-235 for a single or double with a private bathroom and $65-125 for a single or double with a shared bathroom. There is no minimum stay and cancellation requires seven days' notice.

CREDIT CARDS	MasterCard, Visa
BREAKFAST	Full breakfast available on weekends only.
RESTRICTIONS	No smoking, no pets
REVIEWED	*The Best Places to Kiss in the Northwest*

CASH

GRANDVIEW ORCHARD INN

5105 Moody Road, Cash, WA 98815   509-782-2340
J. R. McClendon, Resident Owner

CASTLE ROCK

The U.S. Forest Service's Mount St. Helens Visitor Center is just five miles east of I-5 at Castle Rock. Built shortly after the eruption, which removed the top 1,300 feet of the mountain, the Center commemorates the blast with excellent exhibits, a walk-through volcano, hundreds of historical and modern photos, geological and anthropological surveys, and a film documenting the mountain's destruction and rebirth. On a clear day it is well worth the trip to see the 8,365-foot remains as well as the mountain's regrowth since the incredible eruption of May 18, 1980.

BLUE HERON INN

2846 Spirit Lake Highway, Castle Rock, WA 98611   360-274-9595
John & Jeanne Robards, Innkeepers   800-959-4049
EMAIL jeanne@blueheroninn.com   *WEBSITE www.blueheroninn.com*

LOCATION	One hour north of Portland. Take exit 49 off I-5 and travel five miles up Highway 504; we are across from the Mount St. Helens National Monument.
OPEN	All year
DESCRIPTION	A 1996 three-story country inn set in the woods directly in front of Mount St. Helens.

NO. OF ROOMS	Seven rooms with private bathrooms. The Robardses recommend the Jacuzzi Suite.
RATES	Year-round rates are $125-145 for a single or double and $195 for a suite. The entire B&B rents for $1,200. Monday through Friday, except holidays, the second night is half price. There is no minimum stay and cancellation requires seven days' notice.
CREDIT CARDS	Discover, MasterCard, Visa
BREAKFAST	Full breakfast includes a variety of egg dishes, fruit, assorted pastries, jams, juices, and more. Daily dinner with wine and dessert is included.
AMENITIES	Dinner with wine and dessert, exercise equipment, handicapped access, air conditioning, meeting room, hiking trails, koi pond, music, games, books.
RESTRICTIONS	No smoking, no pets, children over six are welcome.
REVIEWED	*Frommer's; The Best Places to Kiss in the Northwest*
MEMBER	Washington Bed & Breakfast Guild

CATHLAMET

The county seat of Wahkiakum County, Cathlamet is an old-style river town, tied almost as closely to the Columbia as Mark Twain's Hannibal, Missouri, was to the Mississippi. Fishing is everyone's recreation—in season, for trout, salmon, and steelhead; all year long for the Columbia's mammoth, caviar-bearing sturgeon. Nearby Puget Island, reachable by bridge, is flat dairyland, ideal for cycling; a tiny ferry can take you from there directly across to Oregon. Wahkiakum County is the sort of place where nostalgia buffs discover round barns and covered bridges.

BRADLEY HOUSE/COUNTRY KEEPER

61 Main Street, Cathlamet, WA 98612 360-795-3030
Barbara & Tony West, Innkeepers 800-551-1691
EMAIL *bradleyhouse@transport.com*

LOCATION	Located on Main Street, one-and-a-half blocks south of Highway 4 and across the street from the courthouse.
OPEN	All year
DESCRIPTION	A 1907 two-and-a-half-story Eastlake inn decorated with mixed antiques and overlooking the Columbia River.
NO. OF ROOMS	Two rooms with private bathrooms and two rooms share one bathroom. Try the Rose Room.

Bradley House/Country Keeper, Cathlamet

RATES	Year-round rates are $80-95 for a single or double with a private bathroom, $65-80 for a single or double with a shared bathroom, and $325 for the entire B&B. There is a three-day minimum stay during holiday weekends and cancellation requires 72 hours' notice.
CREDIT CARDS	MasterCard, Visa
BREAKFAST	Full breakfast is served in the dining room and includes fresh-squeezed orange juice, homemade muffins, lots of fresh fruit, a hot main course with sausage, bacon, or ham, plus coffee and tea.
AMENITIES	Robes, sherry and port, coffee and tea service all day, games, books, TV in parlor.
RESTRICTIONS	No smoking, no pets, children over 12 are welcome. Mooch is the resident tabby.
REVIEWED	*Northwest Best Places; Fodor's Bed & Breakfasts and Country Inns of the West Coast*
MEMBER	Washington State Bed & Breakfast Guild, Professional Association of Innkeepers International
RATED	AAA 3 Diamonds

THE GALLERY BED & BREAKFAST

4 Little Cape Horn, Cathlamet, WA 98612   *360-425-7395*

REDFERN FARM

277 Cross Dike Road, Cathlamet, WA 98612   *360-849-4108*

CENTRALIA

The Chehalis-Centralia Railroad offers round-trip steam-train rides between those twin cities on weekends, from Memorial Day through September. Shoppers will find a bargain bonanza of factory outlet stores along I-5 outside Centralia, and the 80 antique dealers who work the downtown area offer good finds, too.

CANDALITE MANSION

402 North Rock, Centralia, WA 98531   *360-736-4749*

CHELAN

This resort area is blessed with the springtime perfume of apple blossoms, a 55-mile lake thrusting fjord like into tall mountains, 300 days of sunshine a year, and good skiing, hunting, fishing, hiking, and sailing. The top attraction here is the cruise up Lake Chelan on an old-fashioned tour boat, the *Lady of the Lake*, or the newer *Lady Express*. The lake is never more than two miles wide (it's also one of the deepest in the world), so you have a sense of slicing right into the heart of the Cascades. Fishing for steelhead, rainbow, cutthroats, and Chinooks is very good in Lake Chelan. Chelan Butte Lookout, nine miles west of Chelan, provides views of the lake, the Columbia River, and the orchard-blanketed countryside.

CAPTAIN'S QUARTERS

283 Minneapolis Beach Road, Chelan, WA 98816   *509-682-5886*
WEBSITE www.chelan.com/captain.htm   *FAX 509-682-5886 (call first)*

KUDOS/COMMENTS "Enjoy a great view of Lake Chelan while being served breakfast on the outside deck."

HOLDEN VILLAGE BED & BREAKFAST

21081 South Lakeshore Road, Chelan, WA 98816   509-687-9695
                                                    FAX 509-687-3375

LOCATION	Located 20 miles northwest of Chelan on the south shore of Lake Chelan at the end of the road.
OPEN	All year
DESCRIPTION	A 1982 passive-solar country inn, remodeled in 1991, with a dark slate floor upstairs, wood-beamed ceilings, and large windows.
NO. OF ROOMS	Six rooms with two shared bathrooms. Try the Hart Lake or Holden Lake Rooms.
RATES	June through September, rates are $19-45 for a single or double, and the entire B&B rents for $282. October through May, rates are $17-39 for a single or double, and the entire B&B rents for $246. Family rates are available. There is no minimum stay and cancellation requires two weeks' notice.
CREDIT CARDS	No
BREAKFAST	Full breakfast is served in the dining room and includes homemade pancakes or French toast, fresh fruit, homemade preserves, juice, and coffee. The kitchen is open for guests' use.
AMENITIES	Large front porch with swing overlooking Lake Chelan, nearby beach and hiking trails, fire pit, library.
RESTRICTIONS	No smoking inside. The resident cat is P. K., short for Porch Kitty. There are numerous California quail (P. K. calls them "lunch") and the occasional mule deer on the property.

MARY KAY'S ROMANTIC WHALEY MANSION INN

Route 1, Box 693, Chelan, WA 98816   509-682-5735
Mary Kay & Carol, Resident Owners   800-729-2408
WEBSITE *www.lakechelan.com/whaley.htm*   FAX 509-682-5385

KUDOS/COMMENTS	"Lovely hostess and a fantastic breakfast presentation with candles, fine linens, china, and more food than ever!" (1996)

A Quail's Roost Inn, Chelan

A QUAIL'S ROOST INN

121 East Highland Avenue, Chelan, WA 98816   509-682-2892
Marilee & Brad Stolzenburg, Innkeepers   800-681-2892
WEBSITE *www.lakechelan.com/quailsinn*

LOCATION	Take Highway 97A from Wenatchee for 33 miles. Go left on Woodin Avenue for approximately 0.2 mile and left again on Columbia. Take a left on East Johnson (Highway 150) for 0.4 mile. Go right on East Highland Avenue for four blocks.
OPEN	All year
DESCRIPTION	A 1902 two-story Queen Anne Victorian country inn, restored to its original condition and furnished with period antiques, listed on both the National Historic Register and the Washington Heritage Register. The house is set on a hill with views of the town and Lake Chelan.
NO. OF ROOMS	Three rooms with private bathrooms. Marilee and Brad recommend the Rose and Wicker Room.
RATES	June through September, rates for a single or double are $80-115. October through May rates for a single or double are $65-75. A minimum stay is required on major holidays and seven days' notice is required for cancellation.
CREDIT CARDS	MasterCard, Visa
BREAKFAST	Full breakfast is served in the dining room, guestrooms, or occasionally on the porch. The house specialty is strawberry and

cream French toast served with fresh fruit, yogurt, coffee, and juice. Special diets can be accommodated.

AMENITIES	Picnic lunches, fresh flowers, ice water in antique water carafes, fresh-baked evening treats, library, games in all rooms, meeting facilities, air conditioning.
RESTRICTIONS	No smoking, no pets, and children over 14 are welcome. The resident dog is a golden retriever named Russ.
REVIEWED	*The Best Places to Kiss in the Northwest*

CHIMACUM

About 10 miles south of Port Townsend on Highway 19.

WINDRIDGE COTTAGE

2804 West Valley Road, Chimacum, WA 98325   *360-732-4575*
Nicholas & Lindsay Colitses, Innkeepers
EMAIL *colitses@olympus.net*
WEBSITE *www.olympus.net/getaways/wc/*

LOCATION	Travel west across the Hood Canal Bridge to Route 19, turn right toward Port Townsend, and follow the road eight miles to Chimacum. Pass the café on the left, go around the corner, and turn left onto West Valley Road. Go three miles to Windridge Road and turn right. Continue to the top of the hill and keep going straight past the "private drive" signs. Turn left at the tree with the flower basket in it.
OPEN	All year
DESCRIPTION	A 1980 cedar cabin with cathedral ceilings, natural woods, oak floors, oriental rugs, and some antiques. Located on 140 acres surrounded by forest with stunning views of the Olympic Mountains.
NO. OF ROOMS	One room with a private bathroom.
RATES	April through September, the rate is $115 for the cabin. October through March, rates are $100-110. There is no minimum stay. Ask about a cancellation policy.
CREDIT CARDS	No
BREAKFAST	Full breakfast is set up in the cabin, including juice, cereals, oatmeal, pancake mix, bagels, fresh fruit, eggs, coffee, assorted teas, cocoa, milk, and half-and-half.

Windridge Cottage, Chimacum

AMENITIES	Total seclusion and privacy, fully equipped kitchen with microwave and dishwasher, fireplace, special soaps in bathroom, fresh flowers, TV/VCR, small stereo/CD player, puzzles and games, king-size bed and queen-size pull-out couch, incredible views of lake and mountains, telephone.
RESTRICTIONS	No smoking inside, no pets. There are quarter horses (the Colitses raise them) and a German shepherd named Samba.

CLALLAM BAY

Clallam Bay and its neighboring Sekiu are small coastal towns on the Strait of Juan de Fuca, just off Highway 112. About 20 miles southwest on the Hoko-Ozette Road is Lake Ozette, where trails lead to ocean beaches with eerie, eroded cliffs looming over the water. It was near here that tidal erosion exposed a perfectly preserved 500-year-old Native village. The archaeological dig was closed in 1981; artifacts are on display at the Makah Museum in Neah Bay.

WINTER'S SUMMER INN

16651 Highway 112, Clallam Bay, WA 98326   360-963-2264
Kaye C. (K. C.) Winters, Innkeeper
EMAIL *kcw@olypen.com*   WEBSITE *www.winterssummerinn.usrc.net*

LOCATION	On the Strait of Juan de Fuca in the northwest corner of the Olympic Peninsula, 52 miles west of Port Angeles on Highway 112, a block west of Clallam Bay's town center.

OPEN	All year
DESCRIPTION	A 1982 contemporary inn with an eclectic mix of antiques and native artwork, with views of the Clallam River and the Strait of Juan de Fuca from the three-tiered back deck.
NO. OF ROOMS	Two suites with private bathrooms and two rooms with private half-bathrooms and shared bath or shower.
RATES	Year-round rates are $75-90 for a double with a private bathroom and $95 for a double with a private half-bathroom. An extra person adds $10 per night. There is no minimum stay and cancellation requires 24 hours' notice for a full refund.
CREDIT CARDS	No
BREAKFAST	Full breakfast is served in the dining room, at the kitchen bar, or on the deck. A typical breakfast might be blueberry pancakes or garden vegetable and egg scramble, served with fruit cup, juice, and coffee or tea. Special meals may be accommodated with advance notifice.
RESTRICTIONS	Smoking permitted on the deck. Sitzi is the resident dog and there is an American short-haired cat. Sitzi has been known to sing and loves accompanying people on walks to the beach.
REVIEWED	*Northwest Best Places; Olympic Peninsula Best Places*

Winter's Summer Inn, Clallam Bay

CLARKSTON

Washington's gateway to Hells Canyon, Clarkston sits across the Snake River from Idaho. Check out the Sunflower Days in August, Lewis and Clark Days in October, and the Stocking Festival and Lighted Victorian Village in December.

THE CLIFF HOUSE BED & BREAKFAST

1227 Westlake Drive, Clarkston, WA 98403   509-758-1267

KUDOS/COMMENTS   "Exquisite cottage and award-winning architecture." (1996)

HIGHLAND HOUSE

707 Highland Avenue, Clarkston, WA 99403   509-758-3126
Doreen Bridgmount, Innkeeper   FAX 509-758-3126 *(call first)*

LOCATION	Exit Highway 12 at 6th Street (City Center). Go one mile to the stop sign. Take a right on Highland Avenue. Go one block to the corner of 7th Street. The B&B is on the south side.
OPEN	All year
DESCRIPTION	An 1898 two-story Victorian inn with English furnishings.
NO. OF ROOMS	Three rooms with private bathrooms and two rooms with one shared bathroom. Doreen recommends the Bridal Suite.
RATES	Year-round rates are $70-85 for a single or double with a private bathroom and $50-65 for a single or double with a shared bathroom. There is a two-night minimum stay on some weekends (call for details) and cancellation requires two weeks' notice.
CREDIT CARDS	MasterCard, Visa
BREAKFAST	Full breakfast is served in the dining room and includes juice, fresh fruit, cereal, toast, preserves, eggs, bacon, sausage, hashbrowns, and vegetarian options. Special meals are available on request.
AMENITIES	Meeting room, courtesy in-room tea and coffee, reading room, TV/VCR lounge, air conditioning, wheelchair ramp, patio hot tub.
RESTRICTIONS	No smoking. Shadow, the resident Ridgeback, carries the mail and newspapers, and plays ball with guests.
REVIEWED	*Washington State Hotel & Motel Guide; Be Our Guest; Pets Welcome*

SWALLOWHAVEN BED & BREAKFAST

904 22nd Avenue, Clarkston, WA 99403   509-758-8357
WEBSITE www.busdir.com/swallowhav   800-441-8357

CLE ELUM

Easy access brings travelers from the freeway to Cle Elum, a former coal-mining town now undergoing a modest rediscovery. Check out the Cle Elum Historical Telephone Museum. Open Memorial Day to Labor Day only, this museum incorporates the area's original phone system, which was operating well into the 1960s.

HIDDEN VALLEY GUEST RANCH

3942 Hidden Valley Ranch, Cle Elum, WA 98922   509-857-2344

THE MOORE HOUSE
BED & BREAKFAST COUNTRY INN

526 Marie Avenue, South Cle Elum, WA 98943   509-674-5939
Eric & Cindy Sherwood, Resident Innkeepers

LOCATION	Eastbound on I-90, take exit 84 onto 1st Street, turn right onto South Cle Elum Way, right again onto Madison Street, left onto 6th Street, and right onto Marie Avenue. Westbound on I-90, take exit 84, turn left onto 1st Street, left again onto South Cle Elum Way, and then follow directions listed above, after South Cle Elum Way.
OPEN	All year
DESCRIPTION	A 1909 two-story wood-frame "former Milwaukee railroad crew hotel," furnished with antiques, railroad memorabilia, and old-print wallpaper, plus red cabooses.
NO. OF ROOMS	Six rooms with private bathrooms and six rooms share two bathrooms. The owners recommend the Honeymoon Suite.
RATES	Year-round rates are $75-85 for a single or double with a private bathroom, $50-70 for a room with a shared bathroom, $125 for the suite, and $115-125 for a caboose. There is a two-night minimum

CREDIT CARDS	American Express, Discover, MasterCard, Visa

stay on holiday weekends; cancellations require seven days' notice with a $10 fee.

CREDIT CARDS   American Express, Discover, MasterCard, Visa

BREAKFAST   Full breakfast, served in the dining room, typically includes French toast with sausage and fruit; eggs Benedict with sweet roll; blueberry pancakes with sausage and fruit; scrambled eggs with Canadian bacon, muffin, and fruit; plus choice of beverages.

AMENITIES   Front porch with swing, lobby with wood-burning stove and piano, space for small meetings, year-round outdoor hot tub, air conditioning in most rooms, lacy bridal suite with jetted tub, collection of historic railroad photos and memorabilia, gazebo nestled in aspen grove, caboose suites (with TV, refrigerator, and sun deck), horse paddocks, swing set and slide for children.

RESTRICTIONS   No smoking, no pets, children are welcome. Smokey and Spud are the resident cats and are "kept separate from guest areas."

REVIEWED   *Northwest Best Places; Hidden Pacific Northwest; Washington Off the Beaten Path; Grand Old Hotels of Washington and Oregon; Ultimate Washington*

MEMBER   National Bed & Breakfast Association

RATED   AAA 2 Diamonds

CLINTON

Reached via the mainland ferry from Mukilteo, Clinton is the gateway to Whidbey Island, which boasts pretty towns and communities, historical parks, sandy beaches, and some lovely rolling farmland. The third weekend in August brings the Island County Fair, and art fairs and mystery weekends take place on the island throughout the summer months.

B's GETAWAY

PO Box 15 , Clinton, WA 98236   *360-341-4721*

BAYWATCH

6557 South Columbia Beach Drive, Clinton, WA 98236   *360-341-4561*

FRENCH ROAD FARM

3841 East French Road, Clinton, WA 98236   *360-321-2964*
Linda & Sam Walsh, Innkeepers   *FAX 360-321-4378*
EMAIL FrenchRoadFarm@hotmail.com
WEBSITE www.frenchroadfarm.com

LOCATION	From Seattle, drive north on I-5 to exit 189 (Whidbey Island/Mukilteo Ferry) and take the Mukilteo ferry to Clinton. Drive 2.7 miles up Highway 525 to the stoplight and turn left onto Cultus Bay Road. Drive 2.3 miles and turn right onto French Road. Go 0.3 mile and the farm is on your right.
OPEN	All year
DESCRIPTION	A very private 1924 one-story simple farmhouse with an eclectic mix of Provençal furnishings and antiques, set on 10 acres with extensive perennial gardens, vineyards, and evergreen forests.
NO. OF ROOMS	One room with a private bathroom.
RATES	April through October, rates are $155-170 for a single or double. November through March (except holidays), rates are $145-160. There is a two-night minimum stay during weekends, three nights during some holidays. A 50 percent nonrefundable deposit is required for multinight stays, with the balance due on arrival.
CREDIT CARDS	MasterCard, Visa
BREAKFAST	Continental plus is left for guests in the refrigerator and includes a basket of eggs, fruit, juice, coffee, milk, pastry, and either bagels or homemade muffins.
AMENITIES	Fresh flowers from the garden; bubble bath; spa robes; Jacuzzi tub in the bathroom overlooking gardens and vineyards; large, well-appointed kitchen; Irish enamel pellet stove in the living room; hammock suspended between giant fir trees.
RESTRICTIONS	No smoking, no pets
REVIEWED	*The Best Places to Kiss in the Northwest*
MEMBER	Founding Member, Whidbey Island Bed & Breakfast Association

HOME BY THE SEA
BED & BREAKFAST AND COTTAGES

2388 East Sunlight Beach Road, Clinton, WA 98236   *360-321-2964*

KITTLESON COVE BED & BREAKFAST

4891 East Bay Ridge Drive, Clinton, WA 98236   *360-341-2734*
Al Kittleson, Resident Owner

KUDOS/COMMENTS "Beautiful spot on the water with comfortable accommodations,
privacy."

MARSH HOUSE

6436 Maxwelton Road, Clinton, WA 98236   *360-579-8861*

THE SANDPIPER SUITE

2388 East Sunlight Beach Road, Clinton, WA 98236   *360-321-2964*
Linda Walsh, Innkeeper   *FAX 360-321-4378*

LOCATION   From Seattle, drive north on I-5 to exit 189 (Whidbey
                 Island/Mukilteo Ferry) and take the Mukilteo ferry to Clinton.
                 Drive about 4.2 miles up Highway 525 to Bayview Road and turn
                 left. Proceed about one mile until you see Sunlight Beach Road to
                 your right (marked by a wooden sign featuring a whale). Turn right
                 on Sunlight Beach Road and go to the end of the road. Turn in
                 where you see the sign saying "Home by the Sea." The Sandpiper
                 Suite is down the walkway to the left of the main front door.

OPEN   All year

DESCRIPTION   A 1980 one-story beach house with traditional, eclectic,
                 comfortable decor.

NO. OF ROOMS   One room with a private bathroom.

RATES   Year-round rates are $165-180 for a single or double. There is a
                 minimum stay during weekends and holidays, and a 50 percent
                 nonrefundable deposit is due upon confirmation of reservation,
                 with the balance due upon arrival.

CREDIT CARDS   MasterCard, Visa

BREAKFAST   A breakfast basket left in the refrigerator includes eggs, butter and
                 preserves, bagels or homemade muffins, fresh fruit, coffee, tea,
                 juice, and milk.

AMENITIES   Private deck just steps from the beach; outdoor Japanese soaking
                 tub.

RESTRICTIONS   No smoking, dogs welcome

REVIEWED   *Vacationing with Your Pet: Eileen's Directory of Pet-Friendly Lodging; Fodor's; Northwest Best Places*

MEMBER   Founding Member, Whidbey Island Bed & Breakfast Association

---

SPINK'S OCEAN VIEW

3493 East French Road, Clinton, WA 98236   360-579-2494
Lyle & Ann Spink, Innkeepers   888-799-5979
EMAIL *spink@whidbey.com*   FAX 360-579-1970
WEBSITE *www.whidbey.com/spink*

LOCATION	From Highway 525, go south on Cultus Bay Road for 2.4 miles, turn right onto French Road, and go 1.4 miles.
OPEN	All year
DESCRIPTION	A 1994 four-story country host home decorated with conventional country furnishings and some antiques.
NO. OF ROOMS	Two rooms with private bathrooms and two rooms with two shared bathrooms. Try the Dormer Suite.
RATES	Year-round rates are $125-200 for a single or double with a private bathroom and $200 for a single or double with a shared bathroom. There is no minimum stay and cancellation requires five days' notice.
CREDIT CARDS	MasterCard, Visa
BREAKFAST	Continental breakfast is served in the guestrooms and includes homemade bread, rolls, and pastry; fresh fruit; juice, coffee, and tea.
AMENITIES	Private entrances, CD player, VCR, 1,200 movies, pellet stoves, robes, kitchenette and telescope in Dormer Suite, kitchen in Veranda Suite; gorgeous views of the Olympic Mountains and Admiralty Inlet, laundry room.
RESTRICTIONS	No smoking, no pets
MEMBER	Washington Bed & Breakfast Guild

SWEET WATER COTTAGE

6111 Cultus Bay Road, Clinton, WA 98236   360-341-1604
WEBSITE *www.whidbey.com/sweetwater/*   FAX 360-341-3676

Cascade Mountain Inn, Concrete-Birdsview

CONCRETE

At the southern tip of Lake Shannon on scenic Highway 20, just west of North Cascades National Park. A 10-minute drive east takes you to prime bald eagle-spotting territory along the Skagit River (December through March). Some of the local fetes include the Bald Eagle Festival, Old-Fashioned Fly-In, River Raft Challenge Races, and Good Old Days Festival.

CASCADE MOUNTAIN INN

40418 Pioneer Lane, Concrete-Birdsview, WA 98237   *360-826-4333*
Sally & John Brummett, Innkeepers   *FAX 360-826-3623*
EMAIL casmi1@gte.net

LOCATION	Exit I-5 at Anacortes/Burlington (exit 230), drive through Burlington on Highway 20 east, go 24 miles to Wilde Road, and turn right. Drive 0.25 mile to Pioneer Lane, turn right, and follow the lane to the inn.
OPEN	All year
DESCRIPTION	A 1983 two-story wooden barn-style home on 5 acres in the scenic and primitive mountains of the Upper Skagit Valley.
NO. OF ROOMS	Five rooms with private bathrooms. Sally and John recommend the Sauk Mountain Room.
RATES	Year-round rates are $120 for a single or double and $600 for the entire B&B. There is no minimum stay and cancellation requires 72 hours' notice.
CREDIT CARDS	MasterCard, Visa

BREAKFAST	Full breakfast is served in the dining room or the sun room and includes homemade muffins, breads, jams and spreads, granola and yogurt, fresh fruit and juices, coffee, tea, and a breakfast entrée such as baked stuffed blueberry French toast, south of the border frittata, or seafood quiche. Special diets are accommodated upon request.
AMENITIES	Fresh flowers, two robes in each room, hot tub in the meadow, evening dessert available, pleasant 0.75-mile walk to the Skagit River, retreat and group facilities available.
RESTRICTIONS	No smoking, no pets, children over 10 are welcome. Comanche is the resident pooch.
MEMBER	Washington State Bed & Breakfast Guild, Cascade Loop Association, Tulip Valley Bed & Breakfast Association

OVENELL'S HERITAGE INN

46276 Concrete Sauk Valley Road, Concrete, WA 98237   360-853-8494
Norm & Eleanor Ovenell, Innkeepers   FAX 360-853-8279
EMAIL *breakfast@ovenells-inn.com*   WEBSITE *www.ovenells-inn.com*

LOCATION	At the western edge of Concrete's city limits, turn off Highway 20 onto Concrete Sauk Valley Road. The inn is at milepost 3.
OPEN	All year
DESCRIPTION	A 1915 two-story farmhouse decorated with heirlooms and fine antiques, located on a 450-acre cattle ranch with a "million-dollar" view of Mount Baker.
NO. OF ROOMS	Three rooms with private bathrooms and three rooms share one bathroom. Try the Heirloom Room.
RATES	April through September, rates are $80-115 for a single or double with a private bathroom and $105 for a single or double with a shared bathroom. October through March, rates are $70-105 for a single or double with a private bathroom and $95 for a single or double with a shared bathroom. There is no minimum stay and cancellation requires 24 hours' notice.
CREDIT CARDS	American Express, MasterCard, Visa
BREAKFAST	Full breakfast is served on antique silver and china in the dining room or on the deck with a view of Mount Baker. Breakfast begins with a beautifully garnished fruit tray, quiches, soufflés, frittatas, and a variety of meats, potatoes, and breads. Sack lunches are also available.
AMENITIES	Flowers, robes, chocolate on pillows, hair dryer and toiletries, evening dessert and beverages, fishing gear, bicycles, play yard,

VCR and movies, laundry in the guesthouse, internet and fax use, petting farm.

RESTRICTIONS   No smoking, no pets. There are 150 head of cattle on the property, plus seven horses, four dogs, cats, chickens, ducks, geese, a turkey, sheep, goat, and an abundance of wildlife besides.

MEMBER   Washington Bed & Breakfast Guild, Tulip Valley Bed & Breakfast Association, Professional Association of Innkeepers International

COUGAR

MONFORT'S BED & BREAKFAST

132 Cougar Loop Road, Cougar, WA 98616   360-238-5229

COULEE CITY

MAINSTAY BED & BREAKFAST

110 West Main, Coulee City, WA 99115   509-632-5687

COUPEVILLE

The second-oldest incorporated town in the state dates back to the mid-1850s; no wonder the town has a strict agenda of historic preservation. Coupeville's downtown consists of a half-dozen gift and antique shops and several restaurants. A must-see gallery is the Jan McGregor Studio, open on weekends throughout the year and every day in the summer. McGregor has studied pottery around the world and specializes in rare porcelain techniques. The Island County Historical Museum tells the story of Whidbey Island's early history. Annual community events include the Coupeville Arts & Crafts Festival the second weekend in August and the Penn Cove Mussel Festival in March. An extra bike lane follows

Engle Road three miles south of Coupeville to Fort Casey, a decommissioned fort with splendid gun mounts, beaches, and commanding bluffs. Explore the magnificent bluff and beach at the 17,000-acre Ebey's Landing and Fort Ebey State Park.

THE ANCHORAGE INN

807 North Main Street, Coupeville, WA 98239   *360-376-8282*
Sandra Bronson, Innkeeper   FAX *360-376-8283*
EMAIL sandrab@rockisland.com   *WEBSITE www.anchorageonorcas.com*

LOCATION	Seven miles from the ferry terminal heading toward Eastsound. Take a right on Sunderland Road and drive down to the water.
OPEN	All year
DESCRIPTION	A 1997 two-story Northwest-style inn with eclectic decor on 17 waterfront acres with a private beach overlooking the sound.
NO. OF ROOMS	All rooms with private bathrooms. Try the Ocean View Room.
RATES	June through October, rates are $125-175 for a single or double; November through May, rate is $120. There is a minimum stay from June through October and cancellation requires 14 days' notice.
CREDIT CARDS	Discover, MasterCard, Visa
BREAKFAST	Full breakfast is served in the dining room or delivered in a basket to the guestrooms.
AMENITIES	Flowers; robes; port; cheese, wine, and fruit in the evenings; shampoo, conditioner, body wash, hair dryers, hand lotion, spa towels; hot tub under the trees overlooking Eastsound.
RESTRICTIONS	No smoking, no pets, children over 14 are welcome. Muck, Tuck, and Cosmo are the outdoor cats. Lucy is the goose.
REVIEWED	*The Best Places to Kiss in the Northwest; Frommer's; Fodor's*
MEMBER	Professional Association of Innkeepers International

CAPTAIN WHIDBEY INN

2072 West Captain Whidbey Inn Road,   *360-678-4097*
Coupeville, WA 98239   *800-366-4097*

THE COLONEL CROCKETT FARM
BED & BREAKFAST INN

1012 South Fort Casey Road, Coupeville, WA 98239   360-678-3711
WEBSITE *members.aol.com/crocketbnb*

THE COMPASS ROSE BED & BREAKFAST

508 South Main Street, Coupeville, WA 98239   360-678-5318
WEBSITE *www.whidbey.net/compassrose*   800-237-3881
                                                  FAX 360-678-5318

FORT CASEY INN

1124 South Engle Road, Coupeville, WA 98239   360-678-8792

GARDEN ISLE GUEST COTTAGES

207 Northwest Coveland, Coupeville, WA 98239   360-678-5641
Dan Currier, Resident Owner

THE INN AT PENN COVE

702 North Main Street, Coupeville, WA 98239   360-678-8000
Gladys & Mitchell Howard, Resident Owners   800-688-2683
Some French, Spanish, Italian, and Japanese spoken
EMAIL *penncove@whidbey.net*
WEBSITE *www.whidbey.net/~penncove/pencv.htm*

LOCATION   Turn north at the Coupeville stoplight on Washington Street
                  (Route 20) and go seven blocks to the corner of 7th and North
                  Main Streets.

OPEN   All year

DESCRIPTION	An 1891 two-story Victorian with Victorian interior decor, listed on the National Historic Register.
NO. OF ROOMS	Four rooms with private bathrooms and two rooms share one bathroom.
RATES	Year-round rates are $70-125 for a single or double with a private bathroom, and $55-65 for a single or double with a shared bathroom. There sometimes are discounts during slower months, there is no minimum stay, and cancellation requires seven days' notice.
CREDIT CARDS	American Express, Discover, MasterCard, Visa
BREAKFAST	Full breakfast, served in the dining room, includes seasonal fruit, muffins, coffeecake or pastry, beverages, and a main course of French toast, waffles, and pancakes, plus low-fat turkey sausage.
AMENITIES	Pump organ, antique music box, afternoon tea, plants "all over the place," puzzles and board games in the game room, lots of interesting books in the library.
RESTRICTIONS	No smoking, no pets, ask about children.
REVIEWED	*Northwest Best Places; The Best Places to Kiss in the Northwest; Bed, Breakfast & Bike the Pacific Northwest; Lonely Planet Guide to Washington*
MEMBER	Professional Association of Innkeepers International
RATED	AAA 3 Diamonds

THE OLD MORRIS FARM INN

105 West Morris Road, Coupeville, WA 98239   360-678-6586
Marilyn S. Randock, Innkeeper   800-936-6586
Spanish spoken   FAX 360-678-2090
EMAIL *maricorp@whidbey.net*   WEBSITE *www.whidbey.net/maricorp*

LOCATION	From Seattle, take I-5 north about 25 miles to the Mukilteo ferry exit. Disembark from the ferry at the Clinton terminal and take Highway 525 about 25 miles to its end. At this junction continue going straight on Highway 20 north for three miles. Look for the sign and take a right on West Morris Road.
OPEN	All year
DESCRIPTION	A two-story colonial inn with colonial decor.
NO. OF ROOMS	Four rooms with private bathrooms. Try the La Sala Verde Suite.
RATES	Year-round rates are $85-125 for a single or double. There is a minimum stay during major holidays and cancellation requires three days' notice.

CREDIT CARDS	MasterCard, Visa
BREAKFAST	Full breakfast is served in the dining room or terrace room and includes homemade quiche, blueberry or apple strudel, a large selection of fruit, juices, a variety of omelets, homemade breads, smoked salmon or Penn Cove smelt, and more. Vegetarian diets are accommodated with prior notice and dinner is available with advance reservations.
AMENITIES	Hot tub at the forest edge; robes; hors d'oeuvres; scenic, romantic paths with benches; view of Olympic Mountains; massage by appointment; meeting facility and food service available.
RESTRICTIONS	No smoking, no pets, children over 14 are welcome (infants OK in some rooms). Samantha is the resident black Lab, and Stuffy is the wire-haired terrier. "Samantha is the most loving friend we have; she is kind to all people. Stuffy is two years old and is very loving. He likes to play all day if he can."
REVIEWED	*Northwest Best Places*
RATED	AAA 3 Diamonds

THE VICTORIAN BED & BREAKFAST

602 North Main Street, Coupeville, WA 98239   360-678-5305
Al & Marion Sasso, Innkeepers
WEBSITE *www.whidbey.net/~asasso/*

LOCATION	Coming from the south on Highway 20, turn right on Main Street (turn left when coming from the north). The B&B is at 6th and Main.
OPEN	All year
DESCRIPTION	An 1889 two-story Italianate Victorian host home decorated with a combination of Victorian and country furnishings, antiques, and "just plain family things." Listed on the National and State Historic Registers.
NO. OF ROOMS	Three rooms with private bathrooms. The Sassos recommend the cottage.
RATES	June through October, rates are $80-100 for a single or double. November through May, rates are $70-90. There is a minimum stay during holidays and cancellation requires one weeks' notice.
CREDIT CARDS	American Express, Discover, MasterCard, Visa
BREAKFAST	Full breakfast is served in the dining room and includes "good food and conversation."
AMENITIES	Flowers and wine on anniversaries; robes; soaps, shampoo, and

conditioner; mints on the bed; coffee, tea, hot chocolate, and goodies at all times.

RESTRICTIONS	No smoking. Children and pets are allowed in the cottage only. Shatzy is the resident cat.
REVIEWED	*Pets Welcome*
MEMBER	Whidbey Island Bed & Breakfast Association
RATED	AAA 3 Diamonds

DAVENPORT

A VICTORIAN CHRISTMAS HOUSE BED & BREAKFAST

308 Logan, Davenport, WA 99122   509-725-0308
Tom & Nancy Frees, Resident Owners

DAYTON

With an impressive 88 Victorian buildings on the National Historic Register, Dayton is worthy of a stop. The town profited from an 1861 gold rush because it was on the main stage route between Walla Walla and Lewiston. During the boom years, merchants and farmers built lavish houses. For cross-country and downhill skiing head for the Blue Mountains and Ski Bluewood, 21 miles southeast of Dayton (52 miles from Walla Walla). The Dayton area, boasting the highest base elevation in the state, gets more than 300 inches of snow a year on its 26 runs.

THE PURPLE HOUSE BED & BREAKFAST

415 East Clay Street, Dayton, WA 99328   509-382-3159
D. Christine Williscroft, Resident Owner   800-486-2574
German and French spoken   FAX 509-382-3159

LOCATION	Twenty-nine miles east of Walla Walla. One block off Main Street on Highway 12, in the heart of downtown. Take a right on 3rd Street and a left on East Clay.

The Purple House Bed & Breakfast, Dayton

OPEN	All year
DESCRIPTION	An 1882 two-story Italianate Victorian inn, fully restored and decorated with antiques, listed on the National Historic Register.
NO. OF ROOMS	Two rooms with private bathrooms and two rooms share two bathrooms. The owner recommends the Master Suite.
RATES	Year-round rate for a single or double with a private bathroom is $125, and a single or double with a shared bathroom is $85. There is no minimum stay, and seven days' notice is required for cancellation.
CREDIT CARDS	MasterCard, Visa
BREAKFAST	Full breakfast is served and includes fresh-baked breads, European pastries, and "whatever is in season." Dinners are also available by prior arrangement for a minimum of six people.
AMENITIES	Flowers, robes, hors d'oeuvres, air conditioning, handicapped access, icewater and fruit, often tea and pastries in the afternoon.
RESTRICTIONS	Small pets are OK, and children are welcome by prior arrangement. The resident Shih Tzus, Mollé and Mellé, are very sociable, do not shed, and are bathed every week.
REVIEWED	*Northwest Best Places; On the Road Again with Man's Best Friend; Washington State Bed & Breakfast Cookbook; Teatime in the Northwest; The Official Guide to American Historic Inns*

DEER PARK

About 20 miles north of Spokane on scenic Highway 395. Good skiing, particularly for beginners, can be had at 49 Degrees North Ski and Snowboard Resort.

LOVE'S VICTORIAN BED & BREAKFAST

North 31317 Cedar Road, Deer Park, WA 99006   509-276-6939
Bill & Leslie Love, Innkeepers   FAX 509-276-6939 *(call first)*
EMAIL *LovesBandB@juno.com*   WEBSITE *www.bbhost.com/lovesvictorian*

LOCATION	From the North Division "Y," take Highway 395 north to Staley Road (the first right after Dennison-Chattaroy). Turn right and go to the stop sign. Cross the railroad tracks and follow the road for 2.6 miles.
OPEN	All year
DESCRIPTION	A 1986 two-story Queen Anne Victorian—a romantic country getaway.
NO. OF ROOMS	Three rooms with private bathrooms. Try the Turret Suite.
RATES	Year-round rates are $75-125 for a single or double. There is no minimum stay and cancellation requires 10 days' notice with a $10 charge.
CREDIT CARDS	MasterCard, Visa
BREAKFAST	Full candlelit breakfast is served in the dining room by the fire. Breakfast begins with a fruit compote of strawberries, blueberries, bananas, and yogurt, followed by heart-shaped waffles or French toast, eggs, bacon, juice, and coffee.
AMENITIES	Afternoon tea and cookies served in the sun room; sparkling cider served in the evening; outdoor hot tub; robes and slippers; gazebo (great for outdoor weddings); a Great Room that is perfect for small intimate weddings and afternoon tea parties; central air conditioning and gas fireplaces in the Turret Suite, front parlor, dining room, and Great Room; Turret Suite balcony overlooks the pond, waterfall, and gazebo on the south lawn.
RESTRICTIONS	No smoking, children over 12 are welcome. Miss Pig is the resident potbellied pig. Lilly, Falina, and Mittens are the cats. There are also chickens, a rooster, and a Doberman named Luther, with whom the rooster loves to play chase. "We also have a chow named Shami who greets our guests."
REVIEWED	*The Best Places to Kiss in the Northwest; Fodor's; Victorian Voyages; Pets Welcome; Northwest Getaways*
MEMBER	Spokane Bed & Breakfast Association, Inland Northwest Catering Association

EASTON

SILVER RIDGE RANCH

182 Silver Ridge Ranch Road, Easton, WA 98925   *509-656-0275*

EATONVILLE

Don't miss Northwest Trek just off Highway 7 on the road to Mount Rainier. It's a "zoo" where animals roam free while people tour the 600-acre grounds in small open-air trams. The buffalo herd steals the show. You can also combine your visit with breakfast at the on-site food service concession, the Fir Bough.

MILL TOWN MANOR

116 Oak Street, Eatonville, WA 98328   *360-832-6506*
Gary & Debbi Saint, Resident Innkeepers   *FAX 360-832-6506*
"Choppy" Spanish spoken
EMAIL *milltown@foxinternet.net*
WEBSITE *www.bbonline.com/wa/milltown*

LOCATION	In the small town of Eatonville in the foothills at the base of Mount Rainier.
OPEN	All year
DESCRIPTION	A 1925 three-story colonial/Craftsman decorated as a tribute to the Roaring Twenties with beautiful woodwork, period fixtures, and a growing collection of memorabilia from the 1920s.
NO. OF ROOMS	Four rooms with private bathrooms. One room shares a bathroom. Each room is named after a celebrity from the 1920s. Try the Valentino Suite.
RATES	Year-round rates are $80-115 for a single or double with a private bathroom, $40 for a single or double with the shared bathroom (only available with the rental of another room), and a suite is $115. There is a 10 percent discount on all rooms from September through May, and a two-night minimum stay during July and August. Cancellation requires one week's notice.
CREDIT CARDS	MasterCard, Visa
BREAKFAST	Full hearty "timber town" breakfast is served in the dining room

and includes breakfast breads and pastries or Debbi's famous cracked-wheat cereal, local fruits, and an entrée such as Neptune eggs (featuring Pacific Northwest smoked salmon).

AMENITIES | Hot beverage bar with fresh-baked cookies or dessert, turndown service, big-screen TV/VCR, library, fresh flowers in rooms during the summer, secret passageway to an authentic Prohibition-era speakeasy complete with bar and dance floor, original seven-headed shower in the Rudolph Valentino Suite.

RESTRICTIONS | No smoking, no pets, children over 12 are welcome. Mooch is the resident outdoor sheepdog/shepherd mix and Pumpkin, the red tabby, rules the house.

REVIEWED | *Country Inns of the West; Washington State Bed & Breakfast Cookbook*

MEMBER | Bed & Breakfast Association of Tacoma and Mount Rainier, Washington Bed & Breakfast Guild

KUDOS/COMMENTS | "Outstanding inn. Great decor to match the period of the house. Incredible breakfasts—hearty and well presented."

MOUNTAIN VIEW CEDAR LODGE BED & BREAKFAST

36203 Pulford Road East, Eatonville, WA 98328   *360-832-8080*

EDMONDS

Downtown Edmonds is a throwback to another era, with a small movie theater, friendly shopkeepers, wide sidewalks, and waterfront views that encourage evening strolls. Edmonds bills itself as the City of Celebrations: most popular are the Edmonds Art Festival (in June) and A Taste of Edmonds (the third weekend in August). Brackett's Landing, just north of the ferry terminal, has a jetty and an underwater marinelife park that draws scuba enthusiasts. Edmonds Historic Walk was prepared by the Centennial Committee and offers a look at old Edmonds.

THE DAYTON BED & BREAKFAST

522 Dayton, Edmonds, WA 98020   *425-778-3611*

ENCHANTED GARDEN BED & BREAKFAST

1030 A Avenue South, Edmonds, WA 98020   *425-771-4721*
Bill & JoAnn Morton, Innkeepers   *FAX 425-774-8825*
EMAIL mortowf@ix.netcom.com

LOCATION	From I-5, take exit 177 west to 100th, turn right, then left onto Fir, then right onto A Avenue South.
OPEN	May 15 through October 15
DESCRIPTION	A 1968 two-story contemporary host home with romantic interior, contemporary furnishings, and an outstanding view of Puget Sound.
NO. OF ROOMS	One room with a private bathroom.
RATES	Year-round rate is $80 for a single or double. Ask about minimum stay and cancellation policies.
CREDIT CARDS	No
BREAKFAST	Full breakfast is served in the dining room and includes Seattle's Best Coffee and fresh fruit; guests choose an entrée and a time to eat.
AMENITIES	Robes, fresh flowers from the garden, meeting facility, space for small destination weddings, local tours planned.
RESTRICTIONS	No smoking. Spooky is the resident outdoor tabby.

HARRISON HOUSE

210 Sunset Avenue, Edmonds, WA 98020   *425-776-4748*
Jody & Harve Harrison, Innkeepers

LOCATION	From I-5, take exit 177 to the Edmonds ferry dock. The B&B is one block north of the ferry dock.
OPEN	All year
DESCRIPTION	A 1983 two-story contemporary host home with modern decor.
NO. OF ROOMS	Two rooms with private bathrooms.
RATES	Year-round rates for a single or double are $55-75. There is no minimum stay required.
CREDIT CARDS	No
BREAKFAST	Full breakfast is served in the dining room.
RESTRICTIONS	No smoking, no pets, no children
REVIEWED	*The Road Best Traveled*

HUDGENS HAVEN BED & BREAKFAST

9313 190th Street SW, Edmonds, WA 98020   425-776-2202

MAPLE TREE BED & BREAKFAST

18313 Olympic View Drive, Edmonds, WA 98020   425-774-8420
Hellon Wilkerson, Resident Owner   FAX 425-775-9039

ELLENSBURG

Famous for its Labor Day rodeo, this "college-and-cowboy" town draws many for its slice-of-life view of rural America. The downtown area was rebuilt after a devastating fire in 1889. Among the handsome structures still standing are the Davidson Building, on the corner of Pearl and Fourth, and the Masonic Temple, with its intriguing asymmetrical facade. The Clymer Museum and Gallery honors Ellensburg's own chronicler of the Western frontier, John Clymer, whose work appeared in several editions of the *Saturday Evening Post*. Central Washington's only professional repertory theater presents over 35 performances by the energetic Laughing Horse Company during July and August. Plays are staged in the architecturally stunning Tower Theater on the Central Washington University campus. The hills surrounding Ellensburg are speckled with blue agates found nowhere else in the world.

CARRIAGE HOUSE COTTAGE

140 Rosebriar Lane, Ellensburg, WA 98926   509-925-2108

THE INN AT GOOSE CREEK

1720 Canyon Road, Ellensburg, WA 98926   800-533-0822
Gary & Ylwa Mabee, Resident Owners
Swedish spoken
EMAIL goosecrk@ellensburg.com
WEBSITE www.ellensburg.com/~goosecrk/

LOCATION   Take exit 109 from I-90. Head toward Ellensburg on Canyon Road.

	Turn right at the Texaco station. The inn is located between Texaco and Comfort Inn.
OPEN	All year
DESCRIPTION	A 1997 two-story European inn.
NO. OF ROOMS	Ten rooms with private bathrooms. The owners recommend the Xmas Room.
RATES	May 15 through November 1, rates are $89-109 for a single or double; November 2 through May 14, rates are $69-89. There is no minimum stay and cancellation requires 24 hours' notice.
CREDIT CARDS	American Express, MasterCard, Visa
BREAKFAST	Continental breakfast is served in the dining room and includes orange juice, granola, cereal, bagels, English muffins, assorted jams, cream cheese, peanut butter, coffee, tea, and milk.
AMENITIES	Goose-down comforters, cable TV/VCR, refrigerators in rooms, Jacuzzis, hand-woven wool carpets, in-room coffee, heat and air conditioning with remote control, handicapped facilities, meeting rooms.
RESTRICTIONS	No smoking, no pets

MEADOWLARK FARM GUEST HOUSE

606 North Main Street, Ellensburg, WA 98926　　　　*509-933-1151*

MURPHY'S COUNTRY BED & BREAKFAST

2830 Thorp Highway South, Ellensburg, WA 98926　　　*509-925-7986*
Doris Callahan, Resident Owner
WEBSITE *www.ellensburg-wa.com*

LOCATION	Located 1.8 miles west of exit 106 off I-90. At the KOA turn onto Thorp Highway and continue past Robinson Canyon Road to the second house on the left.
OPEN	All year
DESCRIPTION	A 1915 two-story Craftsman bungalow with leaded-glass windows, original fir woodwork throughout, and a large river-rock porch.
NO. OF ROOMS	Two rooms with private bathrooms.

Murphy's Country Bed & Breakfast, Ellensburg

RATES	Year-round rates are $60 for a single and $70 for a double. There is no minimum stay and cancellation requires seven days' notice.
CREDIT CARDS	American Express, MasterCard, Visa
BREAKFAST	Full breakfast includes fuzzy orange juice, fruits of the season, vegetable quiche or cheese-baked eggs, and a choice of either fresh-baked cinnamon rolls, Danish, muffins, or scones with jam. Special meals are also available.
AMENITIES	In winter, tea and cookies by the fireplace; in summer, iced tea or lemonade; a small conference room is available for meetings or reunions of up to 15 people.
RESTRICTIONS	No smoking, no pets, children over seven are welcome. There are two or three horses pasturing in the summer.
REVIEWED	*Hidden Pacific Northwest*
MEMBER	Washington Bed & Breakfast Guild
RATED	AAA 2 Diamonds
KUDOS/COMMENTS	"The rooms are large and comfortable. Doris's breakfasts are incredible, especially the scones."

ENUMCLAW

The gateway to the northern entrance of Mount Rainier National Park and Crystal Mountain Ski Area. Both Seattle and Tacoma are within easy reach for day trips.

THE WHITE ROSE INN

1610 Griffin Avenue, Enumclaw, WA 98022   *360-825-7194*
Tami & Michael Dunn, Innkeepers   *800-404-7194*
EMAIL *inkeepr@whiteroseinnbb.com*   *FAX 360-802-2472*
WEBSITE *www.whiteroseinnbb.com*

LOCATION	Two blocks from Enumclaw on Highway 164 (also known as Griffin Avenue).
OPEN	All year
DESCRIPTION	A 1922 three-story colonial mansion decorated in a formal, elegant style and constructed of Honduran mahogany and quartersawn oak.
NO. OF ROOMS	Four rooms with private bathrooms. Try the Paradise Room.
RATES	Memorial Day through Labor Day, rates are $85-95 for a single or double. The remainder of the year, rates are $75-85 for a single or double. There is a two-night minimum stay during the Highland Festival and cancellation requires seven days' notice.
CREDIT CARDS	American Express, MasterCard, Visa
BREAKFAST	Full breakfast is served in the dining room.
RESTRICTIONS	No smoking, no pets. Little Buddy is the resident Yorkshire terrier.

EPHRATA

On Highway 28, Ephrata is well situated for short day trips to Moses Lake, Potholes Reservoir, Grand Coulee Dam, Gorge Amphitheater, the Columbia River, and Ginko Petrified Forest.

IVY CHAPEL INN

164 D Street SW, Ephrata, WA 98823   *509-754-0629*
Kirk & Cheryl McClelland, Innkeepers
EMAIL *ivychapel@hotmail.com*
WEBSITE *www.quikpage.com/i/ivychapel*

LOCATION	Two blocks west of Basin Street (Route 28) on 2nd and D Streets.
OPEN	All year
DESCRIPTION	A 1948 two-story, ivy-covered brick church with a cathedral ceiling and theme rooms. Originally a Presbyterian church, it was converted into a B&B in 1994.
NO. OF ROOMS	Six rooms with private bathrooms. The McClellands suggest the Safari Room.
RATES	Year-round rates are $75 for a single or double and $100 for a suite. The entire B&B is $475. There is no minimum stay requirement.
CREDIT CARDS	American Express, Discover, MasterCard, Visa
BREAKFAST	Full gourmet breakfast is served in the breakfast room.
AMENITIES	All rooms with air conditioning and cable TV, large parlor for guests to relax or for meetings. The chapel seats about 160 and is listed for weddings, parties, and business meetings.
RESTRICTIONS	No smoking, no pets, children over 10 are welcome. There are several resident dogs and a cat.
RATED	AAA 3 Diamonds

EVERETT

Though timber still means big business for Everett, the state-of-the-art U.S. Naval Base now adds even more to the city's growing economy and its ever-increasing population. Everett is experiencing new pride, evident in the revitalization of its downtown core. The redevelopment of the Hotel Monte Cristo, a historic landmark boarded up for 20 years, has provided a gorgeous home for the Everett Symphony, the Arts Council, and a stunning display of Pilchuck glass.

GAYLORD HOUSE

3301 Grand Avenue, Everett, WA 98201   425-339-9153
Shirley Anne Gaylord & Theresa Schaudies, Innkeepers   888-507-7177
Italian spoken   FAX 425-303-9713
EMAIL *Gaylord_House@msn.com*   WEBSITE *www.gaylordhouse.com*

LOCATION	Heading north on I-5, take exit 193 (Pacific Avenue) and turn left (west). Continue on Pacific for 1.1 miles to Grand Avenue. Turn left (south) and travel two blocks to the Gaylord House. Heading south on I-5, take exit 194 (Everett Avenue), and turn right (west). Continue on Everett Avenue for one mile to Grand Avenue. Turn left on Grand and travel six blocks.

Gaylord House, Everett

OPEN	All year
DESCRIPTION	A 1910 two-story Craftsman inn on a residential street lined with giant maples. The inn has a parlor, library, covered veranda, and back deck.
NO. OF ROOMS	Five rooms with private bathrooms. Try the Mediterranean Sunrise Room.
RATES	Year-round rates are $85-175 for a single or double. Call about the minimum-stay policy; cancellation requires 72 hours' notice.
CREDIT CARDS	American Express, Discover, MasterCard, Visa
BREAKFAST	Full breakfast is served in the dining room. Lunch, dinner, and special meals are available with 48 hours' notice.
AMENITIES	Flowers, robes, TV/VCR, private phone lines, modem port, desk, bottomless cookie jars and fruit bowl, central air conditioning, some rooms with fireplaces and private balconies, double Jacuzzi tubs, double-headed showers, clawfoot tubs/showers, handicapped access.
RESTRICTIONS	No smoking, no pets
MEMBER	Professional Association of Innkeepers International, Washington State Bed & Breakfast Guild
RATED	AAA 3 Diamonds

EVERSON

This hamlet is 30 minutes northeast of Bellingham.

KALE HOUSE BED & BREAKFAST

201 Kale Street, Everson, WA 98247   360-966-7027
Marvin & Bonnie Litorja, Resident Owners   800-225-2165

WILKINS FARM BED & BREAKFAST

4165 South Pass Road, Everson, WA 98247   360-966-7616
Carmela Wilkins, Innkeeper

LOCATION	From I-5, take exit 255 and head northeast on Mount Baker Highway (Everson Goshen Road) to Everson. Go three miles northeast of Everson on South Pass Road.
OPEN	All year
DESCRIPTION	An 1882 two-story saltbox farmhouse with wood timbers lining the rooms and decorated with antiques.
NO. OF ROOMS	Three rooms share one bathroom.
RATES	Year-round rates are $22 for a single and $35 for a double. There is no minimum stay. Reservations must be made at least two days in advance.
CREDIT CARDS	No
BREAKFAST	Full Italian breakfast is served in the dining room or kitchen. "My parents were from Sicily," Carmela explains. "I cook dishes I was brought up with."
AMENITIES	Flowers in rooms, wine and candies by bedside, hiking areas.
RESTRICTIONS	No smoking, no pets, children are welcome. There are dairy cows grazing on the property.
REVIEWED	*Northwest Budget Traveler*

FERNDALE

The Tennant Lake Interpretive Center and Fragrance Garden in Ferndale offers boardwalk access to an abundance of birdlife in a wetland setting. The garden was developed with the visually and physically impaired in mind, so many of the raised-bed plantings are identified with braille labels and the garden is wheelchair-accessible.

LARSEN DAIRY BED & BREAKFAST

2780 Alder Grove Road, Ferndale, WA 98248   *360-384-4835*
Paul & Alice Larsen, Resident Owners

SAGER BED & BREAKFAST

Ferndale, WA 98248   *360-384-3693*

SLATER HERITAGE HOUSE BED & BREAKFAST

1371 West Axton Road, Ferndale, WA 98248   *360-384-4273*

FORKS

From this little town on the west end of the Olympic Peninsula, you can explore wild coastal beaches, hook a steelhead, or go mountain biking, camping, or hiking. The pristine waters of the Hoh, Bogachiel, Calawah, and Soleduck Rivers all flow near Forks, making it a key destination for fishermen. On the outskirts of town, the Timber Museum tells the story of the West End's logging heritage. Thirty miles south of Forks, the Hoh Rainforest is the wettest location in the contiguous United States. Its steady moisture nurtures the dense vegetation—more than 3000 species of plant life.

BRIGHTWATER HOUSE, A BED & BREAKFAST

440 Brightwater Drive, Forks, WA 98331   *360-374-5453*
Richard & Beth Chesmore, Resident Owners
We speak fly fishing

LOCATION	Four miles west of downtown Forks off La Push Road.
OPEN	All year
DESCRIPTION	A 1972 two-story contemporary ranch house with local wildlife and fly-fishing themes, located on 3,500 feet of riverfront property along the Soleduck River.
NO. OF ROOMS	Two rooms with private bathrooms.
RATES	Please call for current rates and cancellation information.
CREDIT CARDS	MasterCard, Visa
BREAKFAST	Full breakfast is served.
AMENITIES	Flowers, gardens, nature trails, fishing access, bird-watching, wildlife viewing, mushroom picking, guided float trips, archaeological information about the Olympic Peninsula.
RESTRICTIONS	No smoking inside, no pets inside. Children over eight are welcome.
MEMBER	Olympic Peninsula Travel Association

FISHERMAN'S WIDOW

31 Huckleberry Lane, Forks, WA 98331
WEBSITE *www.northolympic.com/fw*

360-374-5693

HOH HUMM RANCH

171763 Highway 101, Forks, WA 98331
Bob Huelsdonk, Resident Owner

360-374-5337

MANITOU LODGE

PO Box 600, Forks, WA 98331

360-374-6295

MILL CREEK INN

1026 Highway 101 South, Forks, WA 98331

360-374-5873

MILLER TREE INN

654 East Division Street, Forks, WA 98331   *360-374-6806*
Bill & Susan Brager, Innkeepers   *FAX 360-374-6807*
EMAIL milltree@ptinet.net   *WEBSITE www.northolympic.com/millertree*

LOCATION	From Highway 101, turn east at the only stoplight in town. The inn is six blocks from the center of town on the right-hand side of the road.
OPEN	All year
DESCRIPTION	A 1917 three-story farmhouse with comfortable, homey decor and some antiques, situated in a grove of trees.
NO. OF ROOMS	Three rooms with private bathrooms and two rooms with two shared bathrooms. The Blue Jay Room is Susan's favorite.
RATES	May 15 through October 15, rates are $75-115 for a single or double with a private bathroom, $45-85 for a single or double with a shared bathroom, and $115 for a suite. October 16 through May 14, rates are $65-100 for a single or double with a private bathroom, $35-65 for a single or double with a shared bathroom, and $100 for a suite. There is a minimum stay during peak season and cancellation requires three days' notice—no charge if the room is rebooked.
CREDIT CARDS	MasterCard, Visa
BREAKFAST	Full breakfast is served in the dining room and includes a self-serve pastry, fruit, juice, and cereal bar. A hot entrée is brought to guests and may include an egg dish, pancakes, waffles, or French toast.
AMENITIES	Cookies, tea, and coffee all day; lemonade available during warm spring, summer, and fall days; sometimes desserts during evenings in the fall; eight-person covered hot tub; robes; guest refrigerator.
RESTRICTIONS	No smoking inside, no pets, children over seven are welcome in the Cedar Creek Room. Children of all ages are welcome in the Orchard Suite. Guinness, the cat, is curious and affectionate. He is allowed in the common rooms, but not the guestrooms.
REVIEWED	*Northwest Best Places; The Best Bed & Breakfast and Country Inns of the West; Inside Out Washington*
MEMBER	Olympic Peninsula Bed & Breakfast Association, Washington Bed & Breakfast Guild
RATED	AAA 2 Diamonds

MISTY VALLEY INN

194894 Highway 101 North, Forks, WA 98331   360-374-9389
Rachel & Jim Bennett, Innkeepers   877-374-9389
EMAIL mistyinn@olypen.com   FAX 360-374-3310
WEBSITE www.olypen.com/pbennett/pbennett/mistyinn.html

LOCATION	Two miles north of Forks on Highway 101 about 100 feet south of milepost 195.
OPEN	All year
DESCRIPTION	A 1977 two-story stone and cedar inn with broad decks overlooking the mist-filled Soleduck River Valley, with comfortable American furnishings and antiques.
NO. OF ROOMS	Four rooms with private bathrooms. Try the Dutch Room.
RATES	Year-round rates are $75-85 for a single or double. There is no minimum stay and cancellation requires 24 hours' notice.
CREDIT CARDS	MasterCard, Visa
BREAKFAST	Full three-course breakfast is served on china with crystal and sterling silver in the formal dining room or on the deck. Breakfast begins with a quiet knock on the door; guests are served a custom tray with fresh beverages and flowers. Guests choose their breakfast times. Breakfast specialties include Irish waffles with orange syrup, Washington apple soufflé, seasonal fruit crepes, or a subtle Moroccan omelet. "Each meal has been hand-tailored to the individual, and personal favorites are readily served." The hostess is a registered dietitian and diet modifications are easily accommodated. "You will never leave the table hungry!"
AMENITIES	Air conditioning and continuously filtered air throughout the inn; ozone hot spa in the rose garden overlooking the Soleduck River Valley; cake, cookies, pastry, and beverages are available throughout the afternoon and evening; fresh well water free of additives; baths stocked with custom linens and quality shampoo, conditioners, and soaps; each room with its own special furnishings; full candy dishes; assistance is provided to guests planning fishing trips, hikes, walks, photography sessions, river rafting, and shopping; hand-drawn maps, reservations, and itineraries are quickly prepared for guests.
RESTRICTIONS	No smoking, no pets, children over 13 are welcome. Jordan is the resident Eskimo dog and Rambo is the blue Manx. Jordan will greet you at the car by barking and then he will roll over to be petted on his stomach.

River Inn Bed & Breakfast

2596 Bogachiel Way, Forks, WA 98331   360-374-6526
Jeff Woodward & Bruno Krebs, Resident Owners   FAX 360-374-6590
Swiss German spoken

LOCATION	Exit Highway 101 into Forks, turn right on Bogachiel Way, and go 2.5 miles; look for the sign.
OPEN	All year
DESCRIPTION	A 1981 two-story Northwest chalet with Northwest interior decor located on the banks of the Bogachiel River among old-growth trees.
NO. OF ROOMS	One room with a private bathroom and two rooms share one bathroom.
RATES	Please call for current rates and cancellation information.
CREDIT CARDS	MasterCard, Visa
BREAKFAST	Full country breakfast is served in the dining room.
AMENITIES	Hot tub and guided fishing trips.
RESTRICTIONS	No smoking inside, children over 10 are welcome.
REVIEWED	*Best of Washington*

Fox Island

A tiny island community just south of Gig Harbor, with plenty of quiet bays for kayaking and fishing.

Beachside Bed & Breakfast

679 Kamus Drive, Fox Island, WA 98333   253-549-2524
Doreen Samuelson, Innkeeper

LOCATION	Approximately 10 miles from Gig Harbor. From the Tacoma Narrows Bridge, take Highway 16 to the first Fox Island exit. Go left across the overpass for two miles to the stoplight at Wollochet. Watch for the green Fox Island signs. Cross Fox Island Bridge and follow Island Boulevard for 3.5 miles to its end at Ninth. Go right one block, then right down the hill until you see the water and a tennis court. Take a sharp right. The B&B is the last house.
OPEN	All year

DESCRIPTION	A 1971 one-story custom-designed beach guesthouse with beamed ceiling. Situated on the beach, with views of the Olympic Mountains and spectacular sunsets.
NO. OF ROOMS	One suite with a private bathroom.
RATES	Year-round rate is $95 per night. There is no minimum stay required; a 50 percent deposit for reservations and one week's cancellation notice are required.
CREDIT CARDS	No
BREAKFAST	Continental plus is served in the guesthouse and includes cereal, bran muffins, fresh fruit, fresh-ground coffee, tea, milk, and sweet rolls.
AMENITIES	Six-person hot tub, wood-burning fireplace surrounded by overstuffed furniture, full kitchen, cable TV/VCR and CD player, flowers, robes, candy, sherry, decorations for special occasions, washing machine, whale- and seal-watching, private entrance.
RESTRICTIONS	No smoking, no pets
REVIEWED	*Northwest Best Places*
MEMBER	Northwest Bed & Breakfast Association, Washington State Bed & Breakfast Guild
RATED	AAA 4 Diamonds
KUDOS/COMMENTS	"Charming English-style waterfront cottage, friendly hosts."

THE BRAMBLES BED & BREAKFAST

1077 12th Avenue, Fox Island, WA 98333
Eve & Dennis Kiehm, Innkeepers
French and some Spanish spoken
EMAIL *evenden@juno.com*

253-549-4959
FAX 253-549-4959

LOCATION	Take I-5 to Highway 16 west (Bremerton/Gig Harbor). Cross the Narrows Bridge and take the third exit (Olympic Drive/Fox Island). Follow the signs to Fox Island. On the island, follow the signs to Historical Museum. Turn left onto Kamus and go toward the water. Stay left (Kamus) and continue to the bottom of the hill. Turn right on Twelfth Avenue.
OPEN	All year
DESCRIPTION	A remodeled 1975 two-and-a-half-story split-entry country host home furnished with European and Asian antiques and accessories, located 100 yards from the Fox Island Yacht Club and Cedrona Bay.
NO. OF ROOMS	One suite with a private bathroom.

RATES	Year-round rate is $80 for the suite. There is no minimum stay and cancellation requires three days' notice.
CREDIT CARDS	No
BREAKFAST	Full breakfast is served in the dining room and includes cereal, tropical juices, fresh fruit, toast, muffins, coffee, tea, and an entrée such as fruit pancakes, "Hawaiian" French toast, huevos rancheros, or egg casseroles.
AMENITIES	Afternoon tea with tiny sandwiches, homemade scones, cake, and cookies—served on the deck when weather permits.
RESTRICTIONS	No smoking inside, no children. Marmalade is the resident cat (a little shy but loving with new friends).

ISLAND ESCAPE BED & BREAKFAST

210 Island Boulevard, Fox Island, WA 98333   253-549-2044
Paula Pascoe, Innkeeper   FAX 253-549-7700
EMAIL paula@island-escape.com   WEBSITE www.island-escape.com

LOCATION	From Seattle, Tacoma, or Olympia: take I-5 to Highway 16 (Bremerton exit). After crossing the Tacoma Narrows Bridge, take the Gig Harbor City Center/Fox Island exit. Follow the signs to Fox Island. After crossing the Fox Island Bridge, drive 0.4 mile and turn right on Cove Road. Turn right again on Island Boulevard. Drive 0.2 mile and turn left on Griffin Lane (gravel driveway). The B&B is the last house on the left at the end of the drive.
OPEN	All year
DESCRIPTION	A 1985 three-story modern German and Hawaiian inn featuring a private, waterfront suite overlooking beautiful Puget Sound.
NO. OF ROOMS	One suite with a private bathroom.
RATES	Year-round rates are $95-115 for a suite. There is no minimum stay and cancellation requires seven days' notice.
CREDIT CARDS	American Express, MasterCard, Visa
BREAKFAST	Full breakfast is served in the suite and includes "whatever the guests want, within reason."
AMENITIES	Spacious suite, large living room with fireplace, large bedroom with king-size bed, private bath with Jacuzzi tub, private entrance, deck and hammock, spectacular views of Puget Sound and Olympic Mountains, special discounts at local shops and restaurants, bedside chocolates, fresh flowers in room, bottle of chilled cider, herbal bath grains, complimentary pass to local health club, luxurious bath robes, massage therapist on request.

RESTRICTIONS	No smoking, no pets. Lucky is the resident Border collie and Alice is the cat.
MEMBER	Professional Association of Innkeepers, Washington Bed & Breakfast Guild
KUDOS/COMMENTS	"Lovely hostess, water view."

FREELAND

The unincorporated town of Freeland, population 1544, is home to Nichols Brothers Boat Builders, manufacturers of cruise boats and stern-wheelers and the town's largest employer. Freeland Park on Holmes Harbor has picnic tables, a play area, and a sandy beach.

BUSH POINT WHARF BED & BREAKFAST

Box 1042, Freeland, WA 98249   360-331-0405
Stanley Yu, Resident Owner   800-460-7219

CLIFF HOUSE & SEACLIFF COTTAGE

727 Windmill Road, Freeland, WA 98249   360-331-1566
Peggy Moore, Innkeeper
WEBSITE www.whidbey.com/cliffhouse

LOCATION	From Seattle, go north on I-5 to exit 189 and follow signs to Mukilteo. Take the ferry to Whidbey Island and head north on Highway 525 for 10.6 miles. Turn left on Bush Point Road, drive 1.5 miles to Windmill Road on the left, go one block, and look for the sign and winding driveway.
OPEN	All year
DESCRIPTION	A 1981 two-story guesthouse with contemporary country decor, lots of glass, and a "gnome house" cottage with country French decor.
NO. OF ROOMS	Two rooms in the Cliff House with private bathrooms and one room in the Seacliff Cottage with private bathroom.
RATES	Year-round rates are $410 for one couple and $510 for two couples; the cottage rents for $165. Ask about a minimum stay. Cancellation requires two weeks' notice.
CREDIT CARDS	No

BREAKFAST	Continental plus is served in both the Cliff House and Seacliff Cottage. "The refrigerator is stocked before your arrival with three varieties of juice, a dozen eggs, ham and cheese, croissants, fruit and crackers, sweet rolls, butter and jam, brioche, cereals, pancake mix and syrup, great coffee, and more."
AMENITIES	Located on the Seattle shipping lanes: huge ships from around the world pass right before the house and cottage. The Cliff House has air conditioning and a flower garden to wander through. The Seacliff Cottage has a deck high in the trees. Miles of driftwood beach, spa overlooking Puget Sound, 14 acres of forest, views of the Olympic Mountains, sunsets over water, fresh flowers, full gourmet kitchen "for those who love to be a chef," 400 videos, 300 CDs, feather beds, robes, jetted tub, atrium in the center of house with native plants (so it rains right into the center of the house), total privacy in house and cottage.
RESTRICTIONS	No smoking, no pets, children over 14 are welcome. "Beautiful bald eagles roost in our trees and fly over the beach."
REVIEWED	*Andrew Harpers Hideaway Report; The Best Places to Kiss in the Northwest; Pacific Northwest: 50 Romantic Getaways; Northwest Best Places; Hidden Pacific Northwest*
MEMBER	Whidbey Island Bed & Breakfast Association, Washington Bed & Breakfast Guild
KUDOS/COMMENTS	"Large, beautiful waterfront home, total privacy and seclusion, warm innkeepers, exquisite interior decor." "Outstanding."

FROGGWELL GARDEN

5508 Double Bluff Road, Freeland, WA 98249   360-321-7308
Ralph Hastings, Innkeeper   FAX 360-321-4378
WEBSITE *www.froggwell.com*

LOCATION	From Seattle, drive north on I-5 for about 35 minutes to exit 189 (Whidbey Island/Mukilteo Ferry) and take the Mukilteo ferry to Clinton. Drive 8.6 miles up Highway 525 to Double Bluff Road and turn right. Proceed 0.2 mile and turn left into the driveway at the Froggwell Garden sign.
OPEN	All year
DESCRIPTION	A very private 1980 two-story English cottage on 10 acres of internationally acclaimed gardens designed by renowned gardener, the late Holly Turner. The cottage was designed and built by Holly's partner Ralph Hastings.
NO. OF ROOMS	Two rooms with private bathrooms.

RATES	Year-round rates are $225-250 for a single or double with a private bathroom. There is a minimum stay during weekends and holidays, and a 50 percent nonrefundable deposit is due upon confirmation of reservation.
CREDIT CARDS	MasterCard, Visa
BREAKFAST	A breakfast basket is left in the refrigerator that includes eggs, butter and preserves, bagels or homemade muffins, fresh fruit, coffee, tea, juice, and milk.
AMENITIES	The main part of the house and one complete bedroom suite are handicapped accessible, including a special Jacuzzi tub; a gas-powered enamel stove warms the living area; the custom kitchen is fully equipped.
RESTRICTIONS	No smoking, no pets. Nepetah is the resident cat.

MUTINY BAY HIDEAWAY BED & BREAKFAST

5939 South Mutiny Bay Road, Freeland, WA 98249   800-262-3308
Carrie & Dan Pike, Innkeepers   FAX 360-331-6010

SEASIDE COTTAGE & GARDEN SUITE

213 East Sandpiper Road, Freeland, WA 98249   360-331-8455
Cliff & Virginia Lindsey, Resident Owners   FAX 360-331-8636
EMAIL seaside@whidbey.com   WEBSITE www.whidbey.com/seaside

LOCATION	From Highway 525, go 2.7 miles out Bush Point Road (past Freeland) and turn left onto Scurlock Road. Follow the yellow line to water's edge and turn left at the restaurant. Go to Sandpiper Road and turn right into the first driveway.
OPEN	All year
DESCRIPTION	A 1920s-era beach cottage and suite with knotty pine decor, situated at the water's edge at Bush Point.
NO. OF ROOMS	One cottage and one suite with private bathrooms.
RATES	Year-round rates are $125 for the cottage and $75 for the suite. There is a minimum stay during weekends in the cottage from July through September, and cancellation requires seven days' notice for a full refund.
CREDIT CARDS	Discover

BREAKFAST	Breakfast in the cottage includes eggs, homemade waffles, and pancakes; fruit, bread, cold cereals, coffee, and tea. Breakfast in the suite includes coffee, tea, fruit, muffins, and bread.
AMENITIES	Lots of flowers, beach fire area, barbecues, miles of sandy beach.
RESTRICTIONS	No smoking, no pets. There are a dog, Corky, and three cats, none of whom is allowed in the cottage or suite.

FRIDAY HARBOR

San Juan Island is the most populated in the archipelago and it supports the biggest town, Friday Harbor. Attractions include the mid-19th-century sites of the American and English Camps, established when ownership of the island was under dispute. The English Camp, toward the island's north end, is wooded and secluded, while the American Camp consists of open, windy prairie and beach, inhabited now only by thousands of rabbits. Either makes a fine picnic spot. So does the beautiful San Juan County Park. The best diving in the archipelago (some claim it's the best cold-water diving in the world) can be had here. Kayaking is a wonderful way to see the island's wildlife up close. If you're lucky (your best chance is in late spring), you may even encounter whales that belong to the three native pods of orcas. Those distrustful of their sea legs can visit the marvelous Whale Museum with exhibits and excursions devoted to the resident cetaceans; or go to the nation's first official whale-watching park at Lime Kiln Point State Park on the island's west side. Bring binoculars and lots of patience. The San Juan Historical Museum is filled with memorabilia from the island's early days. Mid- to late July, throngs of people flock the streets of Friday Harbor for three days of jazz, from blues to Dixieland.

ARBUTUS LODGE

1827 Westside Road North, Friday Harbor, WA 98250   360-378-8840
Susan & Richard Millington, Innkeepers   888-434-8840
EMAIL arbutus@rockisland.com   FAX 360-378-8846
WEBSITE www.friday-harbor.net/arbutus

LOCATION	From Friday Harbor, drive up Spring Street. Turn right on Second Street, which becomes Guard Street. Continue on Guard as it becomes Beaverton Valley Road (6.5 miles) and turn left on Mitchell Bay Road. As the road bears left, becoming Westside Road, watch for our sign on the right.
OPEN	All year
DESCRIPTION	A 1995 two-story Northwest timber-frame lodge with antique and contemporary furnishings.

Arbutus Lodge, Friday Harbor

NO. OF ROOMS	Two rooms with private bathrooms.
RATES	April 1 through October 31, rates are $110-130 for a single or double. November 1 through March 31, rates are $80-100. There is no minimum stay and cancellation requires one weeks' notice.
CREDIT CARDS	MasterCard, Visa
BREAKFAST	Full breakfast is served in the dining room and includes locally roasted coffee, a variety of teas, fresh-squeezed juices, elegant egg dishes, waffles, and French toast. Special meals available to accommodate dietary restrictions.
AMENITIES	Licensed massage services available by owner in home office.
RESTRICTIONS	No smoking, no pets, children over 12 are welcome. Tammy and Bear, the resident Labs, are kept company by Ashes, Checkers, and Modeley, the resident cats.
REVIEWED	*The Best Places to Kiss in the Northwest*
MEMBER	San Juan Islands Bed & Breakfast Association

ARGYLE HOUSE BED & BREAKFAST

685 Argyle Avenue, Friday Harbor, WA 98250   360-378-4084
Bill & Chris Carli, Resident Owners   800-624-3459
EMAIL *bcarli@rockisland.com*
WEBSITE *www.pacificws.com/sj/argyle.html*

LOCATION	From the ferry landing, follow traffic two blocks up Spring Street (main street) to Argyle Avenue and take a left.

OPEN	All year
DESCRIPTION	A 1910 two-story Craftsman-style home with high ceilings, wood floors, and window seats, decorated with light, airy, French country furnishings.
NO. OF ROOMS	Four rooms with private bathrooms and one room with a shared bathroom. The owners recommend the cottage.
RATES	May through September, rates are $100-110 for a single or double with a private bathroom, $90-100 for a single or double with a shared bathroom, $175 for a suite, and the cottage rents for $135. October through April, rates are $75-95 for a single or double with a private bathroom, $65-75 for a single or double with a shared bathroom, $140 for a suite, and $100 for the cottage. There is a two-night minimum stay, and cancellation requires seven days' notice with no charge incurred if the room is rebooked.
CREDIT CARDS	MasterCard, Visa
BREAKFAST	Full breakfast is served in the dining room and features four or five courses, including baked egg dishes (Mexican, Greek, Italian, etc.); oatmeal pancakes (also blueberry, banana Kahlua, etc.); French toast with fresh berries; fruit platters; and home-baked rolls, coffeecakes, and cobblers.
AMENITIES	Flowers and candy in rooms; maps; hot tub under the stars; relax on the patio or by the fountain/fish pond; down comforters; basketball and badminton; summer pick-up service at ferry, seaplane, and airport.
RESTRICTIONS	Children over 10 are welcome, but some exceptions are made for younger kids. Jordon, the resident cat, lives outdoors, and the blind poodle is named Pepperton. Peppy does not go into the main part of the house.
REVIEWED	*The Best Places to Kiss in the Northwest; Fodor's; Essential Guide to the San Juan Islands; Hidden Pacific Northwest*
MEMBER	Washington Bed & Breakfast Guild, San Juan Islands Bed & Breakfast Association
RATED	AAA 2 Diamonds

BEAVERTON VALLEY FARMHOUSE

3580 Beaverton Valley Road, Friday Harbor, WA 98250   *360-378-3276*

Blair House

345 Blair Avenue, Friday Harbor, WA 98250   360-378-5907
Bob Pittman, Resident Owner

Duffy House Bed & Breakfast Inn

760 Pear Point Road, Friday Harbor, WA 98250   360-378-5604
Mary & Arthur Miller, Resident Owners   800-972-2089
EMAIL duffyhouse@rockisland.com   FAX 360-378-6535
WEBSITE www.san-juan.net/duffyhouse

LOCATION	From the ferry landing, follow the traffic about two blocks to Argyle Avenue, take a left, go 0.7 mile to Pear Point Road, and turn left.
OPEN	All year
DESCRIPTION	A 1929 two-story Tudor-style Craftsman inn, decorated with Navajo rugs and antique pieces.
NO. OF ROOMS	Five rooms with private bathrooms. The owners recommend the Panorama Room.
RATES	May through October, rates are $95-115 for a single or double. Low-season rates are $20 less. There is a two-night minimum stay on weekends from July through September and during Christmas and Thanksgiving holidays. Cancellation requires seven days' notice plus a $15 fee.
CREDIT CARDS	MasterCard, Visa
BREAKFAST	Full breakfast includes fresh-squeezed orange juice, fruit compote, fresh-baked pastry, an entrée of eggs, pancakes, or French toast with bacon or sausage, plus coffee, tea, or hot chocolate.
AMENITIES	Flowers in rooms, fresh-baked cookies upon arrival, complimentary soft drinks, fruit juice, tea, fresh fruit in season from Duffy House Orchard, private beach.
RESTRICTIONS	No smoking, no pets, children over eight are welcome. The resident yellow tabby is Mr. Duffy. Watch the sky for Baldette and Baldo, the local bald eagles.
REVIEWED	Northwest Best Places; San Juan & Gulf Islands Best Places; Romantic Getaways in the Pacific Northwest & Western Canada; The Birder's Guide to Bed & Breakfasts; Washington Discovery Guide; Washington State Travelers: Affordable Accomodations
MEMBER	Washington State Bed & Breakfast Guild

RATED	AAA 3 Diamonds
KUDOS/COMMENTS	"Warm, friendly, wonderful innkeepers; great breakfasts; tastefully decorated Tudor-style home with water view." "Wonderful hosts and beautiful location."

FRIDAY'S HISTORICAL INN

35 First Street, Friday Harbor, WA 98250   360-378-5848
Debbie & Steve Demarest, Innkeepers   800-352-2632
WEBSITE *www.friday-harbor.com*   FAX 360-378-2881

LOCATION	Two blocks from the Friday Harbor ferry landing. Turn right from the ferry and left on Spring Street, then go right on First Street. Friday's is the tall gray building with green trim on your left.
OPEN	All year
DESCRIPTION	A renovated 1891 three-story Old West inn with a mixture of oak antiques and modern amenities.
NO. OF ROOMS	Five rooms with private bathrooms and six rooms share three bathrooms. The owners recommend the Eagle Cove Room.
RATES	May through October, a single or double with a private bathroom is $135-175, and a single or double with a shared bathroom is $90-110. November through April, a single or double with a private bathroom is $55-100, and a single or double with a shared bathroom is $45-75. Seven days' notice is required for cancellation.
CREDIT CARDS	MasterCard, Visa
BREAKFAST	Continental plus is served in the parlor and includes homemade baked goods, fresh fruit, real orange juice, gourmet coffee, and hot and cold cereal.
AMENITIES	Complimentary assistance with trip planning.
RESTRICTIONS	No smoking, no pets
REVIEWED	*The Best Places to Kiss in the Northwest; Northwest Best Places*
MEMBER	Bed & Breakfast Association of San Juan Island, Professional Association of Innkeepers International
RATED	Mobil 3 Stars

HALVORSEN HOUSE

1165 Halvorsen Road, Friday Harbor, WA 98250   360-378-2707
John & Cindy Patten, Innkeepers   888-238-4187
EMAIL johnpatten@interisland.net   *FAX 360-378-2707 (call first)*
WEBSITE www.halvorsenhouse.com

LOCATION	From the ferry landing, travel up Spring Street. Turn right onto Second Street and follow it to a three-way stop sign. Turn right onto Tucker Avenue, follow it out of town for two miles, and turn left onto Halvorsen Road. The B&B is the first house on the right.
OPEN	All year
DESCRIPTION	A 1997 two-story country cottage with traditional decor, floral wallpaper, and lace curtains, and situated in an island forest.
NO. OF ROOMS	Four rooms with private bathrooms. Try the Suite Suzanna.
RATES	Mid-May through September 21, rates are $99-105 for a double, $130 for the Suite Suzanna (with Jacuzzi and kitchenette), and $150 for the Ivy Apartment (four rooms). September 22 through October and April through mid-May, rates are $85-89 for a double, $99 for the Suite Suzanna; and $105 for the Ivy Apartment. November through March, rates are $70 for a double, $85 for the Suite Suzanna, and $75 for the Ivy Apartment.There is no minimum stay and cancellation requires 10 days' notice.
CREDIT CARDS	American Express, Discover, MasterCard, Visa
BREAKFAST	Full breakfast is served in the dining room and includes homemade cinnamon rolls, muffins, fresh seasonal fruit, honey-pecan granola, baked blueberry French toast, quiche, or oatmeal pancakes.
RESTRICTIONS	No smoking, no pets. Brighty is the resident miniature horse. Guests can pet, feed, and photograph Brighty.
REVIEWED	*Complete Guide to Bed & Breakfasts, Inns & Guest Houses*
MEMBER	Bed & Breakfast Association of San Juan Island
RATED	AAA 2 Diamonds

HARRISON HOUSE SUITES

235 C Street, Friday Harbor, WA 98250   360-378-3587
Farhad Ghatan, Resident Owner   800-407-7933
EMAIL hhsuites@rockisland.com   *FAX 360-378-2270*
WEBSITE www.rockisland.com/~hhsuites

Harrison House Suites, Friday Harbor

LOCATION	On top of the bluff overlooking the San Juan ferry terminal, 450 feet east of the ferry parking lot.
OPEN	All year
DESCRIPTION	A 1905 three-story Island Craftsman inn overlooking Friday Harbor with an eclectic interior and antiques, a private café, and award-winning gardens.
NO. OF ROOMS	Five rooms with private bathrooms. Try suite 1.
RATES	May through October 15, rates are $100 for a single or double, $100-240 for a suite, $130-150 for the guesthouse, and $800 for the entire inn. October 16 through April, rates are $75 for a single or double, $75-200 for a suite, $100-210 for the guesthouse, and $680 for the entire inn. There is a two-night minimum stay during peak season and on weekends only during low season. Cancellation requires two weeks' notice for a 90 percent refund.
CREDIT CARDS	American Express, Discover, MasterCard, Visa
BREAKFAST	Continental plus is served in the guestrooms. The kitchen is stocked daily with cereals, snacks, juice, milk, coffee, tea, cocoa, and fresh-baked scones. Dinner, gourmet breakfasts, and catering are also available.
AMENITIES	Mountain bikes; Jacuzzis; water views; fresh flowers; fully stocked kitchens; private café with cozy sitting area; meeting space for up to 30; award-winning gardens; internet, email, and fax access; phones in suites; cable TV/VCR and CD players in suites.
RESTRICTIONS	No smoking. Tigger is the resident outdoor cat who is very gentle and patient with kids and adults.

REVIEWED	Northwest Best Places; The Best Places to Kiss in the Northwest
MEMBER	San Juan Island Bed & Breakfast Association
RATED	Mobil 2 Stars, Northwest Best Places 2 Stars, Best Places to Kiss 1.5 Lips, Seattle Sidewalk 2.5 Stars

HILLSIDE HOUSE BED & BREAKFAST

365 Carter Avenue, Friday Harbor, WA 98250   *360-378-4730*
Dick & Cathy Robinson, Innkeepers   *800-232-4730*
EMAIL *hillside@rockisland.com*   *FAX 360-378-4715*
WEBSITE *www.hillsidehouse.com*

LOCATION	From the ferry terminal in Friday Harbor, go right (west) one block to Spring Street, then left (south) two blocks to Second Street. Turn right (west) 0.5 mile to Carter Avenue, then right (north) one block to the house.
OPEN	All year
DESCRIPTION	A three-story contemporary host home built in 1990. The house overlooks the harbor and Mount Baker. The decor is casually elegant with window seats, wooded grounds, gardens, a two-story aviary, and fountains.
NO. OF ROOMS	Seven rooms with private bathrooms. Cathy's favorite is the Eagle's Nest.
RATES	May through October, a single or double is $85-175. November through April ,a single or double is $65-155. There is a two-night minimum stay on Saturdays and for some rooms during the week. Cancellation requires seven days' notice, or there is a charge if the room is not rebooked.
CREDIT CARDS	American Express, Discover, MasterCard, Visa
BREAKFAST	Full breakfast is served in the dining room or in guestrooms on request. "No guest leaves hungry!" A sample breakfast menu: egg and cheese strata, Dick's famous lemon scones, "bluebarb" crunch, fruit plate, granola and toppings, juices, coffee, and teas.
AMENITIES	Dick's banana-chocolate chip cookies, fruit and juices always available, guest refrigerator, Alba Botanica bath products, robes in most rooms, breakfast on the deck all summer, murder mystery weekends.
RESTRICTIONS	No pets, children over 10 welcome, smoking outside only. Two standard poodles, Joe and Anne, are the welcoming committee. The cat, Precious, stays outside and in the owners quarters. Buddy and Crash are the parrots.

REVIEWED	The Best Places to Kiss in the Northwest; AAA Guidebook; Fodor's B&B and Country Inns; Fodor's Pacific Northwest Best B&B's; Quick Escapes in the Pacific Northwest; Recommended Country Inns—West Coast; Northwest Best Places; Birder's Guide to Bed & Breakfasts; Washington Discovery Guide; Washington State Travelers: Affordable Accommodations.
MEMBER	Washington Hotel and Motel Association, Washington Bed & Breakfast Guild, San Juan Island Bed & Breakfast Association
RATED	AAA 2 Diamonds, Mobil 2 Stars
KUDOS/COMMENTS	"Views of the harbor and town, great innkeepers." "A wonderful house. The food is great!"

JENSEN BAY

300 Jensen Bay Road, Friday Harbor, WA 98250   360-378-5318
WEBSITE *www.karuna.com/jensenbay*

MARIELLA INN & COTTAGES

630 Turn Point Road, Friday Harbor, WA 98250   360-378-6868
Arthur & Alison Lohrey, Owners   800-700-7668
          FAX 360-378-6822

LOCATION	From the ferry landing, follow Spring Street and turn left onto First Street, which becomes Harrison Street; go south 0.33 mile to Turn Point Road and turn left (look for the sign).
OPEN	All year
DESCRIPTION	A 1902 three-story inn with Victorian decor, antiques, and a wraparound veranda on a rocky point surrounded by water on three sides.
NO. OF ROOMS	Eleven rooms with private bathrooms.
RATES	Please call for current rates and cancellation information.
CREDIT CARDS	MasterCard, Visa
BREAKFAST	Full breakfast is served in the dining room.
AMENITIES	Bicycle and kayak rentals and tours, boat moorage, hot tub, perennial garden for strolls, croquet, badminton, volleyball, garden canopy for wedding receptions, afternoon tea/coffee and pastries.
RESTRICTIONS	No smoking, no pets

THE MEADOWS BED & BREAKFAST

1980 Cattle Point Road, Friday Harbor, WA 98250   360-378-4004

MOON & SIXPENCE BED & BREAKFAST

3021 Beaverton Valley Road, Friday Harbor, WA 98250   360-378-4138
Evelyn Tuller, Innkeeper
EMAIL *moon6p@rockisland.com*
WEBSITE *www.rockisland.com/~moon6p/inn*

LOCATION	Take the ferry from Anacortes to Friday Harbor. Disembark and go two blocks on Spring Street; then turn right onto Second Street. Angle left onto Guard Street, which becomes Beaverton Valley Road. The inn is about three miles from the ferry on the left before the junction with Egg Lake Road.
OPEN	All year
DESCRIPTION	A restored 1902 two-story classic revival-style country inn on 11 acres of pasture, with comfortable, eclectic furnishings, antiques, and art.
NO. OF ROOMS	Two rooms with private bathrooms. Try the Water Tower Room.
RATES	May through November, rates are $90-125 for a single or double, $240 for a three-room suite (sleeps six), and $365 for the entire B&B. December through April, rates are $80-105 for a single or double, $200 for a three-room suite, and $300 for the entire B&B. There is a two-night minimum stay from May through November, and cancellation requires 72 hours' notice for a full refund of deposit.
CREDIT CARDS	No
BREAKFAST	Continental plus is served in the dining room or on the porch during the summer and includes a buffet of fresh fruits, juices, home-baked pastries, cereals, tea, and coffee.
AMENITIES	Tour of weaving studio and dye porch with weavings available for sale; labyrinth garden for meditative strolls; 11 acres of fenced pasture; kites and croquet.

RESTRICTIONS	No smoking inside, no pets, children are welcome. Chinook and Drumheller are the resident Arabian horses.
REVIEWED	*The Best Places to Kiss in the Northwest; Essential San Juan Islands Guide; American Historic Inns; America's Wonderful Little Hotels & Inns; Birder's Guide to Bed & Breakfasts; Northwest Best Places*
MEMBER	Bed & Breakfast Association of San Juan Island, Washington Bed & Breakfast Guild

OLYMPIC LIGHTS BED & BREAKFAST

4531-A Cattle Point Road, Friday Harbor, WA 98250   360-378-3186
Christian & Lea Andrade, Resident Owners   FAX 360-378-2097
Spanish spoken
WEBSITE *www.san-juan.net/olympiclights*

LOCATION	Take I-5 from Seattle or Vancouver, B.C., to Anacortes (exit 230). Follow signs to the Anacortes Ferry. Take the ferry to San Juan Island and exit onto Spring Street. Olympic Lights is 5.5 miles south. Drive three blocks and bear left to Argyle; the road name will change to Cattle Point. Turn right onto our access road (0.25 mile).
OPEN	All year
DESCRIPTION	An 1895 two-story Victorian farmhouse overlooking the sea and Olympic Mountains, with a mixture of contemporary and antique decor.
NO. OF ROOMS	One room with a private bathroom and four rooms share two bathrooms. The Ra Room is the best.
RATES	Year-round rates are $110 for a single or double with a private bathroom and $75-90 for a single or double with a shared bathroom. There is a two-night minimum stay from July through September and during holiday weekends. Cancellation requires seven days' notice with a $15 fee.
CREDIT CARDS	No
BREAKFAST	Full breakfast, served in the parlor, includes a vegetarian egg dish, muffins, scones, or buttermilk biscuits, fresh fruit, and beverages.
AMENITIES	Fresh flowers, goose-down comforters, unobstructed view of sea and mountains, croquet, horseshoes, boccie ball, hiking trails nearby at American Camp, fresh eggs from resident hens. Also, enjoy the views of the sunrise, sunset, moonrise, and moonset, along with excellent bird-watching.
RESTRICTIONS	No smoking, no pets, children over 10 are welcome. There are five cats and a number of chickens.

Olympic Lights Bed & Breakfast, Friday Harbor

REVIEWED	*Northwest Best Places; The Best Places to Kiss in the Northwest; Best Places to Stay in the Pacific Northwest; Hidden Pacific Northwest; Quick Escapes in the Pacific Northwest; Fodor's Pacific Northwest's Best Bed & Breakfasts; Frommer's Guide to Oregon and Washington; Washington Handbook; The Essential San Juan Islands Guides; Bed, Breakfast & Bike: Pacific Northwest; Inside Out Washington; Lonely Planet—Pacific Northwest*
MEMBER	Washington Bed & Breakfast Guild
KUDOS/COMMENTS	"Serene and welcoming; clear, fresh interior with charm; warm and wonderful innkeepers; impeccable food, furnishings, and garden." "Friendly, relaxed innkeepers. Beautiful older home. Great breakfasts."

PANACEA—A BED & BREAKFAST INN

595 Park Street, Friday Harbor, WA 98250   360-378-3757
Beverly, Jessica & Bruce Schutte, Innkeepers   800-639-2762
EMAIL panacea@pacificrim   FAX 360-378-8543
WEBSITE friday-harbor.net/panacea

LOCATION	Three-tenths of a mile east of the ferry landing. Go up Spring Street and turn right on Blair Street, then left on Park Street. The third house on the left is Panacea.
OPEN	All year
DESCRIPTION	A restored 1907 Craftsman bungalow with a shingled exterior, wraparound veranda, and the original stained glass and woodwork, decorated with vintage arts and crafts.
NO. OF ROOMS	Four rooms with private bathrooms. Try the Veranda Room.

Panacea—A Bed & Breakast Inn, Friday Harbor

RATES	May through September, rates for a single or double are $135-165 and the entire B&B rents for $600. October through April, a single or double is $100-130 and the entire B&B is $450. There is no minimum stay and cancellation requires seven days' notice.
CREDIT CARDS	MasterCard, Visa
BREAKFAST	Full breakfast is served in the dining room, the guestrooms, the parlor, or in bed. Breakfast includes fresh seasonal fruits, homemade granola and yogurt, an entrée and home-baked pastry, plus coffees, teas, and organic, fresh juices. Lunch, picnics, and afternoon tea are also available.
AMENITIES	Birthday, honeymoon, and anniversary in-room gifts; chilled bottled water; house stationery; complimentary use of umbrellas and binoculars; island milled soaps; robes; turndown service.
RESTRICTIONS	No smoking, no pets, no children
REVIEWED	*The Best Places to Kiss in the Northwest; Essential San Juan Islands Guide*
MEMBER	Bed & Breakfast Association of San Juan Island, Professional Association of Innkeepers International, Washington Bed & Breakfast Guild

SAN JUAN INN BED & BREAKFAST

50 Spring Street, Friday Harbor, WA 98250　　　　*360-378-2070*
Skip & Annette Metzger, Resident Owners　　　　*800-742-8210*
Danish, Swedish, Norwegian, and German spoken　　*FAX 360-378-6437*
WEBSITE *www.san-juan.net/sjn*

LOCATION	Exit the ferry, turn west on Front Street, turn south on Spring Street, and the inn is the third building on the west side of Spring Street.

OPEN	All year
DESCRIPTION	An 1873 two-story Queen Anne Victorian with Victorian decor. "One of the first Victorian buildings constructed in Friday Harbor after the Pig War between the United States and England, the inn has served previously as the Bayview Hotel, the Douglas House, and the San Juan Hotel."
NO. OF ROOMS	Four rooms with private bathrooms and five rooms share three-and-a-half bathrooms and two suites.
RATES	May through October 15, rates are $96-102 for a single or double with a private bathroom, $78-92 for a single or double with a shared bathroom, and $160-220 for a suite. Low-season rates are $80-95 for a single or double with a private bathroom, $65-70 for a single or double with a shared bathroom, and $150-210 for a suite. There is no minimum stay and cancellation requires 72 hours' notice.
CREDIT CARDS	American Express, Discover, MasterCard, Visa
BREAKFAST	Continental plus, served buffet style in the parlor, includes bagels with cream cheese and jam, three or four types of warm muffins, fresh fruit tray, gourmet coffee and teas, and orange juice.
AMENITIES	Seven-person Jacuzzi in the Victorian garden, bicycle storage in the garden area, wide variety of magazines and books, lawn furniture in the garden, guest phone in private area.
RESTRICTIONS	No smoking, no pets, children over 10 are welcome (younger children with prior arrangement). Abigail is the resident calico, a "loving inn cat that has been declawed."
REVIEWED	*Washington State Travelers: Affordable Accommodations; The Non-Smokers Guide to Bed & Breakfasts; The National Trust Guide to Bed & Breakfasts, Inns and Small Hotels*
MEMBER	Professional Association of Innkeepers International, Washington Bed & Breakfast Guild, Washington Hotel and Motel Association
RATED	Mobil 3 Stars

STATES INN

2039 West Valley Road, Friday Harbor, WA 98250   360-378-6240
Garreth Jeffers, Resident Innkeeper   FAX 360-378-6241
WEBSITE *www.karuna.com/statesinn*

KUDOS/COMMENTS   "Wonderful horse farm in rural area. Friendly host is a former chef. Food is A-1."

TOWER HOUSE BED & BREAKFAST

1230 Little Road, Friday Harbor, WA 98250   360-378-5464
Chris & Joe Luma, Resident Owners   800-858-4276
French spoken   FAX 360-378-5464
EMAIL *towerhouse@san-juan-island.com*
WEBSITE *www.san-juan-island.com*

LOCATION	Leaving the ferry, follow Spring Street (which becomes San Juan Valley Road) west for 1.7 miles out of town, turn south (left) onto Douglas, go 1.5 miles, and turn west (left) onto Little Road.
OPEN	All year
DESCRIPTION	A 1930s-era two-story Queen Anne Victorian with a blend of contemporary, country, and Victorian decor.
NO. OF ROOMS	Two rooms with private bathrooms.
RATES	Year-round rates are $95-120 for a single or double. There is no minimum stay and cancellation requires one weeks' notice for a full refund unless the room is rebooked.
CREDIT CARDS	American Express, Discover, MasterCard, Visa
BREAKFAST	Full vegetarian breakfast is served in the dining room on fine china with crystal and antique linens, and is garnished with fruit and flowers. Vegan and other special diets are accommodated with advance notice.
AMENITIES	Chocolates on your pillows; a supply of shortbread in your own biscuit tin; antique linens; a piano in the parlor; about 300 videos with fresh popcorn on request; guests are welcome to explore the 10-acre property with trails, ponds, and a friendly guide cat; photos taken during your stay are mailed to your home.
RESTRICTIONS	No smoking, no pets, no children. Fluffy is the resident cat. "Fluffy is an experienced bald eagle dodger since we are a favorite hunting spot of the eagles."
REVIEWED	*Essential San Juan Islands Guide; The Vegetarian Traveler; Victorian Voyages U.S.; Vegetarian Journal's Guide to Natural Foods Restaurants; Washington State Travelers: Affordable Accommodations; The Official Guide to American Historic Inns*
MEMBER	San Juan Island Bed & Breakfast Association, Washington Bed & Breakfast Guild
KUDOS/COMMENTS	"Superb attention to detail, warm hospitality, delicious breakfast, elegant but comfortable." "Two gorgeous suites overlooking the San Juan Valley."

Trumpeter Inn Bed & Breakfast, Friday Harbor

TRUMPETER INN BED & BREAKFAST

420 Trumpeter Way, Friday Harbor, WA 98250
Don & Bobbie Wiesner, Innkeepers
EMAIL *swan@rockisland.com*
WEBSITE *www.friday-harbor.net/trumpeter*

360-378-3884
800-826-7926
FAX 360-378-8235

LOCATION	From the ferry landing, take Spring Street for 1.5 miles and turn right on Trumpeter Way.
OPEN	All year
DESCRIPTION	A 1980 two-story contemporary farmhouse, surrounded by ponds and fields, with a view of the Olympic Mountains and the Strait of Juan de Fuca.
NO. OF ROOMS	Five rooms with private bathrooms. Roberta suggests the Bay Laurel Room.
RATES	May through October, rates for a single or double are $90-130. November through April, rates are $80-115. A three-day stay is required on holiday weekends. Cancellation requires seven days' notice for a refund.
CREDIT CARDS	American Express, Discover, MasterCard, Visa
BREAKFAST	Full breakfast is served in the dining room and includes fruit, juice, fresh-baked bread and muffins, homemade granola, jams, and an entrée such as smoked salmon quiche, French toast with apples, or strawberry pancakes.
AMENITIES	Hot tub in garden, private decks and fireplaces in rooms with king-size beds, fresh flowers in each room, cookies and tea in the afternoons, sitting room on first floor, handicapped access in one room.

RESTRICTIONS	No smoking, no pets, children over 12 are welcome. More and Buddy are the resident outdoor barn cat and black Lab respectively. Migrating birds, including trumpeter swans, winter in the ponds.
REVIEWED	*Northwest Best Places; Best Places to Stay in the Pacific Northwest; Best Places to Kiss in the Northwest; Fodor's; Washington State Travelers: Affordable Accommodations; San Juan & Gulf Island Best Places; Better Bed & Breakfast Inns; Birders' Guide to Bed & Breakfasts.*
MEMBER	Washington Bed & Breakfast Guild, San Juan Island Bed & Breakfast Association, Professional Association of Innkeepers International, Washington State Hotel and Motel Association
RATED	AAA 3 Diamonds
KUDOS/COMMENTS	"Personable owners, lovely rooms."

TUCKER HOUSE BED & BREAKFAST WITH COTTAGES

260 B Street, Friday Harbor, WA 98250   360-378-2783
Annette & Skip Metzger, Resident Owners   800-965-0123
EMAIL *tucker@rockisland.com*   FAX 360-378-6437
WEBSITE *www.san-juan.net/tucker*

LOCATION	From the Anacortes ferry terminal, go west for half a block, turn left on Spring Street for one block, left again on First Street for two blocks, then right on B Street for half a block.
OPEN	All year
DESCRIPTION	An 1898 two-story Victorian home with antique and contemporary decor, plus three cottages.
NO. OF ROOMS	Three cottages with private bathrooms and three rooms share one bathroom. Try the Lilac Cottage.
RATES	May through October 15, rates are $95-150 for a single or double with a shared bathroom and $115-150 for a cottage. Low-season rates are $75-85 for a single or double with a shared bathroom and $105-135 for a cottage (with multiple-day discounts). There is no minimum stay and cancellation requires 72 hours' notice.
CREDIT CARDS	American Express, Discover, MasterCard, Visa
BREAKFAST	Full breakfast, served in the dining room, includes fresh fruit bowl, fresh orange juice, baked eggs or cheese and egg soufflé, and homemade cinnamon bread. Children may have cereal, waffles, and hot chocolate.

AMENITIES	Outdoor seven-person Jacuzzi, patio furniture on upper decks, bicycle storage, guest telephone in the solarium, lawn furniture in selected areas, TV/VCRs and VHS movies, off-street parking.
RESTRICTIONS	No smoking. Young children, infants, and dogs (under 40 pounds) restricted to cottages. The resident cat is restricted to the innkeepers' quarters.
REVIEWED	*Best Places to Stay in the Pacific Northwest; The Non-Smokers Guide to Bed & Breakfasts; Washington State Travelers: Affordable Accommodations*
MEMBER	Professional Association of Innkeepers International, Washington Hotel and Motel Association, Washington Bed & Breakfast Guild
KUDOS/COMMENTS	"A clean, modest Victorian."

WHARFSIDE BED & BREAKFAST
ABOARD THE "JACQUELYN"

Slip K-13, Port of Friday Harbor　　　　　　　　　　　　360-378-5661
Friday Harbor, WA 98250
Captain Clyde & Bette Rice, Resident Owners
WEBSITE *www.san-juan-island.net/wharfside*

LOCATION	Two blocks from Friday Harbor ferry terminal; turn right off the ferry, follow the waterfront for two blocks to port offices and parking, and walk down the main dock to K dock.
OPEN	All year
DESCRIPTION	A 1972 ketch-rigged motorsailer boat, 60 feet long, with "early Nemo, nautical Victorian" interior.
NO. OF ROOMS	One room with a private half-bathroom and one room shares one bathroom. The captain suggests the Aft Room "for short guests."
RATES	Year-round rates are $95 for a single or double with a private or shared bathroom and the entire boat rents for $190 (for four guests). There is a midweek discount from November through April. There is a two-night minimum stay June through September and during holiday weekends. Cancellation requires seven days' notice less a $10 fee.
CREDIT CARDS	American Express, MasterCard, Visa
BREAKFAST	Full all-you-can-eat breakfast, served in the dining room or (weather permitting) on the aft deck, includes fresh fruit tray or compote; fresh-baked coffeecakes or muffins; quiche, frittata, or omelets; breakfast meats; and parmesan potato puffs or latkes; plus beverages. Special diets are accommodated with prior notice.

AMENITIES	Fresh local seafood available on the dock for a "picnic on the poop deck," rowing gig, shrimp nets, crab ring and fishing poles, picnic breakfast for early morning departures on the ferry, Captain Clyde's fish stories optional, owners will "disappear when guests prefer privacy," fresh flowers, robes, tea, coffee, cocoa, fresh fruit bowl, cookies, fireplace, down comforters, dual-control mattress warmers, chocolate "gold doubloons" in a little treasure chest.
RESTRICTIONS	No smoking (except on deck), children and dogs are welcome.
REVIEWED	*Northwest Best Places; San Juan & Gulf Islands Best Places; Ultimate Washington; Best Places to Stay in the Pacific Northwest; Essential San Juan Islands Guide; America's Wonderful Little Inns & Hotels, The Best Places to Kiss in the Northwest; On the Road Again with Man's Best Friend; Washington State Travelers: Affordable Accommodations; Better Bed & Breakfast Inns; Washington Handbook; Frommer's; Fodor's Pacific Northwest's Best Bed & Breakfasts*
MEMBER	Bed & Breakfast Association of San Juan Island

WILDWOOD MANOR

3021 Roche Harbor Road, Friday Harbor, WA 98250   *360 378-3447*
Richard & Victoria Baker, Innkeepers   *FAX 360 378-6095*
EMAIL *wildwdmanor@rockisland.com*
WEBSITE *www.rockisland.com/~wildwdmanor*

LOCATION	Five-and-a-half miles from the ferry landing. Take Spring Street to Second Street and turn right. Follow Second Street to Tucker Avenue and turn right. Tucker Avenue becomes Roche Harbor Road. Continue on Roche Harbor Road past Lakedale Campground and Duck Soup Inn to the manor.
OPEN	All year
DESCRIPTION	A 1988 two-story Queen Anne host home with eclectic decor and old-world elegance, including many antiques, elaborate ceiling designs, and murals.
NO. OF ROOMS	One room with a private bathroom and two rooms with one-and-a-half shared bathrooms. Try the Pink Room.
RATES	May through September, rates are $175 for a single or double with a private bathroom and $155-165 for a single or double with a shared bathroom. October through April, rates are $160 for a single or double with a private bathroom and $140-150 for a single or double with a shared bathroom. There is a minimum stay during weekends from May through September. Ask about a cancellation policy.

Wildwood Manor, Friday Harbor

CREDIT CARDS	MasterCard, Visa
BREAKFAST	Full breakfast is served on china with crystal and silver in the dining room. Breakfast includes coffee and coffeecake (served in the sitting room prior to breakfast), tea, milk, juices, and fresh fruit, plus a variety of egg dishes such as omelets, quiche, or a special baked French toast. Real eggs, cream, and butter are used in all our recipies.
AMENITIES	Fresh flowers in rooms; robes; greeting cards and sparkling cider for special occasions; coffee, tea, and sweets offered at check in and otherwise available upon request; innkeepers will make dinner/tour reservations or other special arrangements; three-zoned climate control system with air conditioning to maintain an even temperature throughout the home; electronic filters to clean air of dust and allergens; walking paths on 11 wooded acres with ocean views.
RESTRICTIONS	No smoking, no pets, children over 12 are welcome. Two-person maximum occupancy in rooms. Caruso and Yoda are the resident Siamese cats; Wolfgang and Cosette are the American longhairs. "Wolfgang is very shy, and Cosette is our hunter." Cats are not allowed in guestrooms or the guest sitting room. Deer, foxes, raccoon, quail, and many other birds may be seen in the backyard and throughout the 11 acres.
MEMBER	Professional Association of Innkeepers International, Washington Bed & Breakfast Guild, Bed & Breakfast Association of San Juan Island

GARDINER

Just east of Gardiner on Sequim Bay, near Blyn, the S'Klallam Indians operate the unique Northwest Native Expressions art gallery. It's worth a look. Seven Cedars, a truly mammoth casino, stands just across the road.

DIAMOND POINT INN

241 Sunshine Drive, Gardiner, WA 98334   360-797-7720
Doug & Barbara Billings, Resident Owners   888-797-0393
EMAIL *dpinn@olypen.com*   FAX 360-797-7723
WEBSITE *www.dynamicgraphics.com/diamonpoint*

LOCATION	Ten miles from Discovery Bay on Highway 101 west. Take a right on Diamond Point Road, a right on Eagle Creek Road, and another right onto Sunshine Drive.
OPEN	All year
DESCRIPTION	A 1979 two-story contemporary inn with country decor, on 10 acres of woods.
NO. OF ROOMS	Four rooms with private bathrooms and two rooms with one shared bathroom.
RATES	April 15 through October 15, rates are $85-125 for a single or double with a private bathroom and $75 for a single or double with a shared bathroom. October 16 through April 14, rates are $75-95 for a single or double with a private bathroom and $65 for a single or double with a shared bathroom. There is a two-night minimum stay during holidays.
CREDIT CARDS	MasterCard, Visa
BREAKFAST	Full breakfast is served. Lunch and dinner are also available with 48 hours' notice.
AMENITIES	Coffee and tea around the clock, ramp for handicapped guests.
RESTRICTIONS	No smoking, no pets, children over five are welcome.
MEMBER	Washington Bed & Breakfast Guild, Sequim Bed & Breakfast Association
RATED	AAA 3 Diamonds, Mobil 2 Stars
KUDOS/COMMENTS	"Nice people. Clean, quiet, and a nice breakfast."

GIG HARBOR

Once an undisturbed fishing village (and still home port for an active commercial fleet), Gig Harbor is now part suburbia, part weekend destination. Boating is still important here, with good anchorage and various moorage docks attracting gunwale-to-gunwale pleasure craft. When the clouds break, Mount Rainier holds court for all. An arts festival in mid-July and a jazz festival in mid-August are two main events. Nearby Kopachuck State Park is a popular destination (follow signs from Highway 16), as are Penrose Point and Robert F. Kennedy State Parks on the Key Peninsula, all with numerous beaches for clam digging. (Purdy Spit and Maple Hollow Park are the most accessible spots.) At Minter Creek State Hatchery the public can watch the different developmental stages of millions of salmon of various species.

ALOHA BEACHSIDE BED & BREAKFAST

8318 State Route 302, Gig Harbor, WA 98329   253-857-8777
Greg & Lalaine Wong, Innkeepers   888-256-4222
EMAIL lalaine@alohabeachsidebb.com
WEBSITE www.alohabeachsidebb.com

LOCATION	On Highway 16, two exits past the city center. Take the Purdy exit and turn left at the light. Go one mile.
OPEN	All year
DESCRIPTION	A 1998 two-story modern beach cabin with Hawaiian decor, situated five feet from the bulkhead on Puget Sound.
NO. OF ROOMS	Two rooms with private bathrooms. Try the Sunrise Room.
RATES	Year-round rate is $95 for a single or double. The entire B&B rents for $150. There is no minimum stay and cancellation requires 72 hours' notice (gift certificate is issued).
CREDIT CARDS	No
BREAKFAST	Full four-course Hawaiian-influenced breakfast includes Kona coffee, guava juice, macadamia nut pancakes, crepes, seafood, and tropical fruits.
AMENITIES	Large lanai upstairs with piped music, large deck off main floor with Adirondack chairs and propane grill.
RESTRICTIONS	No smoking, no pets. Oreo and Buster are the resident pooches, and there are 10,000 or so Chinook salmon fingerlings raised in the pond. "We release the salmon annually," says Lalaine, "but guests love to see them fed."
MEMBER	Professional Association of Innkeepers International

DOCKSIDE BED ON BOATS

8829 North Harborview Drive, Gig Harbor, WA 98332　　253-858-7341

LAGOON LODGE

15419 Goodrich Drive NW, Gig Harbor, WA 98329　　253-858-8827

MARY'S BED & BREAKFAST

8212 Dorotich Street, Gig Harbor, WA 98335　　253-858-2424

NO CABBAGES BED & BREAKFAST

7712 Goodman Drive NW, Gig Harbor, WA 98332　　253-858-7797

THE OLDE GLENCOVE HOTEL

9418 Glencove Road, Gig Harbor, WA 98329　　253-884-2835
WEBSITE www.narrows.com/glencove

PEACOCK HILL GUEST HOUSE

9520 Peacock Hill Avenue, Gig Harbor, WA 98332　　800-863-2318
Suzanne & Steven Savlov, Resident Owners
EMAIL sedonsue@aol.com
WEBSITE www.virtualcities.com/wa/peacock.hem

LOCATION　　　　From Sea-Tac Airport, take I-5 south to Tacoma. Exit to Highway 16 (Bremerton). Then take the City Center exit to Sinnon (straight across from exit). Go down to the bottom of the hill (three stop signs). Turn left on Harborview, then left again on Peacock Hill. Go to the second bus-stop sign on the left and turn left. The inn is located at the first driveway to the left.

OPEN	All year
DESCRIPTION	This 1963 two-story rambler host home features Native American, Southwest, and Northwest decor and sits on a hilltop overlooking Gig Harbor.
NO. OF ROOMS	Two rooms with private bathrooms. Suzanne recommends the Salish Suite.
RATES	Year-round rates are $75-115 for a single or double. May through October, there is a two-night minimum stay on weekends. Cancellation requires seven days' notice.
CREDIT CARDS	None
BREAKFAST	Full breakfast is served in the dining room and includes farm-fresh eggs and home-baked muffins.
AMENITIES	Fresh flowers; mints; robes; coffee, tea, juice, cider, and cocoa available; cake and sparkling cider for special occasions.
RESTRICTIONS	No smoking, no pets. Children over 12 are welcome.
REVIEWED	*Border to Border*
MEMBER	Washington State Bed & Breakfast Guild, Gig Harbor Bed & Breakfast Association

THE PILLARS BED & BREAKFAST

6606 Soundview Drive, Gig Harbor, WA 98335   *253-851-6644*

ROSEDALE BED & BREAKFAST

7714 Ray Nash Drive NW, Gig Harbor, WA 98335   *253-851-5420*
Barbara Beason, Resident Owner

KUDOS/COMMENTS   "A large, clean, spacious suite on the water. Excellent hostess." "Fully loaded with amenities and ambiance."

SUNNY BAY COTTAGE

50 Raft Island Drive NW, Gig Harbor, WA 98335   *253-265-6987*

WATERS EDGE BED & BREAKFAST

8610 Goodman Drive NW, Gig Harbor, WA 98335   253-851-3890

GLACIER

On scenic Highway 542, Glacier lies along the road to Mount Baker Ski Area, Mount Baker National Forest, and Mount Shuksan.

MT. BAKER BED & BREAKFAST

9434 Cornell Circle Road, Glacier, WA 98244   360-599-2299
Vel Dearman & Jacques Massie, Innkeepers   FAX 360-599-2299
Some Spanish spoken
EMAIL *mtbakerbnb@aol.com*
WEBSITE *members.aol.com/mtbakerbnb/index.html*

LOCATION	North of Seattle, south of Vancouver, B.C., and east of Bellingham. Take exit 255 off I-5 and travel east for 31 miles on Highway 542 (Mount Baker Highway). Look for the sign just past milepost 31. Turn right on Cornell Creek Road and go 0.5 mile.
OPEN	All year
DESCRIPTION	A 1997 three-story chalet prow lodge with Southwest decor, located in the secluded wilderness of Glacier with views of Mount Baker.
NO. OF ROOMS	One room with a private bathroom and two rooms with one shared bathroom.
RATES	High-season rates are $85 for a single or double with a private bathroom and $80-85 for a single or double with a shared bathroom. Regular rates are $70 for a single or double with a private bathroom and $70-75 for a single or double with a shared bathroom. There is a minimum stay during high-season weekends and holidays, and cancellation requires five days' notice.
CREDIT CARDS	MasterCard, Visa
BREAKFAST	Full breakfast is served in the dining room or on the deck and includes seasonal fruit, fruit breads, and juice; guests have a choice of breakfast burrito; French toast made with homemade French bread, with ham; oatmeal with apples, raisins, cinnamon, and brown sugar; or blueberry pancakes.
AMENITIES	Quiet seclusion in a wilderness setting, view of Mount Baker from

bed, secluded hot tub, terry robes, slippers, 360-degree mountain views, rooms large enough to accommodate an extra single bed, TV/VCR, queen-size beds.

RESTRICTIONS   No smoking (a smoking area is provided). Bull and Tug are the resident large dogs of mixed breed and Gizmo is the cat. All animals are very friendly.

MEMBER   Whatcom County Bed & Breakfast Guild

GLENWOOD

Bicycle the backroads, hike the abundant trails, observe the birds in the Convoy Wildlife Refuge, or ski Mount Adams—all are within easy distance of Glenwood.

FLYING L RANCH—
A MT. ADAMS COUNTRY INN

25 Flying L Lane, Glenwood, WA 98619   *509-364-3488*
WEBSITE www.mt-adams.com   *FAX 509-364-3634*

GOLDENDALE

Maryhill Museum, a stately Palladian mansion, perches rather obtrusively upon the barren Columbia River benchlands near Goldendale and features one of the largest collections of Rodin sculptures in the world, a whole floor of classic French and American paintings and glasswork, unique exhibitions such as chess sets and Romanian folk textiles, and splendid Northwest tribal art. Just up the road is a not-quite-life-size replica of Stonehenge, built to honor World War I veterans. Goldendale Public Observatory, on a hill overlooking town, was a popular spot when Halley's comet dropped in. High-powered telescopes give incredible celestial views through unpolluted skies.

TIMBERFRAME COUNTRY INN

223 Golden Pine, Goldendale, WA 98620   *509-773-3660*
Dor Creamer, Innkeeper   *800-861-8408*
          FAX 509-773-3660

LOCATION	From Highway 97 in Goldendale, take the Broadway exit (Highway 142) and turn right on 3rd Street (the first road to the right). Go one block and turn right onto Pipeline Road. Drive 2.7 miles, keep left where Pipeline veers, and continue for 1.2 miles. Turn left at the entrance to Ponderosa Village. Go one block and turn right onto Golden Pine Road.
OPEN	All year
DESCRIPTION	A 1995 two-story, authentic German timber-frame country inn decorated with antiques and nestled among the ponderosa pines and meadowlands of the Simcoe Mountains.
NO. OF ROOMS	Two rooms with private bathrooms. Dor recommends the **Tree Top Room**.
RATES	Year-round rates are $95-125 for a single or double. There is no minimum stay and cancellation requires seven days' notice, longer during holidays.
CREDIT CARDS	No
BREAKFAST	Full country breakfast is served in the dining room and includes juice, coffee and tea, scrambled eggs, enchiladas, smoked bacon, strawberry shortcake, homemade breads and muffins, jams, jellies, and more.
AMENITIES	Private spa on the deck surrounded by flower boxes, porch swing, wicker furniture, total privacy, full-size refrigerator, goblets for sparkling cider, flowers, skylight in large tiled shower, coffee/coffee-maker, TV/VCR and movies, private entrances.
RESTRICTIONS	No smoking inside, no pets, no children. Butch and Sundance are the resident tabbies.
REVIEWED	*The Best Places to Kiss in the Northwest*

THE VICTORIAN HOUSE BED & BREAKFAST

415 East Broadway, Goldendale, WA 98620 509-773-5338
Jeffrey & Audrey Bright, Resident Owners

LOCATION	Seventy miles south of Yakima on Highway 97, take the Broadway exit (SR 142) to Goldendale west and go 0.75 mile to the B&B.
OPEN	All year
DESCRIPTION	A 1910 three-story Victorian with partial Victorian decor.
NO. OF ROOMS	Four rooms share one bathroom.

RATES	Year-round rates are $40-62 for a single or double. There is no minimum stay and cancellation requires 24 hours' notice.
CREDIT CARDS	MasterCard, Visa
BREAKFAST	Full breakfast, served in the dining room, features a choice of three menus including scrambled eggs with bacon, ham, or sausage; hashbrowns; waffles or pancakes; Victorian scramble; plus fruit; toast; English or fruit muffins; and beverages. Continental breakfast is also available.
AMENITIES	Parlor, cable TV, air conditioning, privacy when dining, distinctive staircase and original oak woodwork, home-baked goods, home-canned fruit and jams, early coffee and tea service.
RESTRICTIONS	No pets, children are welcome. Pug and Sweet Pea are the resident dogs. There are three indoor cats: Rusty, Snowball, and Buttons.

GRAHAM

COUNTRY HOUSE BED & BREAKFAST

25421 99th Avenue Court East, Graham, WA 98338   *253-846-1889*
Jim & Sue Tulare, Resident Owners

GRAND COULEE

Grand Coulee Dam is one of the largest structures on the earth: tall as a 46-story building, with a spillway twice the height of Niagara and a length as great as a dozen city blocks. The heroic scale of the concrete is quite magnificent, especially when illuminated by the inspirational nighttime laser light show. There are daily self-guided tours of the dam; hours vary according to season.

FOUR WINDS GUEST HOUSE

301 Lincoln Street, Coulee Dam, WA 99116   *509-633-3146*
Dick & Fe Taylor, Resident Owners   *800-786-3146*

THE GOLD HOUSE INN

411 Partello Park, Grand Coulee, WA 99133   509-633-3276
WEBSITE www.grandcouleedam.com

GRANDVIEW

COZY ROSE BED & BREAKFAST

1220 Forsell Road, Grandview, WA   509-882-4669
Mark & Jennie Jackson, Resident Owners

GRAYLAND

Just south of Grays Harbor and north of Willapa Bay on Highway 105, Grayland offers plenty of beach access. Each spring, a half-million Arctic-bound shorebirds migrate from as far south as Argentina and congregate on the tidal mud flats at the wildlife refuge of Bowerman Basin.

GRAYLAND BED & BREAKFAST

1678 State Route 105, Grayland, WA 98547   360-267-6026
Dale & Terry Walter, Innkeepers

LOCATION	From I-5 north, take exit 101 and stay left heading toward the Montesano/Aberdeen exit. State Road 8 becomes Highway 12 west, then Highway 101 south. Turn right at State Route 105 and go 3.2 miles.
OPEN	All year
DESCRIPTION	A 1937 two-story coastal shake host home with a homey, country feel.
NO. OF ROOMS	Two rooms share one bathroom.

RATES	May through September, rates are $100-125 for a single or double. October through April, rates are $75-90. There is no minimum stay. Ask about a cancellation policy.
CREDIT CARDS	No
BREAKFAST	Full country breakfast is served in the dining room and includes waffles, pancakes, hashbrowns, eggs, sausage, bacon, and fresh fruit.
AMENITIES	Flowers; large living room with big-screen TV/VCR and lots of videos; library; rest with the relaxing sounds of the ocean.
RESTRICTIONS	No smoking. Sophie and Tucker are the resident Maltese dogs.

GREENBANK

Here on the narrowest part of Whidbey Island, stop by Greenbank Farm, at one time the largest loganberry farm in the country, and sample their Loganberry Liqueur or Whidbey Port.

GUEST HOUSE LOG COTTAGES

24371 South Highway 525, Greenbank, WA 98253   *360-678-3115*
Don & MaryJane Creger, Owners   *FAX 360-678-3115 (call first)*
French spoken
EMAIL guesthse@whidbey.net   *WEBSITE www.whidbey.net/logcottages*

LOCATION	Take the Mukilteo-Clinton ferry and drive 16 miles up Highway 525.
OPEN	All year
DESCRIPTION	A 1927 log lodge and five log cottages decorated with antiques, country furnishings, and early American decor, and scattered across 25 acres of woods.
NO. OF ROOMS	A log lodge and five log cabins (for two occupants each) with private bathrooms.

RATES	March 15 through October, rates are $160-295 for a cottage for two with a private bathroom; November through mid-March, rates are $125-295. There is usually a two-night minimum stay on weekends and cancellation requires 21 days' notice less a $25 fee.
CREDIT CARDS	American Express, Discover, MasterCard, Visa
BREAKFAST	Continental plus is set up in the dining room of each cottage.
AMENITIES	Jacuzzi tubs in all cottages; outdoor hot tub; swimming pool; robes, fireplaces, and kitchens in all cottages; exercise rooms; TV/VCR; CD players; fresh flowers; special romantic touches; privacy.
RESTRICTIONS	No smoking inside, no pets, no children. There are egg-producing chickens and geese on the property.
REVIEWED	*Weekends for Two in the Pacific Northwest; 50 Romantic Getaways; The Best Places to Kiss in the Northwest; Northwest Best Places; Frommer's*
MEMBER	Professional Association of Innkeepers International, Whidbey Island Bed & Breakfast Association
RATED	AAA 4 Diamonds

NORTH BLUFF BED & BREAKFAST

2419 Surf Paradise, Greenbank, WA 98253   360-678-6775
Ron & Kathy Hill, Innkeepers

LOCATION	From Seattle, take the Mukilteo ferry to Clinton on Whidbey Island. Take Highway 525 for 17 miles to Greenbank. Turn right on North Bluff Road and continue for 1.5 miles to Surf Paradise and turn right.
OPEN	All year
DESCRIPTION	A 1994 two-story contemporary waterfront host home overlooking Puget Sound.
NO. OF ROOMS	One room with a private bathroom.
RATES	Please call for rates and cancellation information.
CREDIT CARDS	MasterCard, Visa
BREAKFAST	Continental plus is served in the dining room.
AMENITIES	Whirlpool, exercise room, barbecue.
RESTRICTIONS	No smoking. You may see flower-eating rabbits roaming the property.

SMUGGLER'S COVE HAVEN

3258 Smuggler's Cove Road, Greenbank, WA 98253   360-678-7100
WEBSITE www.smugglerscove.com   800-772-7055

HOQUIAM

Tour Hoquiam Castle, a 20-room mansion built for a prominent lumberman in 1897. Right next door is the equally splendid house his brother built—now the Lytle House Bed & Breakfast. Polson Park is a fine house by Arthur Loveless, with a rose garden.

LYTLE HOUSE BED & BREAKFAST

509 Chenault Avenue, Hoquiam, WA 98550   360-533-2320
Robert & Dayna Bencala, Resident Owners   800-677-2320
EMAIL benchmrk@techline.com   FAX 360-533-4025
WEBSITE www.lytlehouse.com

LOCATION	From the intersection of Highways 101 and 109 in Hoquiam, go three blocks west on Highway 109 to Grant Street. Turn right and drive until Grant deadends at Chenault Avenue. Turn left.
OPEN	All year
DESCRIPTION	An 1897 four-story, four-color painted lady Queen Anne Victorian inn decorated with antiques overlooking the harbor. Listed on the National and State Historic Registers.
NO. OF ROOMS	Six rooms with private bathrooms and two rooms with one shared bathroom. Try the Balcony Suite.
RATES	June through September, rates are $80-125 for a single or double with a private bathroom, $75 for a single or double with a shared bathroom, and $790 for the entire B&B. October through May, rates are $70-115 for a single or double with a private bathroom, $65 for a single or double with a shared bathroom, and $710 for the entire B&B. There is no minimum stay and cancellation requires 72 hours' notice.
CREDIT CARDS	American Express, MasterCard, Visa
BREAKFAST	Full breakfast is served in the dining room. Guests order from a 10-choice menu the evening before. Meals for special events are available for eight or more people.
AMENITIES	Robes; candy and apples in room; evening dessert; two TV rooms; four parlors; space for meetings, weddings, and parties.

Lytle House Bed & Breakfast, Hoquiam

RESTRICTIONS	No smoking, no pets. Chelsea is the resident chocolate Lab, China and Squeekers are the cats, and Tangles is the Angora rabbit who runs loose in the yard and thinks she's a cat. She also loves pets on the nose.
REVIEWED	*Northwest Best Places; The Best Places to Kiss in the Northwest; Washington Backroads; Fodor's; Hidden Pacific Northwest*
MEMBER	Olympic Peninsula Bed & Breakfast Association, Olympic Peninsula Travel Association
RATED	AAA 3 Diamonds
AWARDS	1995–1998, "Best of Twin Harbors," *Daily World* newspaper

ILWACO

Named after a Chinook Indian chief, Ilwaco is best known as the sport-fishing hub of the lower Columbia River. Because of intermittent ocean closures for sport fishing, many charter operators are now offering eco-tours. The Ilwaco Heritage Museum is a fine example of a small-town museum. It offers a look at southwest Washington history (including Native American artifacts and a scale-model glimpse of the peninsula in the 1920s). Fort Canby State Park covers 2,000 acres spanning North Head and Cape Disappointment at the Columbia's mouth. Check out the Lewis and Clark Interpretive Center, which depicts the explorers' journey from St. Louis to the Pacific, explains the history of the Cape Disappointment and North Head lighthouses, and enjoys the best view of the Columbia River bar—a great storm-watching spot.

CHICK-A-DEE INN AT ILWACO

120 Williams Street NE, Ilwaco, WA 98624   360-642-8686
Chick & DeLaine Hinkle, Resident Owners   FAX 360-642-8642

CHINA BEACH BED & BREAKFAST RETREAT

222 Captain Robert Gray Drive   360-642-5660
Ilwaco, WA 98624   360-642-2442
Laurie Anderson & David Campiche, Innkeepers

LOCATION	Located on the perimeter of Fort Canby State Park.
OPEN	All year
DESCRIPTION	A restored 1907 Craftsman-style home with views of Baker Bay.
NO. OF ROOMS	Three rooms with private bathrooms.
RATES	Year-round rates are $189 for a single or double and $229 for a suite.
CREDIT CARDS	American Express, MasterCard, Visa
BREAKFAST	Full breakfast is served.
AMENITIES	Next to 400 feet of waterfront; workshops and classes offered on such subjects as watercolor painting, needlepoint, seashore ecology, and plant and bird identification; and wine and cooking courses taught by Northwest oenologists and chefs.

KOLA HOUSE BED & BREAKFAST

211 Pearl Avenue, Ilwaco, WA 98624   *360-642-2819*

INCHELIUM

Inchelium is pleasantly remote. It is situated below the bluffs along the Columbia River in northeastern Washington. No major highways lead to Inchelium from the west and to get here from the east will necessitate a brief, fun ferry ride across the Columbia. Coulee Dam National Recreation Area lies just to the south; Colville National Forest is to the north.

THE LOG HOUSE

Silver Creek Road, Inchelium, WA 99138   *509-722-3784*
Sue Jacobsen, Innkeeper

LOCATION	From Spokane, take exit 277 onto Highway 2 west. Go 38 miles to Davenport and turn right onto Highway 25 (Kettle Falls and Fort Spokane). Go approximately 57 miles to the Gifford ferry. After the ferry ride, go 2 miles to Inchelium-Covada Road. Turn left and go 2.7 miles to the stop sign. Turn left again and go 4.8 miles on Silver Creek Road to the driveway.
OPEN	All year
DESCRIPTION	A 1983 two-story log house featuring comfortable country furnishings, hardwood floors, and braided rugs. The home overlooks the Columbia River, with a spectacular seven-mile view upriver.
NO. OF ROOMS	Three rooms share two bathrooms.
RATES	May through October, rates are $60-100 for a single or double with a shared bathroom. November through April, rates are $50-75 for a single or double with a shared bathroom. There is a two-night minimum stay during weekends. Ask about a cancellation policy.
CREDIT CARDS	MasterCard, Visa
BREAKFAST	Breakfast baskets are provided on the first morning; they include homemade muffins, granola, and juice. Thereafter, full kitchen is available for guests to use.
AMENITIES	Wood heater, clawfoot tub upstairs, modern kitchen.

No smoking. The Log House is located on part of a working ranch, so it is not uncommon to see livestock passing through the area. The family's horses are often kept nearby, and the chicken coop is nearby, too.

INDEX

Here's where rock climbers go to climb "The Wall." Challenging cliffs loom just behind this tiny town in Snoqualmie National Forest, about 40 miles east of Everett on Highway 2.

A STONE'S THROW BED & BREAKFAST

406 Index Avenue, Index, WA 98256   360-793-0100
David & Lynn, Resident Owners

BUSH HOUSE COUNTRY INN

300 Fifth Street, Index, WA 98256   360-793-2312
Dennis Breen & Rick Brown, Resident Managers

A RIVER'S EDGE COUNTRY COTTAGE

911 Avenue A, Index, WA 98256   360-793-0392
Mike & Dawna Finley, Innkeepers

LOCATION   From the west, take Highway 2 about eight miles east of Goldbar. Turn left at the Index sign and go one mile. Turn left again, drive over the bridge, and take an immediate right.

OPEN   All year

DESCRIPTION   A 1910 guest cottage with old-fashioned country decor and Victorian touches.

NO. OF ROOMS   One room with a private bathroom.

RATES	Year-round rate is $80 for the cottage. There is no minimum stay. Ask about a cancellation policy.
CREDIT CARDS	MasterCard, Visa
BREAKFAST	Full breakfast is delivered to guestrooms in a large country basket and includes blueberry muffins, Scottish eggs, fresh seasonal fruit, cereals, and coffee.
AMENITIES	Fresh-cut flowers from cottage grounds, therapeutic spa with a view of Mount Index, oversized shower, separate entrance, propane fireplace.
RESTRICTIONS	No smoking. Children are welcome. The cottage is suitable for families of up to four. Dinah and Tigger are the resident cats; Big Red is the rabbit.
REVIEWED	*Hot Showers, Soft Beds, and Dayhikes in the North Cascades*

ISSAQUAH

The center of this old coal-mining town still resembles small-town America, complete with a butcher shop, a well-respected community theater, and a working dairy. On clear days, Mount Rainier appears between the hills that form the town's southern and eastern borders. The Issaquah Farmers Market is held on Saturdays, mid-April to mid-October. Nearby Lake Sammamish State Park offers swimming and boat access. Tiger Mountain, the sprawling 13,000-acre state forest that looms to the east, is a favorite weekend destination for hikers and mountain bikers. Trails wind through alder and evergreen forests and past old mine shafts.

ISSAQUAH BED & BREAKFAST

140 6th Avenue SE, Issaquah, WA 98027   *425-557-7924*

POPLARS ON LAKE SAMMAMISH

3527 East Lake Sammamish Shore Lane   *425-392-7079*
Issaquah, WA 98029

TIGER MOUNTAIN CHALET

12900 246th Avenue SE, Issaquah, WA 98027   425-392-9905
David & Renee Moe, Innkeepers   FAX 425-391-4534
EMAIL dmoe@motivater.com
WEBSITE www.motivater.com/dmoe/chalet.htm

LOCATION	Two-and-a-half miles south of Issaquah on the Issaquah-Hobart Road, turn left onto 132nd Way SE. Go up the hill 1 mile. Just past Tiger Mountain Stables on your left is 246th Avenue SE. Turn left down the dirt road and go 0.25 mile to the last house on the right.
OPEN	All year
DESCRIPTION	A spacious 1978 two-story A-frame host home set in a grove of cedar trees and decorated with a mix of old and new.
NO. OF ROOMS	Two rooms with private bathrooms and one room with one shared bathroom. Try the Master Suite.
RATES	Year-round rates are $85 for a single or double with a private bathroom, $65 for a single or double with the shared bathroom, $135 for a suite, and $225 for the entire B&B. There is no minimum stay and cancellation requires 48 hours' notice.
CREDIT CARDS	Visa
BREAKFAST	Full breakfast is served in the dining room and includes waffles with ham or bacon, fruit, and coffee. Guests can request substitutes.
AMENITIES	Hot tub in forest setting, hiking trails, horseback riding next door, piano, and maybe a song or two performed by the host on guitar and washtub bass.
RESTRICTIONS	No smoking. Sheba is the resident Belgian sheepdog, Rosey is the Tennessee walking horse, and Panda, Baby Girl, and Airplane are the cats.
MEMBER	Seattle Eastside Bed & Breakfast Association

KENT

VICTORIAN GARDENS 1888 BED & BREAKFAST

9621 South 200th, Kent, WA 98031   253-850-1776

KETTLE FALLS

On the National Scenic Byway, Highway 20, in northeastern Washington, Kettle Falls offers access to excellent cross-country skiing in the winter and floating the Colville River, hiking, and playing in the water at nearby Franklin D. Roosevelt Lake in the summer.

MY PARENTS' ESTATE BED & BREAKFAST

719 Highway 395 N, Kettle Falls, WA 99141   509-738-6220
Al & Bev Parent, Innkeepers

LOCATION	A little over seven miles north of Colville on Highway 395. Look for a long white fence and the house on the left as you are going north.
OPEN	April through October 15
DESCRIPTION	A 1900 two-story traditional host home, renovated in 1985, decorated with Laura Ashley furnishings, and situated on 43 acres with mountain and pastoral views in every direction.
NO. OF ROOMS	Four rooms with private bathrooms. Al recommends the suite.
RATES	Year-round rates are $75-100 for a single or double. The suite is $100 and the guesthouse is $45-100. There is a two-night minimum stay in the guesthouse and cancellation requires seven days' notice.
CREDIT CARDS	MasterCard, Visa
BREAKFAST	Full breakfast is served in the dining room and includes juice, coffee, fruit, and a main dish.
AMENITIES	Central air conditioning.
RESTRICTIONS	No smoking, no pets, no children
REVIEWED	*Mobil Travel Guide; Hidden Pacific Northwest; Northwest Best Places; Fodor's Pacific Northwest Best Bed & Breakfasts; Washington Handbook*
RATED	Mobil 3 Stars
KUDOS/COMMENTS	"Friendly, neat, hospitable."

KINGSTON

KINGSTON HOUSE BED & BREAKFAST

26117 Ohio Avenue NE, Kingston, WA 98346   *360-297-8818*

KIRKLAND

This city's comfortable downtown on Lake Washington's Moss Bay is a popular strolling ground, especially in summer. Art galleries, restaurants, and boutiques line the two-story main street. Several restaurants look out over boats docked at the marina. On Yarrow Bay at the south end of town lies Carillon Point, a high-end hotel and shopping complex lining a round, red-brick courtyard with pretty views of the lake and the distant Olympic Mountains. At Saint Edward State Park, just north of Kirkland, spectacular rolling trails amble through old stands of Douglas fir and western red cedar, eventually winding up on the lakefront.

SHUMWAY MANSION

11419 99th Place NE, Kirkland, WA 98033   *425-823-2303*
Richard & Salli Harris, Innkeepers   *FAX 425-822-0421*
EMAIL shumway@nwpages.com   *WEBSITE www.shumway.nwpages.com*

LOCATION	From I-405 north, take exit 20A (NE 116th Street) and go west under the freeway, then turn left onto 99th Place NE. From I-405 south, take exit 20 (NE 124th Street) and turn left onto 116th Avenue NE, turn right onto NE 116th Street, and take another left onto 99th Place NE.
OPEN	All year
DESCRIPTION	A restored 1909 four-story New England shingle-style mansion furnished with antiques, silk floral arrangements, and oriental carpets. Listed on the State Historic Register.
NO. OF ROOMS	Eight rooms with private bathrooms. Try the Kirkland Suite.
RATES	Year-round rates are $70-105 for a single or double. There is no minimum stay and cancellation requires one week's notice.
CREDIT CARDS	American Express, MasterCard, Visa

Shumway Mansion, Kirkland

BREAKFAST	Full breakfast is served buffet style in the dining room and includes a variety of cereals, yogurt, fresh and/or baked fruit, and a main entrée that changes daily, plus muffins, scones, bagels, coffee, tea, and juices. Catering for business functions is also available.
AMENITIES	Meeting facilities for up to 75 in the ballroom; other large rooms available for weddings and receptions; full use of Columbia Athletic Club; homemade snacks, coffee, tea, and hot chocolate in the evenings; one bedroom with handicapped access; covered veranda, patio, and gazebo; walk to the beach.
RESTRICTIONS	No smoking inside, no pets, children over 12 are welcome. Dudley, the director of public relations, doubles as an Old English sheepdog.
MEMBER	Washington Bed & Breakfast Guild
RATED	AAA 3 Diamonds, Mobil 3 Stars
AWARDS	1986 Washington Trust for Historic Preservation

LA CONNER

La Conner was founded in 1867 by John Conner, a trading-post operator, who named the town after his wife, Louisa A. Conner. Much of what you see today was built when the fishing and farming communities of Puget Sound traded almost entirely by water—before the railroads arrived in the late 1880s. In an age of conformity and efficiency, the town became a literal backwater, and something of a haven for nonconformists (Wobblies, WWII COs, McCarthy-era escapees, beatniks, hippies, and bikers), always with a fair smattering of artists and writers, including Mark Tobey, Morris Graves, Guy Anderson, and Tom Robbins.

ART'S PLACE

511 Talbott Street, La Conner, WA 98257   *360-466-3033*
Art & Rita Hupy, Innkeepers

LOCATION	From Seattle, take I-5 north to exit 221. Go west five miles to La Conner. Take the first left to Maple Avenue and go two blocks south to Talbot. Turn right—we are the second house on the right.
OPEN	All year
DESCRIPTION	A 1993 one-and-a-half-story contemporary guesthouse with a modern interior, 18 original paintings, and skylights. The guesthouse is near the owners' 100-year-old Victorian home.
NO. OF ROOMS	One room with a private bathroom.
RATES	Year-round rate for a double is $60 and $10 for each additional guest. There is no minimum stay and no charge for cancellation.
CREDIT CARDS	MasterCard, Visa
BREAKFAST	Continental breakfast is provided in the guesthouse and includes homemade coffeecake or muffins, juice, coffee, tea, or cocoa.
AMENITIES	Refrigerator; popcorn; microwave; TV/VCR; fresh berries, plums, and tomatoes from the garden.
RESTRICTIONS	No smoking. All children and pets are welcome. Crib for babies and toddler gate for stairway available on request. The cat is called Little Orphan Annie.
MEMBER	Tulip Valley Bed & Breakfast Association

THE HERON IN LA CONNER

117 Maple, La Conner, WA 98257   360-466-4626
See the description listed under The Wild Iris.

KATY'S INN

503 South Third Street, La Conner, WA 98257   360-466-3366
Bruce & Kathie Hubbard, Resident Owners   800-914-7767
WEBSITE *www.home.ncia.com/katysinn/*

LOCATION	As you enter La Conner on Morris Street, continue west toward the waterfront. Turn left on Second, go one block, then turn left on Washington Street. Go one block up the hill.
OPEN	All year
DESCRIPTION	An 1882 two-story Victorian inn with cozy Victorian decor and wraparound porches. The inn is nestled against a hillside two blocks above historic La Conner and offers views of town, water, and gardens.
NO. OF ROOMS	Three rooms with private bathrooms and two rooms with one shared bathroom. Try the Captain's Suite.
RATES	Year-round rates are $82-120 for a single or double with a private bathroom, $62-82 for a single or double with a shared bathroom, $110-120 for a suite, and $461 for the entire B&B. From mid-October through mid-March, stay two nights from Sunday through Thursday and the second night is half price. There is no minimum stay and cancellation requires three days' notice.
CREDIT CARDS	MasterCard, Visa
BREAKFAST	Full breakfast is served in the dining room or delivered on a silver tray to your door.
AMENITIES	Robes and fresh flowers in all rooms; hot tub under the gazebo; evening goodies, plus spiced cider, tea, and cocoa; beautiful gardens, ponds, and waterfalls.
RESTRICTIONS	No smoking, no pets. Smudge is the resident mixed breed outdoor cat.
REVIEWED	*The Best Places to Kiss in the Northwest*
MEMBER	Washington Bed & Breakfast Guild, Tulip Valley Bed & Breakfast Association, Washington State Hotel and Motel Association
RATED	Mobil 3 Stars, Best Places to Kiss in the Northwest, 2.5 Lips

KUDOS/COMMENTS "Beautifully decorated Victorian within walking distance of downtown; congenial hosts, great food." (1996) "Cozy B&B right in town with very nice innkeepers."

LA CONNER CHANNEL LODGE

205 North First Street, Box 573, La Conner, WA 98257   *360-466-1500*

LA CONNER COUNTRY INN

107 S Second Street, La Conner, WA 98257   *360-466-3101*
Gary Tachiyama, Resident Manager   *FAX 360-466-5902*

RIDGEWAY "FARM" BED & BREAKFAST

14914 McLean Road, Mount Vernon, WA 98273   *360-428-8068*
Louise & John Kelly, Resident Owners   *800-428-8068*
EMAIL *ridgeway@halcyon.com*   *FAX 360-428-8068*
WEBSITE *www.placestostay.com/lacon-ridgewayfarm*

LOCATION	Midway between La Conner and Mount Vernon. Take exit 221 (or 230) off I-5 and follow the signs toward La Conner, then Ridgeway. The B&B is 11 miles from exit 221 and eight miles from exit 230.
OPEN	All year
DESCRIPTION	A 1928 three-story Dutch colonial brick farmhouse uniquely decorated with antiques, quilts, and wallpaper, with views of gardens, farm fields, and mountains.
NO. OF ROOMS	Four rooms with private bathrooms and two rooms with one shared bathroom. Louise and John suggest the Nicole Room (penthouse).
RATES	Year-round rates are $95-155 for a single or double with a private bathroom, $75-95 for a single or double with a shared bathroom, and the entire B&B rents for $635. There is a two-night minimum stay during the Skagit Valley Tulip Festival and cancellation requires five days' notice.
CREDIT CARDS	Discover, MasterCard, Visa
BREAKFAST	Full farm-style breakfast is served in the dining room and includes fresh fruit with juice, homemade granola and yogurt, special egg dishes with meat, pancakes, and toast or muffins.

AMENITIES	Fresh flowers, terry robes, and "if-you-forgot" items in every room; luxury linens; handmade quilts; comforters on premium queen- and king-size beds; therapeutic hot tub off the patio; homemade dessert.
RESTRICTIONS	No smoking, no pets, children over 12 are welcome. Murphy and Paddy O'Kelly, the resident cats, are the official house greeters.
REVIEWED	*Quick Escapes; Ultimate Washington; America's Favorite Inns and Bed & Breakfasts; Fodor's; The Best Places to Kiss in the Northwest*
MEMBER	Washington Bed & Breakfast Guild, Tulip Valley Bed & Breakfast Association, Professional Association of Innkeepers International
RATED	AAA 3 Diamonds, Mobil 3 Stars
AWARDS	1996 and 1997, Best Bed & Breakfast of Skagit Valley, Business Pulse
KUDOS/COMMENTS	"Wonderful B&B, charming, comfortable and homey; John and Louise are excellent hosts."

SKAGIT BAY HIDEAWAY

17430 Goldenview Avenue, La Conner, WA 98257   360-466-2262
Earlene Beckes & Kevin Haberly, Innkeepers   888-466-2262
Spanish spoken   FAX 360-466-7493
EMAIL *hideaway@skagitbay.com*   WEBSITE *www.skagitbay.com*

LOCATION	From Seattle, follow I-5 north to exit 221 (Conway/La Conner). Go left (west) over the freeway and take the first right (Conway/La Conner). Go over the Skagit River on Fir Island Road and continue until you see a left turn to La Conner. Take the first left in La Conner onto Maple Avenue. After the bridge, take the second left on Snee-oosh Road. Drive about 1.7 miles and take Sunset Drive. Take the second left onto Goldenview Avenue. The inn is the third home on the right.
OPEN	All year
DESCRIPTION	A 1998 two-story Northwest shingled guesthouse decorated with casual elegance.
NO. OF ROOMS	Two suites with private bathrooms.
RATES	Year-round rate is $195 for a suite. There is no minimum stay and cancellation requires seven days' notice, 14 days for stays of more than three days.
CREDIT CARDS	MasterCard, Visa
BREAKFAST	Full breakfast is served in the guestrooms. The house special features fruit with yogurt, homemade muffins, a Dungeness crab and Havarti omelet, and juice.

AMENITIES	Fresh flowers, thick terry robes and spa wraps; the two-person spa is on a private deck that looks out over the bay; fireplace, stereo in living room; spectacular sunsets; waterfront property and beach walks; large shower has two showerheads and four body sprays; chocolates; mango iced tea; refrigerator and microwave; coffee- and tea-makers.
RESTRICTIONS	No smoking, no pets, no children. Misty is the resident shorthaired cat and Stormy is the Norwegian forest cat. The cats are not allowed in the guesthouse. "You are welcome to pet them outdoors on the property."
MEMBER	Tulip Valley Bed & Breakfast Association, Washington State Bed & Breakfast Guild

STORYVILLE BED & BREAKFAST

1880 Chilberg Road, La Conner, WA 98257   *360-466-3207*

THE WILD IRIS INN AND THE HERON INN

117-121 Maple Avenue, La Conner, WA 98257   *360-466-1400*
Susan Sullivan, Innkeeper   *FAX 360-466-1221*
EMAIL pathy@wildiris.com   *WEBSITE www.wildiris.com*

LOCATION	Entering La Conner, turn left at the first block onto Maple Avenue and go one block south.
OPEN	All year
DESCRIPTION	A 1992 two-story Victorian inn with Victorian and Northwest eclectic decor and sweeping views.
NO. OF ROOMS	Thirty-two rooms with private bathrooms. Susan recommends the Cloud Room.
RATES	March 15 through November 15, rates are $85-120 for a single or double, $140-160 for a suite with a queen-size bed, and $180 for a suite with a king-size bed. Mid-November through mid-March, rates are $95-130 for a single or double and $120-130 for a suite. There is no minimum stay and cancellation requires 24 hours' notice.
CREDIT CARDS	American Express, MasterCard, Visa
BREAKFAST	Full breakfast is served in the dining room and includes fresh fruits, fresh juices, excellent coffee and tea with two baked goods, an

The Wild Iris Inn and The Heron Inn, La Conner

	inspired egg dish, imported cheeses, and jams. Dinner is also available, as are New Year's Eve and Valentine's Day meals.
AMENITIES	Renowned guest service; guests' special events (honeymoons, anniversaries) are celebrated with sparkling cider, crystal, and ribbons; bath bombs; surprises.
RESTRICTIONS	No smoking, no pets
REVIEWED	*The Best Places to Kiss in the Northwest; America's Wonderful Little Inns & Hotels; Northwest Best Places; The Great Towns of America*
AWARDS	1998, Best Bed & Breakfast Inn in the Northwest, *Seattle* magazine's readers poll.

LAKE BAY

RANSOM'S POND OSTRICH FARM BED & BREAKFAST

3915 Mahnke Road KPS, Lakebay, WA 98351

253-884-5666
FAX 253-884-5666

LANGLEY

The nicest town on Whidbey still carries its small-town virtues well, though it may be getting a little too spit-and-polished for some—with the addition of Langley Village on Second Street, it has grown into a two-street town. Look for original Northwest art, from paintings and pottery to sculpture and glass, at Childers-Proctor Gallery on First Street. At the Hellebore Glass Studio you can watch glassblower George Springer at work. Other fun stuff to do in Langley includes the Mystery Weekend in February, the Choocho Kum arts and crafts festival in July, the County Fair in August, and the Harvest Ball in September.

COUNTRY COTTAGE OF LANGLEY

215 Sixth Street, Langley, WA 98260   360-221-8709
Bob & Kathy Annecone, Resident Owners   800-713-3860

DOVE HOUSE/CHAUNTECLEER HOUSE/ THE POTTING SHED

3557 Saratoga Road, Langley, WA 98260   360-221-5494
Bunny Meals, Resident Owner   800-637-4436
EMAIL bunny@dovehouse.com   FAX 360-221-0397
WEBSITE www.dovehouse.com

LOCATION	From Seattle, take I-5 north to exit 189, following signs to the Mukilteo ferry. Follow Highway 525. Once on Whidbey, go to the first traffic light and turn right onto Langley Road. Take 2nd Street to Saratoga Road. Dove House is on the right.
OPEN	All year
DESCRIPTION	Three artfully appointed, fully furnished private cottages within walking distance to Langley.
NO. OF ROOMS	Three rooms with private bathrooms.
RATES	Year-round rates are $175-225 for a single or double. There is a two-night minimum stay and cancellation requires seven days' notice.
CREDIT CARDS	MasterCard, Visa
BREAKFAST	Continental plus includes egg soufflé or quiche, muffins, fruit, granola, coffee, and juice.

AMENITIES	Six acres of meadows, ponds, and gardens; bluff views; private hot tubs; stereo, CD players, TV/VCR, and movies; robes; fireplaces.
RESTRICTIONS	No smoking, no pets, children over 10 are welcome. The resident pets are Molly and Rudy—both yellow Labs—and Boots the cat.
REVIEWED	*The Best Places to Kiss in the Northwest; Northwest Best Places; America's Favorite Inns, Bed & Breakfasts and Small Hotels; Sweetheart's Getaway Guide*
MEMBER	Washington State Bed & Breakfast Guild, Whidbey Island Bed & Breakfast Association
KUDOS/COMMENTS	"Lovely private cottages." "Charming."

EAGLE'S NEST INN BED & BREAKFAST

3236 East Saratoga Road, Langley, WA 98260   360-221-5331
Joanne & Jerry Lechner, Resident Owners   FAX 360-221-5331
WEBSITE *www.eaglesnestinn.com*

LOCATION	One-and-a-half miles north of Langley on Saratoga Road.
OPEN	All year except Christmas
DESCRIPTION	A 1987 four-story contemporary Northwest octagon with contemporary decor.
NO. OF ROOMS	Four rooms with private bathrooms.
RATES	Year-round rates are $95-125 for a single or double. There is a two-night minimum stay on Saturday nights and some holiday weekends, and cancellation requires seven days' notice.
CREDIT CARDS	American Express, Discover, MasterCard, Visa
BREAKFAST	Full "Northwest gourmet" breakfast includes seasonal berry delights, omelets, soufflés, stuffed French toast, and summer fruit sorbets.
AMENITIES	Jacuzzi under the sun, well-stocked video library, bottomless jar of homemade chocolate chip cookies, complimentary beverage bar, fresh flowers from the garden, robes, local guide maps, culinary garden, wildlife and bird-watching on property.
RESTRICTIONS	No smoking, no pets, children over 12 are welcome. Mory is the resident tabby.
REVIEWED	*The Best Places to Kiss in the Northwest; Pacific Northwest's Best Bed & Breakfasts; Best Places to Stay in Washington; Americas Wonderful Little Hotels & Inns; Ultimate Washington; Northwest Best Places*

MEMBER	Professional Association of Innkeepers International, Whidbey Island Bed & Breakfast Association, Washington Bed & Breakfast Guild
RATED	AAA 3 Diamonds

THE EDGECLIFF COTTAGES

PO Box 758, Langley, WA 98260

360-221-8857
800-243-5536

GALITTOIRE BED & BREAKFAST

5444 South Coles Road, Langley, WA 98260
Mahesh Massand, Resident Innkeeper

360-221-0548

KUDOS/COMMENTS "Elegant and very sophisticated. A wonderful indulgence."

THE GALLERY SUITE BED & BREAKFAST

302 1st Street, Langley, WA 98260
Ron Childers & Richard Proctor, Resident Owners
EMAIL randr@whidbey.com

360-221-2978

LOCATION	Take the Mukilteo ferrry to Whidbey Island, then go 7.5 miles to Langley.
OPEN	All year
DESCRIPTION	Artfully appointed suite adjacent to a 1939 one-story art gallery.
NO. OF ROOMS	One suite with a private bathroom.
RATES	Year-round rates are $110 for the first night; the second night is $100; and the third and subsequent nights are $90. There is a minimum stay during weekends and holidays.
CREDIT CARDS	American Express, Discover, MasterCard, Visa
BREAKFAST	Continental plus is served in the suite's kitchen and includes fresh croissants, orange juice, milk, coffee, fruit, cheese, English muffins, homemade granola, jam, and jelly.
AMENITIES	Unobstructed views of Saratoga Passage and Camano Head, spacious deck.

THE GARDEN PATH

PO Box 575, Langley, WA 98260   *360-221-5121*
                                                   FAX 360-221-6050

HERON HAVEN BED & BREAKFAST

513 Anthes Avenue, Langley, WA 98260   *360-221-9121*

THE INN AT LANGLEY

400 First Street, Langley, WA 98260   *360-221-3033*
Stephen & Sandy Nogal, Innkeepers   *FAX 360-221-3033 (call first)*

LOCATION	In the center of Langley, four miles from the highway stoplight at Route 525 and Langley Road, and two miles from the Clinton ferry terminal.
OPEN	All year
DESCRIPTION	A 1989 four-story Craftsman country inn with cedar-shake exterior and an interior featuring Asian design, natural wood tones, and neutral colors.
NO. OF ROOMS	All rooms with private bathrooms.
RATES	Year-round rates are $189-199 for a single or double and $279-395 for the suites. There is a minimum stay during weekends. Reservations are guaranteed with a credit card and cancellation requires 48 hours' notice.
CREDIT CARDS	American Express, MasterCard, Visa
BREAKFAST	Full breakfast is served in the dining room and includes homemade muesli (the innkeepers' own recipe), fresh fruit, juices, coffees and teas, fresh muffins, toast and toaster biscuits, and homemade jams and jellies. Weekend dinners and holiday meals are also available.
AMENITIES	Each room is on the waterfront and has a porch, fireplace, Jacuzzi, robes, hair dryers, small refrigerator, TV/VCR, coffee-maker, coffee, and tea. Conference room seats up to 15.

The Inn at Langley, Langley

RESTRICTIONS	No smoking, no pets, children over 12 are welcome. Kelly is the resident Lab/retriever. Kelly is a professional couch-warmer with a fondness for home-baked dog biscuits.
REVIEWED	*Harper's Hideaway; Weekends for Two in the Pacific Northwest; Northwest Best Places; Fodor's; Frommer's; The Best Places to Kiss in the Northwest*
RATED	AAA 2 Diamonds
KUDOS/COMMENTS	"The perfect Whidbey getaway."

ISLAND FOREST RETREAT

5851 South Pioneer Park Place, Langley, WA 98260   *360-321-8095*
Charline Denny, Resident Owner
WEBSITE *www.nwculture.com*

ISLAND TYME BED & BREAKFAST INN

4940 South Bayview Road, Langley, WA 98260   *360-221-5078*
Lyn & Phil Fauth, Resident Owners   *800-898-8963*
WEBSITE *www.moriah.com/inns*

LOCATION	From the ferry dock at Clinton, take Highway 525 for 6.4 miles to Bayview Road, turn right, and go 2.1 miles. From Langley, take 3rd Street and drive two miles from the edge of town.
OPEN	All year
DESCRIPTION	A 1994 two-story Victorian inn with a country Victorian interior decorated with antiques on "10 acres of peace and quiet."
NO. OF ROOMS	Five rooms with private bathrooms.
RATES	Year-round rates are $95-140 for a single or double. There is a two-night minimum stay during the summer and cancellation requires seven days' notice.
CREDIT CARDS	American Express, Discover, MasterCard, Visa
BREAKFAST	Full breakfast, served in the dining room, includes fresh fruit compotes; yogurt; granola; varied hot entrées including Dutch babies, omelets, quiche, and stuffed French toast; muffins; desserts; gourmet coffee and other beverages.
AMENITIES	Three Jacuzzi tubs, decks, chocolates by the bed, homemade cookies and beverages in common room, pool table and fireplace in common area, phones in rooms, customized gift baskets, three fireplaces in rooms, one room with handicapped access.
RESTRICTIONS	No smoking inside. Butch is the resident golden retriever; Mork is the short-haired cat. There are also eight goats.
REVIEWED	*The Best Places to Kiss in the Northwest*
MEMBER	Bed & Breakfasts of the Northwest
RATED	AAA 3 Diamonds

LOG CASTLE BED & BREAKFAST

3273 East Saratoga Road, Langley, WA 98260   360-221-5483
Phil & Karen Holdsworth, Resident Innkeepers

LONE LAKE COTTAGE AND BREAKFAST

5206 South Bayview Road, Langley, WA 98260   360-321-5325
Delores Renfrew, Innkeeper
WEBSITE *www.whidbey.com/lonelake*

LOCATION	Take the ferry from Mukilteo to Clinton, follow Highway 525 for 5.5 miles, take a right on Bayview Road, and go one mile.

OPEN	All year
DESCRIPTION	Two waterfront cottages, one Honeymoon Suite, and a sternwheel houseboat are decorated with an Asian theme.
NO. OF ROOMS	Four rooms with private bathrooms.
RATES	April through October, rate is $140 for a single or double. November through March, rate is $125 for a single or double. There is a two-night minimum stay on weekends and cancellation costs $10 unless the room is rebooked.
CREDIT CARDS	No
BREAKFAST	Continental plus, provided in cottages and on the houseboat, includes fruit, juice, muffins, homemade bread and jam, cream, butter, cereals, coffee, tea, and hot chocolate.
AMENITIES	Boats, canoes, bicycles, fireplaces, TV/VCR and video library, stereo with CDs, fishing, swimming, Jacuzzi tubs for two in each accommodation, exotic bird aviary.
RESTRICTIONS	Smoking on covered deck only, no pets, children over 15 (and babies) are welcome. There is an aviary with over 400 exotic birds and swans in a natural setting with koi ponds and waterfalls.
REVIEWED	*The Best Places to Kiss in the Northwest; Northwest Best Places; Sweethearts Getaway Guide; Where to Stay and Play on the West Coast; Non-Smokers Guide to Bed & Breakfasts*
MEMBER	Whidbey Island Bed & Breakfast Association
KUDOS/COMMENTS	"Warm innkeeper; reasonably priced." (1996)

PINE COTTAGE BED & BREAKFAST

3827 McKay Drive, Langley, WA 98260   *360-730-1376*

PRIMROSE PATH COTTAGE

3191 East Harbor Road, Langley, WA 98260   *360-730-3722*
John & Sarah Primrose, Innkeepers   *800-333-4724*
EMAIL primrose@whidbey.com

LOCATION	On Whidbey Island, 35 miles north of Seattle and six miles northwest of Langley. Take the Whidbey Island ferry in Mukilteo. Drive off the ferry in Clinton and follow Highway 525 north to the second stoplight. Turn right onto Langley Road and follow it for about 2.5 miles into Langley. Turn left onto 2nd Street, which will

become Saratoga Road. Follow it for 6.3 miles. The cottage is the first house on the left after a sharp curve.

OPEN	All year
DESCRIPTION	A 1928 rustic beach cottage decorated with informal English country decor with a vaulted ceiling and skylights, and nestled on wooded acreage.
NO. OF ROOMS	All rooms have private bathrooms.
RATES	May through November, rates are $145-195 for the private cottage. December through April (excluding holidays), rates are $115-155 for the private cottage. There is a two-night minimum stay during weekends and holidays.
CREDIT CARDS	MasterCard, Discover
BREAKFAST	Continental breakfast is left in the kitchen and includes breads or muffins, fruit, coffee, and tea.
AMENITIES	Fresh flowers, robes, private hot tub; TV/VCR/stereo with CD player and phone in the kitchen; wood-burning stove and firewood; private beach access less than a block away.
RESTRICTIONS	No smoking, no pets. Sylvia is the Border collie, Teddy is the mixed shepherd, and the three cats are Zaire, Taz, and Kazoo. All animals reside at the owners' home and are never permitted in the cottage.

SARATOGA SUNRISE GUEST HOUSE

3770 South Bells Beach Road, Langley, WA 98260   *360-730-8407*

THE TREE HOUSE

PO Box 326, Langley, WA 98260   *360-221-5159*

TWICKENHAM HOUSE INN

5023 Langley Road, Langley, WA 98260   *360-221-6131*
Maureen & Raymond Cooke, Innkeepers   *FAX 360-221-8393*
Fluent French spoken
EMAIL *twcknham@whidbey.com*
WEBSITE *www.whidbey.com*

LOCATION	From the Clinton ferry terminal, go north on Highway 525 to the first traffic light and turn right onto Langley Road. Go about 2.5 miles. The inn is on the right.
OPEN	All year
DESCRIPTION	A 1990 rambling two-story rustic country inn with French-Canadian and European furnishings, antiques, heavy dark beams, and white walls.
NO. OF ROOMS	Six rooms with private bathrooms. Try the Kingston Suite.
RATES	Year-round rates are $85-120 for a single or double. There is no minimum stay and reservations require a one-night deposit.
CREDIT CARDS	MasterCard, Visa
BREAKFAST	Full three-course breakfast is served in the dining room and includes an appetizer, entrée, and dessert: for example, a croissant with preserves, a gourmet omelet with fruit, and warm spiced bananas. Coffee, tea, and juices are also served. Dinner is also available.
AMENITIES	Three common rooms with fireplaces for winter getaways and a patio for summer visits; the quiet room has books, puzzles, and a wet bar with refrigerator.
RESTRICTIONS	No smoking, no pets, no children. Whidbey is the resident tabby cat. Loving and gentle, Whidbey loves to have guests around.
REVIEWED	*Fodor's; The Best Places to Kiss in the Northwest*
RATED	AAA 3 Diamonds

VILLA ISOLA BED & BREAKFAST INN

5489 South Coles Road, Langley, WA 98260
Gary & Gwen Galeotti, Innkeepers
EMAIL *villa@villaisola.com*
WEBSITE *www.villaisola.com*

360-221-5052
800-246-7323
FAX 360-221-5823

LOCATION	Approximately seven miles from the Clinton ferry dock on Highway 525. Go past the stoplight (Maxwalton Road) and proceed 0.5 mile to Coles Road and turn right. Go another 0.5 mile. The B&B is on the right side of the road.
OPEN	All year
DESCRIPTION	Two 1986 one- and two-story Italian country villas with Italian and Northwest decor, nestled among tall pines and situated on 3.5 beautifully landscaped acres.
NO. OF ROOMS	Six rooms with private bathrooms. Gary and Gwen recommend the Tuscany Suite.

RATES	Year-round rates are $85-140 for a single or double. There is no minimum stay and cancellation requires 14 days' notice.
CREDIT CARDS	MasterCard, Visa
BREAKFAST	Full breakfast is served in the dining room and may include hazelnut French toast, poached pears in orange butter sauce, lemon tart, berry cobbler, pear tart, apples in phyllo dough, double-chocolate cranberry bread, *pesche repiene*, or Italian stuffed peaches, to name a few. Special meals are available upon request. Breakfast is heart-healthy whenever possible.
AMENITIES	Fresh flowers in all rooms, robes, Jacuzzi bath in each room, acres of gardens to walk through, boccie ball court, mountain bikes, food tastings.
RESTRICTIONS	No smoking, no pets, children over 12 are welcome.
REVIEWED	*Northwest Best Places; The Best Places to Kiss in the Northwest*
RATED	AAA 3 Diamonds

THE WHIDBEY INN

106 First Street, Langley, WA 98260   360-221-7115
Richard Francisco, Resident Owner   888-313-2070
WEBSITE *www.whidbeyinn.com*

LOCATION	Take I-5 north from Seattle to exit 189, follow the signs to the Mukilteo ferry, take the ferry to Clinton, and go north on Highway 525 to Langley Road; turn right and follow Langley Road into Langley. The inn is in the heart of Langley.
OPEN	All year
DESCRIPTION	A 1934 two-story early American/Victorian inn on the waterfront, with country Victorian decor.
NO. OF ROOMS	Six rooms with private bathrooms. Try the Gazebo Suite.
RATES	Year-round rates are $95-160 for a single or double and $130-160 for a suite. There is no minimum stay and cancellation requires seven days' notice.
CREDIT CARDS	American Express, MasterCard, Visa
BREAKFAST	Full breakfast, served in the dining room or brought to guestrooms in a basket, includes an egg dish, fruit, orange juice, croissants, bagels, homemade breads, and muffins.
AMENITIES	Cheese plate and sherry in guestrooms upon arrival, English soaps and bath gel, chocolate truffles on the bed.
RESTRICTIONS	No smoking, no pets, children over 14 are welcome.
REVIEWED	*Recommended Country Inns; The Best Places to Kiss in the Northwest*

LEAVENWORTH

Located in a stunning alpine setting in the Cascade Range, Leavenworth, once a railroad yard and sawmill town, decided years ago to recast itself as a Bavarian-style town with tourism as its primary industry. Popular festivals are the Autumn Leaf Festival (the last weekend in September and the first weekend in October), the Christmas Lighting Festival (the first two Saturdays in December), and Maifest (the second weekend in May). Outdoor activities include river rafting on the Wenatchee; fishing and hiking along Icicle Creek; golfing at the scenic 18-hole Leavenworth Golf Club; downhill skiing at Stevens Pass or Mission Ridge; fabulous cross-country skiing around the area; walking along the river on a new city-center trail system that leads via wheelchair-accessible ramps to Blackbird Island; and rock climbing in Peshastin Pinnacles State Park, just 10 miles east of Leavenworth.

ABENDBLUME PENSION

12570 Ranger Road, Leavenworth, WA 98826   509-548-4059
Randy & Renee Sexauer, Innkeepers   800-669-7634
EMAIL abendblm@rightathome.com   FAX 509-548-9032
WEBSITE www.abendblume.com

LOCATION	From Highway 2, take Ski Hill Drive north for 0.7 mile. Turn left onto Ranger Road for 0.1 mile and then turn right at the sign—you should see four rock pillers and a carved sign that reads Abendblume.
OPEN	All year
DESCRIPTION	A 1993 two-story Austrian guesthouse with carved pine ceilings and walls, deep inset archways and windows, a handcrafted wrought-iron curved stairway, and 3,000 square feet of natural marble and limestone. "We studied the architecture in Austria and built from the ground up."
NO. OF ROOMS	Seven rooms with private bathrooms. Randy and Renee recommend the Almrosen Room.
RATES	Year-round rates are $77-159 for a single or double, $105-159 for a suite, and $790 for the entire pension. There is a minimum stay during weekends and in December; cancellation requires 10 days' notice, 30 days for festivals and in December.
CREDIT CARDS	American Express, Discover, MasterCard, Visa
BREAKFAST	Full buffet-style breakfast is served in the dining room and includes meats, cheese, pastries, a variety of fruits, breads, and fresh granola. A hot dish is brought to the table along with French-press coffees and teas. "Choose your time for breakfast, sit at your own table, and serve yourself from the buffet."

AMENITIES	Robes; candles; flowers; VCR and CD players with videos and CDs; most lights are on dimmers to give a very romantic feel; most marble and tile floors are heated; some rooms have large all-marble showers with six shower heads; most rooms have balconies and wood-burning fireplaces.
RESTRICTIONS	No smoking, no pets, children over 12 are welcome. Heather and Heidi are the cashmere goats. There are also Arabian horses on the property. "The two little cashmere goats are very spoiled—they live in an authentic Bavarian barn with a grass roof. Their fiber is used to spin and weave cashmere sweaters."
REVIEWED	*Northwest Best Places; The Best Places to Kiss in the Northwest; Frommer's; Fodor's; Sweethearts Getaway Guide*
MEMBER	Professional Association of Innkeepers International, Leavenworth Lodging Association
RATED	AAA 3 Diamonds
AWARDS	1995, Best Holiday Interior Design, and 1997, Finest Lodging Facility in Leavenworth, both awarded by the Leavenworth Chamber of Commerce
KUDOS/COMMENTS	"The house was built by the owners, a real labor of love; very talented, gentle, conscientious people." "Gorgeous, elegant B&B."

ALL SEASONS RIVER INN

8751 Icicle Road, Leavenworth, WA 98826   *509-548-1425*
Kathy & Jeff Falconer, Innkeepers   *800-254-0555*
Spanish spoken
EMAIL *allriver@rightathome.com*
WEBSITE *www.allseasonsriverinn.com*

LOCATION	From Highway 2, drive exactly one mile south on Icicle Road. The inn is the second house on the left side of the road after the bridge.
OPEN	All year
DESCRIPTION	A two-story Northwest cedar inn decorated with an elegant and inviting blend of antiques, country furnishings, and Kathy's creations.
NO. OF ROOMS	Six rooms with private bathrooms.
RATES	June through October and during December, rates are $100-150 for a single or double; January through May and during November, rates are $95-145. There is a minimum stay during weekends, holidays, and festivals; cancellation requires 30 days' notice during December, 10 days during the rest of the year.
CREDIT CARDS	MasterCard, Visa

BREAKFAST	Full breakfast is served in the dining room. A typical breakfast might include an orange juice and pineapple blend; kiwi-peanut butter parfait; pumpkin muffins; egg puff with black bean sauce, sausage and apples; and "inspirational" hashbrowns. An in-room fruit and bread basket is available upon request .
AMENITIES	Catered candlelight dinner in private dining room by special request; in-room riverview seating areas; private decks; soothing music; chocolates on the bed; lulling sounds of the river; robes in some rooms; complimentary bikes; air conditioning; evening goodies; hot cider on arrival during cold winter season; three common rooms including library/TV room with video library and refrigerator, game room with a large selection of games, and a large living room with fireplace and wraparound deck; concierge service includes scheduling in-room massages, and carriage rides; breakfast served in special rooms with advance notice only.
RESTRICTIONS	No smoking, no pets, no children
REVIEWED	*Weekends for Two in the Pacific Northwest; The Best Places to Kiss in the Northwest; Northwest Best Places; Fodor's Bed & Breakfast Country Inns and Other Weekend Pleasures; Ultimate Washington; The Non-Smokers Guide to Bed & Breakfasts; America's Most Charming Towns & Villages; Hot Showers, Soft Beds, and Day Hikes in the North Cascades*
MEMBER	Professional Association of Innkeepers International, Washington Bed & Breakfast Guild

AUTUMN POND BED & BREAKFAST

10388 Titus Road, Leavenworth, WA 98826
Roger & Pamela Kirkpatrick, Resident Owners

509-548-4482
800-222-9661
FAX 509-548-7278

BOSCH GARTEN

9846 Dye Road, Leavenworth, WA 98826
Myke (Ruth) & Cal Bosch, Innkeepers
Some German spoken
EMAIL popity@nwi.net

509-548-6900
800-535-0069
FAX 509-548-6076
WEBSITE www.boschgarten.com

LOCATION	Located 0.4 mile east of the center of town. Take Highway 2 to East Leavenworth Road, take a right and go one block to Mountain Home Road, then take a left and go one block to Dye Road. Bosch Garten is on the corner.

OPEN	All year
DESCRIPTION	A 1992 two-story Bavarian home with classic and elegant interior.
NO. OF ROOMS	Three rooms with private bathrooms.
RATES	Year-round rates are $98-105 for a double. There is a two-night minimum stay during festivals and holidays and cancellation requires 10 days' notice.
CREDIT CARDS	Discover, MasterCard, Visa
BREAKFAST	Full breakfast is served in the dining room and includes three courses, such as a fruit dish, sausage and apple sauté, fluffy French toast fingers with fruit syrups, and Hawaiian banana dessert.
AMENITIES	Hot tub in Japanese teahouse; air conditioning; waterfall and stream; flower gardens; wicker porch furniture on deck by rooms; apples in rooms; tea, coffee, and biscotti in afternoons.
RESTRICTIONS	No smoking, no pets, children over six are welcome.
MEMBER	Washington State Bed & Breakfast Guild
RATED	AAA 3 Diamonds
KUDOS/COMMENTS	"Very friendly, warm, and accommodating; good food." (1996)

DAS WIESENHAUS

8089 Icicle Road, Leavenworth, WA 98226   509-548-6746
Delbert & Gloria Schmidt, Resident Owners   800-448-1293
German spoken

LOCATION	Turn off Highway 2 onto Icicle Road. The B&B is two miles from the highway on the left side of the road.
OPEN	All year
DESCRIPTION	A 1994 two-story German pension decorated with German and American accents, with views of the mountains from every direction.
NO. OF ROOMS	Three rooms with private bathrooms. Try the Lavender Room.
RATES	Year-round rates are $55-110 for a single or double. There is a two-night minimum stay during festival weekends and cancellation requires 14 hours' notice plus a $10 fee.
CREDIT CARDS	MasterCard, Visa
BREAKFAST	Bavarian breakfast is served in the dining room and includes German hard rolls, cold cuts, cheese, jellies, fruit or melon, and muffins or sweet bread.
RESTRICTIONS	No smoking, no pets, children over 14 are welcome.

DER BEAR-VARIAN INN

337 Whitman Street, Leavenworth, WA 98826   509-548-7021
Bob & Nancy Kelly, Resident Owners

FEATHERWINDS BED & BREAKFAST

17033 River Road, Leavenworth, WA 98826   509-763-2011

LOCATION	About 20 minutes out of Leavenworth in the recreation area on the Beaver Valley plain.
OPEN	All year
DESCRIPTION	A 1992 two-story cedar-shake country farmhouse with French country decor.
NO. OF ROOMS	Four rooms with private bathrooms.
RATES	Year-round rates are $95-125 for a single or double. There is a minimum stay during holidays and festival weekends.
CREDIT CARDS	MasterCard, Visa
BREAKFAST	Full breakfast, served in the dining room, includes a main dish, such as apple sausage and cheese-filled crepes with fresh fruit sauce and a dollop of whip cream, plus meats and beverages.
AMENITIES	Flowers in room, large spa towels, VCR and nice selection of movies, hot tub, coffee service to guestrooms an hour before breakfast.
RESTRICTIONS	No smoking, no pets, no children
REVIEWED	*The Best Places to Kiss in the Northwest*

HAUS LORELEI INN

347 Division, Leavenworth, WA 98826   509-548-5726
Elisabeth Sanders, Resident Owner   800-514-8868
German spoken   FAX 509-548-6548
WEBSITE *www.hauslorelei.com*

LOCATION	At the only traffic light in downtown Leavenworth, turn south and go two blocks to Commercial, turn east and go two blocks to Division, then go south for one block.

OPEN	All year
DESCRIPTION	A 1903 two-story mansion with high ceilings filled with German antiques.
NO. OF ROOMS	Ten rooms with private bathrooms.
RATES	Year-round rates are $95 for a single or double on the mountain side and $109 for a single or double on the river side. There is a two-night minimum stay on weekends and cancellation requires two weeks' notice.
CREDIT CARDS	No
BREAKFAST	Full breakfast, served in the dining room, varies but includes a hot entrée such as chile egg puff, crepes, eggs Benedict, or French toast, plus coffeecake, English muffins, fruit, meats, and beverages.
AMENITIES	Teatime with desserts; special treats for honeymoons, birthdays, and anniversaries; tennis court, rackets, and balls; hot tub, mountain bikes, swings; meeting room for up to 40 with tables, projector, screen, and white board.
RESTRICTIONS	No smoking, no pets. Colonel Klinck is the resident Bouvier dog.
REVIEWED	*Northwest Best Places; The Best Places to Kiss in the Northwest*
MEMBER	Hotel & Motel Association of Leavenworth
KUDOS/COMMENTS	"Great rooms on the river just off downtown; friendly, good service and extras!"

HAUS ROHRBACH PENSION

12882 Ranger Road, Leavenworth, WA 98826   509-548-7024
Bob & Kathryn Harrild, Resident Owners   800-548-4477
WEBSITE *www.comhausrohrbach*

HOTEL-PENSIONE ANNA

926 Commercial Street, Leavenworth, WA 98826   509-548-6273

INN VIENNA WOODS BED & BREAKFAST

12842 Prowell Street, Leavenworth, WA 98826   509-548-7843

MOONLIGHT AND ROSES BED & BREAKFAST

12590 Spring Street, Leavenworth, WA 98826   509-548-6766
Jim & Laurie Mooney, Innkeepers

LOCATION	On Highway 2 toward Leavenworth, turn left at Ski Hill Drive. (If coming west, turn right at Ski Hill Drive.) Go one mile, turn left onto Spring Street, and go to the third home on the right.
OPEN	All year
DESCRIPTION	A 1991 two-story traditional French country home.
NO. OF ROOMS	Two rooms with one shared bathroom. The Mooneys recommend the English Garden Room.
RATES	Year-round rates are $85-95 for a single or double. There is a minimum stay on festival and holiday weekends and cancellation requires two weeks' notice.
CREDIT CARDS	MasterCard, Visa
BREAKFAST	Full breakfast is served in the dining room and includes fruit, homemade granola, rum-raisin rice pudding, and a main course.
AMENITIES	Tea tray with coffee, tea, hot water, cocoa, orange juice.
RESTRICTIONS	No smoking, no pets, no children. Nakita, the resident dog, loves people.

MOUNTAIN HOME LODGE

8201-9 Mountain Home Road, Leavenworth, WA 98826   509-548-7077
Brad & Kathy Schmidt, Resident Owners   800-414-2378
Spanish spoken   FAX 509-548-5008
EMAIL mhl@televar.com   WEBSITE www.mthome.com

LOCATION	Take I-90 east to exit 85, which becomes State Route 97 north, then drive to State Route 2 west; turn left toward Leavenworth, turn left again onto East Leavenworth Road just before the bridge across the Wenatchee River, turn left onto Mountain Home Road, and go 2.5 miles.
OPEN	All year
DESCRIPTION	A 1977 four-story Northwest lodge with pine and maple interior and "lots of windows overlooking a 20-acre meadow and the spectacular Cascades."
NO. OF ROOMS	Ten rooms with private bathrooms. The Mountain View Suite is the best.

Mountain Home Lodge, Leavenworth

RATES	November through March, rates are $200-300 for a single or double; April through October, rates are $100-180. There is a two-night minimum stay from Thanksgiving through March 31.
CREDIT CARDS	Discover, MasterCard, Visa
BREAKFAST	Full breakfast, served in the dining room, includes homemade muffins, mountain home granola, eggs with cream cheese, sausage, fruit, and freshly squeezed orange juice.
AMENITIES	Hot tubs, wine and hors d'oeuvres, air conditioning, surround-sound movie room, tennis, swimming pool, snowmobile tours, hiking, snow-cat rides, toboggan run, cross-country skiing, snowshoes.
RESTRICTIONS	No smoking, no pets, children over 16 are welcome. Oggie is the resident shepherd and the lodge's official guide dog. Ernie and Oscar are the resident cats.
REVIEWED	*The Best Places to Kiss in the Northwest; Northwest Best Places; Recommended Country Inns*
MEMBER	Professional Association of Innkeepers International
RATED	Mobil 3 Stars, Northwest Best Places 3 Stars, Best Places to Kiss 3.5 Lips

MRS. ANDERSON'S LODGING HOUSE

917 Commercial Street, Leavenworth, WA 98826   *509-548-6173*
Al & Dee Howie, Resident Owners   *800-253-8990*
EMAIL info@quiltersheaven.com   *FAX 509-548-9113*
WEBSITE www.quiltersheaven.com

LOCATION	Right in downtown Leavenworth.
OPEN	All year
DESCRIPTION	An 1895 two-story small-town lodging house decorated with turn-of-the-century antiques, quilts, and vintage clothing.
NO. OF ROOMS	Seven rooms with private bathrooms and two rooms with one shared bathroom.
RATES	Year-round rates are $50-70 for a single or double with a private bathroom and $39-45 for a single or double with a shared bathroom. There is no minimum stay and cancellation requires 72 hours' notice.
CREDIT CARDS	Discover, MasterCard, Visa
BREAKFAST	Continental plus is served in the dining room.
RESTRICTIONS	No smoking, no pets
REVIEWED	*Northwest Best Places*

Mrs. Anderson's Lodging House, Leavenworth

PHIPPEN'S BED & BREAKFAST

10285 Ski Hill Drive, Leavenworth, WA 98826

509-548-7755
800-666-9806

PINE RIVER RANCH BED & BREAKFAST

19668 Highway 207, Leavenworth, WA 98826
Michael & Mary Ann Zenk, Resident Owners
Some German and some Spanish spoken
EMAIL lodger@televar.com

509-763-3959
800-669-3877
FAX 509-763-3959
WEBSITE www.lakewenatchee.com

LOCATION	Fourteen miles west of Leavenworth, turn off Highway 2 and head north 1.8 miles on Highway 207 toward Lake Wenatchee.
OPEN	All year
DESCRIPTION	A 1941 two-story ranch house with contemporary funishings and accented with pine and river rock, on 32 acres, surrounded by uninterrupted territorial views.
NO. OF ROOMS	Five rooms with private bathrooms. The Lodgepole Room is the best.
RATES	Year-round rates are $89-135 for a single or double and $135-155 for a suite. There is a minimum stay and cancellation requires two weeks' notice.
CREDIT CARDS	American Express, Discover, MasterCard, Visa
BREAKFAST	Full breakfast, served in the dining room or delivered to suites, typically includes rice pudding, baked barn cat (a specialty apple dish), Cascade Mountain stuffed French toast, link sausage with fried apples, and beverages. Special diets are accommodated.
AMENITIES	Robes, hot tub, all rooms have TV/VCRs and stereos with CD players, common area with beautiful brick fireplace, guest beverage area with refrigerator and sink, 800 feet of river frontage, fresh flowers in season, natural pond frequented by wild ducks and Canada geese, cross-country skiing and snowshoeing on 32 private acres.
RESTRICTIONS	No smoking, no pets, children over 12 are welcome. Resident critters are Daisy the Wonderdog, a yellow Lab mix, and BC the cat, who is almost reaching mountain lion proportions at 22 pounds. Other animals include a llama, horses, and a goat.

Pine River Ranch Bed & Breakfast, Leavenworth

REVIEWED	*Northwest Best Places; The Best Places to Kiss in the Northwest; Fodor's; Washington State Travelers: Affordable Accommodations; America's Most Charming Towns and Villages; Lanier's Complete Guide to B&Bs, Inns and Guesthouses*
MEMBER	Professional Association of Innkeepers International, Washington Bed & Breakfast Guild, Gail Greco's Cooking and Baking Association
RATED	AAA 2 Diamonds

PONDEROSA COUNTRY INN

11150 Highway 209, Leavenworth, WA 98826

509-548-4550
800-443-3304
FAX 509-548-8024

RUN OF THE RIVER

9308 East Leavenworth Road, Leavenworth, WA 98826 509-548-7171
Monty & Karen Turner, Innkeepers 800-288-6491
Spanish spoken FAX 509-548-7547
EMAIL rofther@runoftheriver *WEBSITE www.runoftheriver.com*

LOCATION	Turn south at the intersection of Highway 2 and East Leavenworth Road, which is 0.25 mile east of Leavenworth toward Cashmere, and drive exactly one mile. Watch for the sign and turn right as directed down the little country lane toward the river.
OPEN	All year
DESCRIPTION	A luxurious 1986 two-story log lodge decorated with natural pine and lots of river rock situated on the banks of a quiet oxbow of the Icicle River, surrounded on two sides by a bird refuge.
NO. OF ROOMS	Six rooms with private bathrooms.
RATES	Year-round rates are $100-135 for a single or double and $155 for a suite. There is a minimum stay and cancellation requires 10 days' notice.
CREDIT CARDS	Discover, MasterCard, Visa
BREAKFAST	Full breakfast is served in the dining room and begins with fresh-ground, locally roasted coffee, a hearty platter of seasonal fruit, and a basket of warm muffins ... and then comes breakfast! Entrées might be cinnamon-swirl French toast and a vegetable frittata garnished with fresh herbs from the garden. "Add lots of laughter and lies about who had the best hike or cross-country ski!"
AMENITIES	Each room comes with an array of goodies: soft cotton robes, hiking sticks, a picnic basket with a map for fine wilderness dining, and a daypack; top-flight Specialized mountain bikes and a Cannondale tandem for guests' use; Redfeather snowshoes for treks through the snow on quiet winter trails. The innkeepers, avid hikers, bikers, and skiers, have written their own "field tested" guides and maps that get guests off the beaten path. "We specialize in going the extra yard for guests so that getaway time is just that."
RESTRICTIONS	No smoking, no pets, no children. Jasper is the resident Airedale.
REVIEWED	*Best Places to Kiss; Northwest Best Places; Quick Escapes in the Pacific Northwest; Outside Guide to the Pacific Northwest; America's Favorite Small Hotels and Inns; Recommended Romantic Inns; Hidden Pacific Northwest; Best Places to Stay in the Pacific Northwest; Weekend Pleasures/Frommer; Ultimate Washington*
MEMBER	Professional Association of Innkeepers International, Washington State Bed & Breakfast Guild
RATED	AAA 3 Diamonds, Mobil 3 Stars

"One of the top operations in Washington, rustic and elegant. Great, professional hosts and a terrific woodsy setting with panoramic Cascade and river views. Original and inviting. A perfect romantic getaway."

LONG BEACH

A popular hangout here is the half-mile-long elevated boardwalk (with night lighting) stretching between South 10th and Bolstad Streets, accessible by wheelchairs, baby strollers and, of course, feet. Kite lovers should visit the Long Beach World Kite Museum and Hall of Fame. August's International Kite Festival brings thousands of soaring creations to the skies. The entire peninsula swells with visitors for this event, so plan ahead.

BOREAS BED & BREAKFAST INN

607 North Ocean Beach Boulevard, Long Beach, WA 98631 360-642-8069
Susie Goldsmith & Bill Verner, Innkeepers   888-642-8069
Some Spanish spoken   FAX 360-642-5353
EMAIL boreas@boreasinn.com   WEBSITE www.boreasinn.com

LOCATION	Follow Pacific Highway north through Long Beach and take a left onto North Sixth Street, go one block and turn right onto North Boulevard.
OPEN	All year
DESCRIPTION	An artistically remodeled 1920 two-story beach bungalow on the ocean with an elegant mix of art, antiques, and contemporary furnishings.
NO. OF ROOMS	Five rooms with private bathrooms. The Dunes suite is the best.
RATES	May through October, rates are $120-135 for a single or double and $625 (negotiable) for the entire inn. November through April, rates are $110-125 for a single or double and $575 (negotiable) for the entire inn. There is a two-night minimum stay during weekends and holidays, and cancellation requires seven days' notice—14 days during holidays and festivals.
CREDIT CARDS	American Express, Diners Club, Discover, MasterCard, Visa
BREAKFAST	Full breakfast, served in the dining room, features regional fruits and vegetables (including local mushrooms), home-baked pastries, smoked salmon or sturgeon fritattas, ginger pancakes, coffee, and teas.
AMENITIES	Fresh flowers, fluffy robes, luscious brownies all day, high-tech spa by the sand dunes, ocean views, feather beds, candies, custom bathroom amenities, large common areas with fireplace, baby

Boreas Bed & Breakfast Inn, Long Beach

grand piano, private path through the dunes to the beach, gardens, gazebo.

RESTRICTIONS	No smoking. Children welcome with prior arrangement. D.O.G. is the resident pooch, who resides with the owners in separate quarters.
REVIEWED	*The Best Places to Kiss in the Northwest; Northwest Best Places; America's Wonderful Little Inns and Hotels; America's Favorite Inns, B&Bs and Small Hotels; Bed & Breakfasts and Country Inns*
MEMBER	Washington Bed & Breakfast Guild, Professional Association of Innkeepers International, Bed & Breakfast Association of the Long Beach Peninsula
RATED	Mobil 2 Stars

SCANDINAVIAN GARDENS BED & BREAKFAST

1610 California Avenue South, Long Beach, WA 98631   360-642-8877
Rod & Marilyn Dakan, Resident Owners   800-988-9277
WEBSITE *www.aone.com/~rdakan*   FAX 360-642-8764

LOCATION	Three-quarters of a mile north of the junction of Highways 101 and 103. Take a right on 16th Street, go one block to California, and take a left.

OPEN	All year
DESCRIPTION	A 1977 two-story ranch-style inn with modern and antique Scandinavian furniture.
NO. OF ROOMS	Five rooms with private bathrooms. The Swedish Suite is the best.
RATES	Year-round rates are $95-115 for a single or double and $140 for a suite. There is a minimum stay most weekends and holidays, and cancellation requires seven days' notice.
CREDIT CARDS	Discover, MasterCard, Visa
BREAKFAST	Full five-course breakfast features Scandinavian specialties, such as Shrimp in a Cloud or sour cream waffles, plus creamed rice fruit soup, three kinds of pastries (including homemade Danish), and beverages.
AMENITIES	Finnish sauna, 500-gallon hot springs hot tub, robes, large library, beautiful gardens with deck, maintained path through dunes to the beach, fresh fruit and homemade cookies always available.
RESTRICTIONS	No smoking, no pets, children over three are welcome.
REVIEWED	*Where to Stay in the American Northwest; Washington State Travelers: Affordable Accommodations; The Pacific Northwest's Best Bed & Breakfasts*
MEMBER	Professional Association of Innkeepers International, Washington Bed & Breakfast Guild, Long Beach Peninsula Bed & Breakfast Association
KUDOS/COMMENTS	"Friendly couple, good Scandinavian food, close to beach."

LOPEZ ISLAND

Lopez Island, flat and shaped like a jigsaw-puzzle piece, is a sleepy, rural place, famous for its friendly locals (drivers always wave) and its cozy coves and full pastures. It has the easiest bicycling in the islands: a 35-mile circuit suitable for the whole family to ride in a day. There are numerous public parks. Two day parks (Otis Perkins and Agate County) are great for exploring, with good beach access. Seals and bald eagles can often be seen from the rocky promontory off Shark Reef Park, on the island's western shore.

ALECK BAY INN

45 Finch Lane & Aleck Bay Road   360-468-3535
Lopez Island, WA 98261   FAX 360-468-3533
May Mendez, Resident Owner
Chinese (Mandarin and Cantonese) and Spanish spoken
EMAIL *ABI@Pacificrim.net*   WEBSITE *www.pacificrim.net/~abi/abi.html*

LOCATION	From the ferry landing, turn right onto Center Road; continue for two miles on Center Road, which changes into Mud Bay Road. At Aleck Bay Road, take a right; continue to the inn, on left.
OPEN	All year
DESCRIPTION	A 1990 ranch-style waterfront B&B with formal decor.
NO. OF ROOMS	Four rooms with private bathrooms. May recommends the Captain's Quarters.
RATES	May 15 to September 15, rates are $109-179 for a single or double, and the entire B&B rents for $600 a day. October 1 through May 14, rates are $89-149 for a single or double, and the entire B&B rents for $700 a day. There is no minimum stay. Call about the cancellation policy.
CREDIT CARDS	American Express, Diners Club, Discover, MasterCard, Visa
BREAKFAST	Full breakfast is served in the dining conservatory and includes fresh fruit juices, coffees, teas, cider, and gourmet main dishes.
AMENITIES	Fresh flowers, robes, piano concerts in the morning, hot tub overlooking Aleck Bay, bike and kayak rentals, meeting room, game room, wine, hors d'oeuvres.
RESTRICTIONS	No smoking, no pets. There are peafowls on the premises.
MEMBER	Washington State Bed & Breakfast Association

EDENWILD INN

Eads Lane at Village Road North   *360-468-3238*
Lopez Island, WA 98261
Sue Aran, Resident Owner
WEBSITE *www.edenwildinn.com*

INN AT SWIFTS BAY

Route 2, Box 3402, Lopez Island, WA 98261   *360-468-3636*
Rob Aney & Mark Adcock, Resident Owners   *FAX 360-468-3637*
WEBSITE *www.swiftsbay.com*

LOCATION	On Lopez Island in the San Juan Islands. Disembark at the first stop on the ferry ride from Anacortes, drive one mile up Lopez Drive to Odlin Park on the right, turn left on Port Stanley Road, and drive approximately one mile.

OPEN	All year
DESCRIPTION	A 1971 two-story Pacific Northwest Tudor-style inn with comfortable English country decor.
NO. OF ROOMS	Three rooms have private bathrooms and two rooms share one bathroom. The owners suggest room 5.
RATES	Year-round rates are $95-105 for a room with a shared bathroom and $145-175 for the suites. There is no minimum stay and cancellation requires 10 days' notice.
CREDIT CARDS	American Express, Discover, MasterCard, Visa
BREAKFAST	Full breakfast is served in the dining room and includes crab cakes with lemon tarragon sauce; smoked salmon and chive potato pancakes; sautéed apple, ham, and brie omelets; fresh muffins; fresh juice; and coffee blends. Special meals are provided and are "a big part of staying at the inn."
AMENITIES	Video library with headphones and VCR, "left-it-at-home basket;" walking sticks, sherry, apples, popcorn for microwaving, 24-hour tea and coffee, Evian water, hot tub, sauna, robes, flowers, shower and sewing kits, library, private beach.
RESTRICTIONS	No smoking inside, no pets, children over 16 are welcome.
REVIEWED	*The Best Places to Kiss in the Northwest; Northwest Best Places; Pacific Northwest Bed & Breakfast Guide; The Essential San Juan Islands Guide; The Non-Smokers Guide to Bed & Breakfasts*
MEMBER	Washington Bed & Breakfast Guild, Professional Association of Innkeepers International
RATED	Mobil 3 Stars
KUDOS/COMMENTS	"Professionally run, great setting, wonderful hosts, a true gourmet breakfast served in a delightful breakfast room."

MacKaye Harbor Inn

Route 1, Box 1940, Lopez Island, WA 98261   *360-468-2253*
Robin & Mike Bergstrom, Resident Owners   *FAX 360-468-2393*
WEBSITE *www.san-juan.net/mackayeharbor*

LOCATION	From the ferry dock, turn left on Center Road and go south about eight miles—Center becomes Mud Bay Road. Turn right onto MacKaye Harbor Road (if you pass a service station you've gone too far).
OPEN	All year
DESCRIPTION	A 1927 two-story colonial revival inn, a restored sea captain's home with Victorian interior.

NO. OF ROOMS	Three rooms with private bathrooms and two rooms share one bathroom. Try the Harbor Suite.
RATES	May through October, rates are $99-159 for a single or double with a private bathroom and $89-99 for a double with a shared bathroom. Low-season rates are $109-139 for a single or double with a private bathroom and $89 for a double with a shared bathroom. There is a two-night minimum stay during high season and cancellation requires 14 days' notice.
CREDIT CARDS	MasterCard, Visa
BREAKFAST	Full breakfast, served in the dining room, includes large servings of international main entrées such as Barcelona chile-puff, *aebleskivers*, Finnish *panukaku*, or Louisiana pecan pancakes, with meats, fruits, and breads. Continental breakfast available to carriage house guests.
AMENITIES	Afternoon dessert; chocolate truffles every evening; 24-hour coffee, tea, and hot cocoa bar; complimentary bikes; kayak rentals.
RESTRICTIONS	No smoking, no pets, children over nine are welcome. Mickey is the resident cat. "She acts like a dog; goes for walks on the beach with guests; usually outside but frequents the parlor."
REVIEWED	*Northwest Best Places; The Non-Smokers Guide to Bed & Breakfasts; Washington State Travelers: Affordable Accommodations; Paddle America*
MEMBER	International Inn and Bed & Breakfast Exchange

LUMMI ISLAND

Located just off Gooseberry Point northwest of Bellingham, Lummi is one of the most overlooked islands of the ferry-accessible San Juans. It echoes the days when the San Juan Islands were still a hidden treasure, visited only by folks who preferred bucolic surroundings and deserted beaches to a plethora of restaurants and gift shops. To stretch your limbs, head for the peaceful beaches (a few of which are publicly accessible), or bring bikes and enjoy the quiet country roads. Plan ahead; dining options tend to be seasonal.

SUNNYHILL BED & BREAKFAST

4080 Sunny Hill Lane, Lummi Island, WA 98262   *360-758-2927*

WEST SHORE FARM BED & BREAKFAST

2781 West Shore Drive, Lummi Island, WA 98262   360-758-2600
FAX 360-758-2722

THE WILLOWS INN BED & BREAKFAST

2579 West Shore Drive, Lummi Island, WA 98262   360-758-2620
Gary & Victoria Flynn, Resident Owners
EMAIL *willows@lummi-island.com*
WEBSITE *www.lummi-island.com/willows*

LOCATION	On the west shore of Lummi Island, 3.5 miles from the ferry landing, which is 10 miles west of exit 260 off I-5, just north of Bellingham.
OPEN	All year
DESCRIPTION	A 1910 two-story bungalow and guesthouse overlooking the water with an interior design circa 1930.
NO. OF ROOMS	Three rooms with private bathrooms. Try the Thistle Suite.
RATES	Year-round rates are $145-185 for a single or double and $245 for the guesthouse. There is a minimum stay during weekends from Memorial Day through Labor Day. Cancellation requires 10 days' notice.
CREDIT CARDS	MasterCard, Visa
BREAKFAST	Continental breakfast is served in the guestrooms and includes fresh fruit, juice, yogurt, bagels and cream cheese, and coffee or tea. Picnic baskets and, occasionally, full dinners are also available.
AMENITIES	Fresh flowers in rooms, robes, TV/VCR, full kitchen (with stove, microwave, coffee-maker, and refrigerator). The guesthouse has a whirlpool tub, fireplace, decks, award-winning gardens, and a private beach.
RESTRICTIONS	No smoking, no pets, children over 12 are welcome.
REVIEWED	*Northwest Best Places; The Best Places to Kiss in the Northwest*
KUDOS/COMMENTS	"Unsurpassed in making your weekend a very special occasion."

LYNDEN

This neat and tidy community, with immaculate yards and colorful gardens lining the shady avenue into downtown, has adopted a Dutch theme in tribute to its early inhabitants. Be sure to visit the charming Pioneer Museum, full of local memorabilia and antique buggies and motorcars.

CENTURY HOUSE BED & BREAKFAST

401 South BC Avenue, Lynden, WA 98264   360-354-2439
Jan & Ken Stremler, Resident Owners

DUTCH VILLAGE INN

655 Front Street #7, Lynden, WA 98264   360-354-4440
Elaine Oostra, Resident Manager

MAPLE FALLS

About 25 miles east of Bellingham, Maple Falls is a stone's throw from the Canadian border and sits on the doorstep to Mount Baker National Forest. The Mount Baker ski area features the longest season in the state. The mountain never lacks for snow, and runs are predominantly intermediate, with bowls, meadows, and trails. Hiking in the area is extensive and beautiful, especially in late summer, when the foliage is turning, the wild blueberries are ripe, and the days are hot and dry. In mid-September, celebrate Sasquatch Days.

COUNTRY HILL BED & BREAKFAST
AT MOUNT BAKER

7968 Silver Lake Road, Maple Falls, WA 98266   360-599-1049
Dolores LaBounty, Resident Owner

THURSTON HOUSE BED & BREAKFAST

9512 Silver Lake Road, Maple Falls, WA 98266   360-599-2261
Pete & Betty Zylstra, Resident Owners
Some Dutch spoken
EMAIL bzylstra@juno.com

LOCATION	Exit I-5 onto Highway 542, drive into Maple Falls. Turn north onto Silver Lake Road (the only major crossroad in Maple Falls) and drive five miles.
OPEN	All year
DESCRIPTION	A 1950 one-story contemporary host home on the shore of Silver Lake with rustic "homey atmosphere and some antiques."
NO. OF ROOMS	Two rooms with private bathrooms and a one-room cabin.
RATES	Year-round rates are $65 for the two-room suite and $65 for the one-room cabin. There is no minimum stay.
CREDIT CARDS	MasterCard, Visa
BREAKFAST	Full breakfast is served in the dining room and includes a scrambled egg dish or French toast, blueberry muffins, fresh fruit, and beverages.
AMENITIES	Paddle boats in summer; ice skates in winter; trout fishing May through October; year-round views of eagles, osprey, and water fowl; hot tub on lake's edge.
RESTRICTIONS	None. Baxter the Newfoundland is the resident dog. "He's sometimes mistaken for a bear," says Betty.

YODELER INN

7485 Mt. Baker Highway, Maple Falls, WA 98266   360-599-1716
Bethnie & Jeff Morrison, Resident Owners   800-642-9033
                                         FAX 360-599-1389

LOCATION	From Bellingham, head east on Highway 542 for 26 miles. The inn is on the right.
OPEN	All year
DESCRIPTION	A 1917 two-story Bavarian country inn and satellite cabins with country decor.
NO. OF ROOMS	Three rooms with private bathrooms.
RATES	Year-round rates are $65-75 for a single or double. There is a two-night minimum stay on weekends during high season, three nights during holiday weekends. Cancellation requires 48 hours' notice.

CREDIT CARDS	American Express, Discover, MasterCard, Visa
BREAKFAST	Continental breakfast is served in the coffee shop next door and includes muffins, bagels, breakfast sandwiches, espresso, coffee, juice, and fresh fruit.
AMENITIES	Cable TV; coffee, tea, and hot chocolate; games to play; central hot tub.
RESTRICTIONS	No smoking. Maggie is the resident husky/golden retriever mix. Tom, Jerry, and Oscar are the cats.
REVIEWED	*Hot Showers, Soft Beds and Dayhikes in the North Cascades*

MAPLE VALLEY

Just 30 minutes southeast of Seattle in the foothills of the Cascade Mountains, Maple Valley offers quick and easy access to both city and outdoor amenities. Mount Rainier National Park is less than an hour to the south.

MAPLE VALLEY BED & BREAKFAST

20020 SE 228th, Maple Valley, WA 98038   *425-432-1409*
Clarke Hurlbut, Resident Innkeeper   *888-432-1409*
WEBSITE *www.nwlink.com/hilihedg/ssbba.html*   FAX *425-413-1459*

LOCATION	From Seattle, go south on I-5 to Highway 405 (exit from left lane just before Southcenter Mall). Go to exit 4 and go southeast on Highway 169 (Maple Valley/Enumclaw) for about 10 miles to the stoplight at 231st. Turn right (west) and go one mile to 204th. Go 0.2 mile and turn left at SE 228th.
OPEN	All year
DESCRIPTION	A 1971 three-story Northwest country chalet with hand-hewn cedar railings, exposed beams, country furnishings, and antiques.
NO. OF ROOMS	Two rooms with one shared bathroom.
RATES	Year-round rates are $75-85 for a single or double. There is a two-night minimum stay (or $10 extra for a one-night stay) and cancellation requires two weeks' notice.
CREDIT CARDS	No
BREAKFAST	Full breakfast is served on crystal and silver in the breakfast nook and includes plate-size Dutch babies with fresh strawberries, whipped cream, syrup, powdered sugar, and almonds, plus orange juice, coffee, and tea.

Maple Valley Bed & Breakfast, Maple Valley

AMENITIES	Bird-watching; many nature reference books; rose and herb gardens; pond and trail; massive stone fireplace; porches and decks; French doors with screens for summer; nite-nite trays and "hot babies" on cool nights.
RESTRICTIONS	No smoking, no pets. King Kitty is the resident cat. There are also two Japanese quail on the property.
REVIEWED	*Hidden Pacific Northwest*
MEMBER	Bed & Breakfast Association of Suburban Seattle

MARYSVILLE

EQUINOX BED & BREAKFAST

13522 12th Avenue NW, Marysville, WA 98271   *360-652-1198*

Mazama

In recent years, Mazama has become a high-end mecca for fishing and climbing. West of North Cascades National Park in the Okanogan National Forest on Highway 20.

Chokecherry Inn Bed & Breakfast

PO Box 251, Mazama, WA 98833   509-996-2049
Marlene & Darrell Ford, Resident Owners

Mazama Country Inn

42 Lost River Road, Mazama, WA 98833   509-996-2681
George Turner, Innkeeper   800-843-7951
Spanish spoken   FAX 509-996-2646
EMAIL *mazama@methow.com*   WEBSITE *www.mazama.com*

LOCATION	Fourteen miles west of Winthrop on Highway 20.
OPEN	All year
DESCRIPTION	A 1985 two-story cedar board and batten lodge with a log beam dining room and a huge stone fireplace.
NO. OF ROOMS	Fourteen rooms with private bathrooms.
RATES	High-season rates are $70-180 for a single or double and $115-250 for a suite. Low-season rates are $65-75 for a single or double and $115-250 for a suite. There is a minimum stay during holiday weekends and cancellation requires 30 days' notice.
CREDIT CARDS	Discover, MasterCard, Visa
BREAKFAST	Breakfast is served various ways at various times. Expect a full menu to choose from in the summer, a family-style arrangement in the winter, and continental breakfast in the off season. Lunch and dinner are also available. A family-style dinner is available in the winter.
AMENITIES	Outdoor hot tub, sauna, tennis court, hors d'oeuvres in winter, maps of area and trails.
RESTRICTIONS	No smoking, no pets, children 13 or older are welcome in the winter. Cabins are available for families with younger children.
REVIEWED	*Northwest Best Places; The Best Places to Kiss in the Northwest*
MEMBER	Professional Association of Innkeepers International

Mazama Country Inn, Mazama

NORTH CASCADES BASECAMP

Star Route Box 36, Mazama, WA 98833　　　　　　　509-996-2334

MOCLIPS

RUBY SLIPPER BED & BREAKFAST

4876 Pacific Avenue, Moclips, WA 98562　　　　　　360-276-8173

MONROE

THE FROG CROSSING BED & BREAKFAST

306 South Lewis, Monroe, WA 98272　　　　　　　360-794-7622

MONTESANO

ABEL HOUSE BED & BREAKFAST

117 Fleet Street South, Montesano, WA 98563　　　360-249-6002
Victor Reynolds, Resident Owner　　　　　　　　800-235-2235

MORTON

ST. HELENS MANORHOUSE

7476 Highway 12, Morton, WA 98356   *360-498-5243*

MOSES LAKE

It's the RV capital of the state, with many campers and boaters lured by the fishing and hunting around the lakes. The anglers come for trout and perch. You can rent a boat, then motor out to a sandy island in Potholes Reservoir for a picnic.

THE CARRIAGE HOUSE BED & BREAKFAST INN

2801 West Peninsula Drive, Moses Lake, WA 98837   *509-766-7466*
WEBSITE *www.wsu.edu:8000/~joshr/carriage/carriage.htm*   *800-761-7466*

MOUNT VERNON

To travelers on I-5, Mount Vernon is little more than a blur except during the spring, when the lush farmlands are brilliantly swathed in daffodils (mid-March to mid-April), tulips (April through early May), and irises (mid-May to mid-June). The pastoral countryside is flat and ideal for bicyclists, except for the gridlock that occurs on the small farm lanes during the Tulip Festival (usually late March to early April). Mount Vernon is really all about fresh food and beautiful flowers, products of surrounding Skagit Valley farms. Check out the many harvest festivals (June is Strawberry Month, September Apple Month, and October Redleaf Month).

COLONIAL MANOR BED & BREAKFAST

17550 McLean Road, Mount Vernon, WA 98273   *360-424-3237*
Bonnie & Howard Anderson, Innkeepers   *800-893-1022*
EMAIL *cmanor@fidalgo.net*   *FAX 360-428-2009*
WEBSITE *www.fidalgo.net~cmanor/*

LOCATION	On the tulip route between La Conner and Mount Vernon, 1.2 miles from downtown.
OPEN	All year
DESCRIPTION	A 1907 three-story plantation inn with Victorian decor and antiques.
NO. OF ROOMS	Five rooms with private bathrooms. Try the Bonnie Jean Suite.
RATES	April through October, rates are $95-150 for a single or double, $150 for a suite, and $535 for the entire B&B. November through March, rates are $85-140 for a single or double, $140 for a suite, and $500 for the entire B&B. There is no minimum stay and cancellation requires one weeks' notice.
CREDIT CARDS	MasterCard, Visa
BREAKFAST	Three-course breakfast is served in the dining room or guestrooms and includes espresso, smoothies, homemade granola, and an entrée with fresh fruit.
AMENITIES	Air conditioning; antiques; cable TV/VCR in each room; robes, candles, bath salts, soaps, and lotions; espresso; down comforters.
RESTRICTIONS	No smoking, children welcome. Madison is the resident pooch.
MEMBER	Skagit Valley Tulip Association, Washington Bed & Breakfast Guild

FULTON HOUSE

420 East Fulton Street, Mount Vernon, WA 98273   *360-336-2952*
WEBSITE www.halcyon.com/phyllis

THE INN AT THIRTEEN FIRS BED & BREAKFAST

2329 B Highway 9, Mount Vernon, WA 98274   *360-445-3571*

RAINBOW INN

12757 Chilberg Road, Mount Vernon, WA 98273   *360-466-4578*
Squires Family, Innkeepers   *888-266-8879*
EMAIL rainbow@rainbowinnbandb.com   *FAX 360-466-3844*
WEBSITE www.rainbowinnbandb.com

LOCATION	Half a mile east of the flagpole on the edge of La Conner; 10 miles from I-5 exit 221 northbound following the signs to La Conner; or 10.5 miles from I-5 exit 230 southbound following the signs to La Conner—turn left at the flagpole.
OPEN	All year
DESCRIPTION	A cozy 1908 three-story Craftsman inn, a "solid and unpretentious" turn-of-the-century farmhouse decorated with some antiques and set among farm fields and flower gardens.
NO. OF ROOMS	Five rooms with private bathrooms and three rooms with one shared bathroom. Try the Rose Room.
RATES	March 15 through September, rates are $100-115 for a double with a private bathroom, $80 for a double with a shared bathroom, and $765 for the entire inn. October through mid-March, rates are $90-105 for a double with a private bathroom, $70 for a single or double with a shared bathroom, and $685 for the entire inn. There is no minimum stay and cancellation requires four days' notice.
CREDIT CARDS	Discover, MasterCard, Visa
BREAKFAST	Full three-course breakfast is served on the porch and includes bread or muffins, fruit or custard, a main entrée such as waffles, pancakes, or an egg dish, with a choice of juice and/or a hot beverage.
AMENITIES	Robes in each room; hot tub on the deck in the ivy-covered gazebo with views of farm fields and Mount Baker; living area with piano and theater organ, puzzles, a library, candy dishes, nut bowls, three jars of homemade cookies (accessible at any time, just like the beverages); air conditioning (for the rare days it is needed); hammock under the 90-year-old chestnut tree; bench under the old apple tree; lawn for croquet; flower gardens.
RESTRICTIONS	No smoking, no pets, children are welcome "with limits." Peanut and Cracker Jack are the resident orange tabbies. They are not allowed inside the B&B.
REVIEWED	*The Best Places To Kiss in the Northwest; Northwest Best Places; Fodor's*
MEMBER	Washington Bed & Breakfast Guild, Professional Association of Innkeepers International, Tulip Valley Bed & Breakfast Association
RATED	Mobil 2 Stars
KUDOS/COMMENTS	"Beautiful setting, lovely inn."

WHISPERING FIRS BED & BREAKFAST

1957 Kanako Lane, Mount Vernon, WA 98273 360-428-1990
Vic & Linda Benson, Resident Owners 800-428-1992
Japanese spoken FAX 360-428-1990

LOCATION	Heading north on I-5, take exit 221 and turn right, then immediately left onto Cedardale Road. Drive north two miles and turn right onto Stockpole. At the base of the hill, turn right onto the bridge (Kanako Lane). As you come off the bridge, take a hard right and follow the gravel road, keeping left at each fork.
OPEN	All year
DESCRIPTION	A 1981 one-story ranch-style host home with a cathedral ceiling, huge stone fountain, and fireplace.
NO. OF ROOMS	Two rooms with private bathrooms and one room shares one bathroom.
RATES	April through October, rates are $85-95 for a single or double with a private bathroom and $65 for a single or double with a shared bathroom. The suite rents for $95. Low-season rates are $10 less for everything but the room with a shared bathroom.
CREDIT CARDS	Yes
BREAKFAST	Full breakfast is served in the dining room and includes Dutch puff pancakes with lemon juice and powdered sugar, Italian hash (sausage, potatoes, onions, peppers, and herbs), and rainbow tart (cream cheese crust with filling and fresh fruit topping), plus beverages. Dinner and special meals are available at additional cost.
AMENITIES	Flowers, fireplace in living room, view of San Juan Islands and Olympic Mountains, hot tub, private fishing at trout-stocked ponds, 250 acres of wooded hiking, room for weddings and catered family reunions.
RESTRICTIONS	No smoking inside, pets accepted by arrangement only. Perkins is the resident outdoor Irish setter and Dugin is the tabby cat.
REVIEWED	*The Non-Smokers Guide to Bed & Breakfasts*
MEMBER	Tulip Valley Bed & Breakfast Association, National Bed & Breakfast Association
AWARDS	1995 Finalist for the People's Choice Award, *Business Pulse* magazine

THE WHITE SWAN GUEST HOUSE

15872 Moore Road, Mount Vernon, WA 98273   360-445-6805
Peter Goldfarb, Resident Owner
WEBSITE *www.chw.com/~wswan/*

LOCATION	Take exit 221 off I-5 and drive five miles west toward La Conner on Fir Island Road, turn onto Moore Road at the blinking yellow light, and drive one mile. Or, from La Conner, go straight out on Chilberg Road and take a right at Best Road. Go three miles to North Fork Bridge and take a left on Moore Road.
OPEN	All year
DESCRIPTION	A restored 1898 two-story Queen Anne Victorian farmhouse with an old-fashioned, vine-covered porch and comfy country and eclectic furnishings. There is also a private housekeeping cottage.
NO. OF ROOMS	One cottage with a private bathroom and three rooms in the main house share two bathrooms.
RATES	July and August and tulip season (the first three weeks in April), rates are $135-150 for a double in the cottage (add $15 per additional person) and $75-85 for a single or double with a shared bathroom. During the rest of the year, rates are $125-135 for a double in the cottage (add $15 per additional person and $75-80 for a single or double with a shared bathroom. There is a minimum stay during tulip-season weekends. There is a five-day cancellation policy—no charge when the room is rebooked.
CREDIT CARDS	MasterCard, Visa
BREAKFAST	Continental plus is served in the dining room or brought out to the cottage and will typically include fresh fruit-filled muffins or scones, French toast, a plate of assorted seasonal fruit with a dollop of yogurt, homemade apple or rhubarb sauce, a fresh juice smoothie, and coffee. "I aim for low-fat, vegetarian, not-too-rich, healthy food," says Peter.
AMENITIES	Chocolate chip cookies, fluffy robes, cozy nooks, magazines and books everywhere, swans and wild birds in the winter, daffodil and tulip fields nearby in March and April, English country gardens for walking and relaxing, fresh flowers in rooms, Peter's "New York schtick," romance and memories.
RESTRICTIONS	No smoking, no pets, children are welcome in the cottage (which can sleep four or five), no extra charge for small children. Shadow is the old German shepherd, Andy is the golden retriever/chow mix, and Willy and Harley are the black Labs. All are friendly, outdoor dogs.
REVIEWED	*Northwest Best Places; The Best Places to Kiss in the Northwest; Hidden Pacific Northwest; Ultimate Washington; Best Places to*

Stay in the Pacific Northwest; America's Wonderful Little Hotels & Inns; Wake Up and Smell the Coffee cookbook

MEMBER Washington Bed & Breakfast Guild, Tulip Valley Bed & Breakfast Association

RATED Mobil 2 Stars

AWARDS 1995, Best Bed & Breakfast in Skagit Valley, Target Publications (a local business journal); 1998, Small Business of the Year, La Conner Chamber of Commerce

KUDOS/COMMENTS "A true getaway, country charm, wonderfully comfortable and refreshing, friendly innkeeper, garden lovers' paradise, delicious cookies." "Peter is a great host. Very cozy and warm, beautiful setting and gardens." "Wonderfully restored Victorian farmhouse."

NACHES

An ideal location for all manner of outdoor activity, from hiking and fishing to alpine and cross-country skiing.

APPLE COUNTRY

4561 Old Naches Highway, Naches, WA 98937   *509-965-0344*

COZY CAT BED & BREAKFAST

12604 Highway 410, Naches, WA 98937   *509-658-2953*

NAHCOTTA

Nahcotta has become almost synonymous with oysters. At the Nahcotta Oyster Farm, on the old rail line, you can pick up some pesticide-free 'sters or gather your own for half-price. Two places help explain the oyster story: The Willapa Field Station has outdoor interpretive signs, maps, and information; the Willapa Bay Interpretive Center (on the Nahcotta pier, open in summer only) features a viewing deck and indoor exhibits.

MOBY DICK HOTEL & OYSTER FARM— BED & BREAKFAST

Sandridge Road, Nahcotta, WA 98637 360-665-4543
Linda Jackson, Innkeeper FAX 360-665-6887
EMAIL *mobydickhotel@willapabay.org*
WEBSITE *www.nwplace.com/mobydick.html*

LOCATION	On the Long Beach Peninsula, go north on Highway 103 to Ocean Park. Turn right at the only stop sign onto Bay Avenue and go about 0.6 mile to Sandridge Road. Turn right and the B&B is on the left.
OPEN	All year
DESCRIPTION	A 1929 two-story "railroad hotel" inn with artisan-welded staircases, lots of art, and casual, comfortable furnishings. During World War II, the inn was home to the USCG horse patrol.
NO. OF ROOMS	One room with a private bathroom and nine rooms share seven bathrooms. Linda suggests room 1 or 2.
RATES	Year-round rates are $90 for a single or double with a private bathroom, $70-95 for a single or double with a shared bathroom, and the entire B&B rents for between $650 and $800. There is a minimum stay during weekends and holidays and cancellation requires 48 hours' notice, longer during special events.
CREDIT CARDS	American Express, MasterCard, Visa
BREAKFAST	Full American-style breakfast is served in the dining room and includes homemade breads, fruit, juice, coffee and tea, plus scrambled eggs, potatoes, and bacon, or pancakes, frittatas, and oysters fresh from the farm's beds. Dinner is available during the summer as part of a visiting chef program and during special events as well.
AMENITIES	Sauna pavilion on the bay during fall and winter; rambling grounds, including an extensive organic garden, oyster beds, picnic areas; meeting facilities; extensive library; video collection; fireplace in public area; hiking trails; canoeing.

RESTRICTIONS	No smoking
REVIEWED	*Northwest Best Places; Lonely Planet; Hidden Pacific Northwest; Frommer's On the Road Again with Man's Best Friend; Fodor's; Northwest Budget Traveler*
MEMBER	Long Beach Bed & Breakfast Association

OUR HOUSE IN NAHCOTTA BED & BREAKFAST

PO Box 33, Nahcotta, WA 98637   360-665-6667

NORTH BEND

ROARING RIVER BED & BREAKFAST

46715 SE 129th Street, North Bend, WA 98045   425-888-4834

OAK HARBOR

Named for the thriving Garry oak trees, Oak Harbor is Whidbey's largest city and home to Whidbey Island Naval Air Station, a large air base for tactical electronic warfare squadrons. Nearby Deception Pass, the beautiful, treacherous gorge, has a lovely, if crowded, state park with 2300 acres of forests and beach.

HARBOR POINTE BED & BREAKFAST

720 West Bonnie View Acres Road   360-675-3379
Oak Harbor, WA 98277
Les & Diane, Resident Owners
WEBSITE www@whidbey.net/harborpointe/

INN AT THE BAY

5129 North Alto Lane, Oak Harbor, WA 98277　　　360-679-8320
Irmgard Pierson, Resident Owner

MARANATHA SEA HORSE BED & BREAKFAST

4487 North Moran Beach Lane, Oak Harbor, WA 98277　360-679-2075

THE VICTORIAN ROSE

438 East Sea Breeze Way, Oak Harbor, WA 98277　　360-675-8197

OAKESDALE

THE HANFORD CASTLE BED & BREAKFAST

PO Box 23, Oakesdale, WA 99158　　　509-285-4120

OCEAN PARK

Founded as a religious settlement, Ocean Park is now a tranquil retirement community with a quiet beach—except in June, when the Garlic Festival takes over the town. Needless to say, there's lots of stinkin' good food at this event. The Wiegardt Watercolors Gallery displays Eric Wiegardt seascapes in a restored Victorian house. Nearby, the Shoalwater Cove Gallery exhibits nature scenes in soft pastels.

CASWELL'S ON THE BAY

25204 Sandridge Road, Ocean Park, WA 98640　　360-665-6535
Marilyn Caswell, Resident Owner　　　FAX 360-365-2534

LOCATION	From the intersection of Highway 101 south and Highway 103—the entrance to Long Beach Peninsula—turn right, heading north 12 miles to the Ocean Park stop sign; turn right and go 0.5 mile to the next stop sign and turn right again onto Sandridge Road and drive for 0.5 mile.
OPEN	All year
DESCRIPTION	A 1995 two-story Queen Anne Victorian with traditional decor and "antiques galore," set at the edge of Willapa Bay on three secluded acres.
NO. OF ROOMS	Five rooms with private bathrooms. Try the Terrace Room.
RATES	High-season (April through October), rates are $85-150 for a single or double and $550 for the entire B&B. Low season rates are $85-150 for the rooms and $550 for the entire B&B. There is no minimum stay and cancellation requires seven days' notice.
CREDIT CARDS	MasterCard, Visa
BREAKFAST	Full breakfast is served in the breakfast room and includes a choice of juices and hot beverages, fresh fruit, fresh-baked muffins or scones, hot entrée that varies daily, plus bacon, sausage, or ham.
AMENITIES	Ralph Lauren all-cotton linens and towels; Caswell-Massey soaps, shampoo, hand creams; mending kits; antique bedroom sets with sitting area; cable TV; individual temperature control in each room; covered veranda; and 3.5 acres of trees and flowers.
RESTRICTIONS	No smoking, no pets, children over 12 are welcome. Sheba, Patches, Princess, and Fraidy are the "strictly outdoor" cats.
MEMBER	Long Beach Bed & Breakfast Association, Washington State Bed & Breakfast Guild
RATED	AAA 3 Diamonds
KUDOS/COMMENTS	"Lovely new Victorian home. Meticulously cared for, very spacious, furnished with antiques. Fabulous breakfast; helpful, friendly innkeepers." "Stunning facility, beautiful view, wonderful hosts."

COAST WATCH BED & BREAKFAST

PO Box 841, Ocean Park, WA 98640   *360-665-6774*

KUDOS/COMMENTS	"Close to a beautiful beach, quiet and peaceful area, good for unwinding." (1996)

THE DOVESHIRE

21914 Pacific Highway 103, Ocean Park, WA 98640   *360-665-3017*
Gene & Sharon Miller, Innkeepers   *888-553-2320*
EMAIL *doveshire@willapabay.org*   *FAX 360-665-3017*

LOCATION	From Long Beach, head north on Highway 103. Turn into the first driveway north of milepost 9
OPEN	All year
DESCRIPTION	A 1997 one-story Gothic home. Each guestroom has a different theme.
NO. OF ROOMS	Four rooms with private bathrooms.
RATES	Call for year-round rates. There is a minimum stay during two festivals.
CREDIT CARDS	American Express, MasterCard, Visa
BREAKFAST	Continental plus is served in the dining room and includes homemade granola, hot fruit dish or quiche, hot muffins, and fresh fruit.
AMENITIES	Hot drinks available day or night, snacks available, TV/VCR in each room, vaulted ceilings, and lots of windows that look out onto beautiful grounds.
RESTRICTIONS	No smoking, no pets, no children. Two doves and two finches live in the aviary.
MEMBER	Washington Bed & Breakfast Guild, Bed & Breakfast Association of the Long Beach Peninsula
RATED	AAA 3 Diamonds

THE WHALEBONE HOUSE

2101 Bay Avenue, Ocean Park, WA 98640   *360-665-5371*
Jim & Jayne Nash, Innkeepers   *888-298-3330*
"Southern" spoken
EMAIL *whalebone@willapabay.org*
WEBSITE *www.willapabay.org/2whalebone*

LOCATION	At the intersection of State Roads 101 and 103, go north on 103 about 10 miles to Ocean Park. At the flashing red light in Ocean Park, turn right onto Bay Avenue and drive 0.25 mile.
OPEN	All year

The Whalebone House, Ocean Park

DESCRIPTION	A restored 1889 two-story Victorian farmhouse, reminiscent of coastal Maine, with beautiful gardens. Listed on the State Historic Register.
NO. OF ROOMS	Four rooms with private bathrooms.
RATES	May through October, rates are $95-110 for a single or double. November through April, rates are 20 percent off for multiple-night stays. There is a two-night minimum stay during weekends from May through October, three nights during Labor Day weekend. Cancellation requires five days' notice.
CREDIT CARDS	MasterCard, Visa
BREAKFAST	Full breakfast is served in the dining room and includes fruit juice, fresh fruit, a main course such as stuffed French toast, frittatas, smoked salmon hash, muffins, quick breads, scones, and a special blend of organically grown coffee.
AMENITIES	Afternoon treats (cookies, biscotti, brownies) always available, fresh flowers and candy in rooms, a welcoming gift, robes, bicycles, kayaks, canoes.
RESTRICTIONS	No smoking, no pets, children over 12 are welcome. There are six outdoor cats of all shapes, sizes, and colors on the property.
MEMBER	Washington State Bed & Breakfast Guild, Long Beach Peninsula Bed & Breakfast Association
KUDOS/COMMENTS	"Beautifully restored 1890s farmhouse. Authentic feeling. Great antiques, unique and delicious breakfasts, good hosts."

OLALLA

Between Gig Harbor and Port Orchard, Olalla provides access to Mount Rainier and the Olympic Peninsula. Those with ice in their veins may want to inquire about the doings at the Olalla Polar Bear Club. In the summer, slap your knees and tap your toes at the local bluegrass festival.

CHILDS' HOUSE BED & BREAKFAST

8331 SE Willock Road, Olalla, WA 98359   253-857-4252
Ken & Susan Childs, Innkeepers   800-250-4954
EMAIL *ChildsHse@aol.com*   WEBSITE *users.aol.com/childshse/BnB.htm*

LOCATION	Go east on Mullenix from Highway 16 for three miles to Orchard (the end of Mullenix), south one mile on Orchard to Willock, and east on Willock for approximately one mile. Stay to the left into the woods upon entering the driveway.
OPEN	All year
DESCRIPTION	A 1992 two-story Victorian country host home on 5 acres of woods and a half-acre of lawn with numerous flower gardens and trails.
NO. OF ROOMS	One room with a private bathroom and two rooms share one bathroom. Try the Lilac Room.
RATES	Year-round rates are $95 for a single or double with a private bathroom and $65 for a single or double with a shared bathroom. There is no minimum stay and cancellation requires seven days' notice.
CREDIT CARDS	MasterCard, Visa
BREAKFAST	Full gourmet breakfast is served in the dining room and includes seasonal fruit, baked goods, and a hearty entrée. "No one has ever left hungry!" Lunch and dinner are also available, and dietary needs can be accommodated.
AMENITIES	Fresh flowers, refreshments reflecting the season, air conditioning, wood-burning stove, hot tub, player piano, large meeting room perfect for special occasions or meetings, space for indoor or outdoor weddings or receptions, on-site (or off-site) catering available.
RESTRICTIONS	No smoking, no pets, children over 16 are welcome. Smoking is OK outside on the decks. Kodi is the resident chow. "He has us trained very well!"
MEMBER	Washington Bed & Breakfast Guild

STILL WATERS BED & BREAKFAST

13202 Olympic Road SE, Olalla, WA 98359   253-857-5111
Cynthia Sailor, Resident Innkeeper

LOCATION	Eight miles north of Gig Harbor on Highway 16, turn right on Burley-Olalla Road, go to Olympic Road, and turn right.
OPEN	All year
DESCRIPTION	A 1964 two-story colonial plantation home with restored antiques and country comfort interior, located on 5 acres with a 100-year-old orchard and views of the Olympic Mountains and Burley Valley.
NO. OF ROOMS	One room with a private bathroom and two rooms share one bathroom. The best room is Cloe's Wedding Room.
RATES	Year-round rates are $65 for a single or double with a private or shared bathroom and $85 for the guesthouse. The entire B&B rents for $250. There is no minimum stay and cancellation requires 48 hours' notice.
CREDIT CARDS	MasterCard, Visa
BREAKFAST	Full "healthy, hearty" breakfast, served in the dining room, includes homemade hot cereals, fresh fruit, scones, jams, German apple pancakes, and beverages. Various gourmet dishes are available with prior notice. Special dietary needs are accommodated.
AMENITIES	Hot tub under the stars; fresh flowers in rooms; extensive gardens; fireplace in common room; tea or coffee; croquet; volleyball; basketball hoop; 50-year-old lawn swing; special packages include massage, facials, and wraps.
RESTRICTIONS	No smoking inside, no pets, no children. "With no dogs, we are visited by many varieties of birds, bunnies, and chipmunks."
REVIEWED	*Northwest Budget Traveler*
MEMBER	Gig Harbor Bed & Breakfast Association

OLYMPIA

Washington's capitol city is easily identified by the classic dome of its legislative building, a lavish Romanesque structure adorned with bronze and marble. There are museums and plenty of impressive buildings to see, including the stately Governor's Mansion. Thanks in part to the Washington Center for the Performing Arts, Olympia's downtown scene has been injected with new life. A community focal point, Percival Landing (a waterfront park), is the site of harbor festivals of all kinds. The historic heart of the whole area (Olympia, Lacey, and Tumwater) is Tumwater Falls, where the Deschutes River flows into Capitol Lake. This is the site of the chief local industry, the Tumwater Division of the Pabst Brewing Company, which brews Olympia beer.

FOREST HAVEN BED & BREAKFAST

7800 Brown Road SW, Olympia, WA 98512   *360-956-7800*

HARBINGER INN BED & BREAKFAST

1136 East Bay Drive, Olympia, WA 98506   *360-754-0389*

PARKER HOUSE BED & BREAKFAST

1919 East Bay Drive NE, Olympia, WA 98506   *360-357-7988*
Liliane Bartha & Craig Southwell, Innkeepers
Spanish, French, Portuguese, and Hungarian spoken   *FAX 360-357-6443*
EMAIL healthohrc@telebyte.com

LOCATION	Take exit 105B from I-5 and follow the signs for Port of Olympia and City Center. Traveling on southbound I-5, the exit becomes Plum Street. Traveling on northbound I-5, stay on the right side of the exit lane and complete a 360-degree turn to the right, passing under the freeway; turn left onto Plum Street at the first traffic light. Stay on Plum Street, which becomes East Bay Drive after crossing State Street (0.6 mile after the first intersection), and drive 1.1 miles past State Street to the B&B, on the left.
OPEN	All year

DESCRIPTION	A 1917 three-story Craftsman waterfront bungalow tastefully
	decorated with a mix of antiques and wicker furniture. Listed on the State Historic Register.
NO. OF ROOMS	One suite with a private bathroom.
RATES	April through October, the suite is $110-130. November through March, the suite is $100-120. There is a minimum stay during major holidays and cancellation requires seven days' notice.
CREDIT CARDS	No
BREAKFAST	Full breakfast is served in the guest room or on the terrace and features all organically grown food, including fresh juice, fresh fruits, homemade granola, omelets, pancakes, soufflés, huevos rancheros, scones, muffins, and oatmeal. No meat is served. Special dietary needs are accommodated.
AMENITIES	Fresh flowers, robes, chocolate, TV/VCR, videos, tapes, books, filtered air and water, organic coffee and tea, microwave, fridge, fax, telephone in suite, emergency laundry service, handmade soap, aromatherapy bath salts, water view from every room, pebble beach.
RESTRICTIONS	No smoking, no pets, children over 12 (and infants) are welcome. The resident cats are not allowed into the guest areas.
MEMBER	Washington Bed & Breakfast Guild

PUGET VIEW GUESTHOUSE

7924 61st Avenue NE, Olympia, WA 98516   *360-413-9474*
Dick & Barbara Yunker, Innkeepers
WEBSITE *www.bbonline.com/wa/pugetview*

LOCATION	Five minutes off I-5 on the southern shore of Puget Sound between Johnson Point and the Nisqually Delta, 500 feet before the entrance to Tolmie State Park. Take exit 111 off I-5 and follow Marvin Road north 3.5 miles to 56th Avenue NE, turn right and go one mile, and turn left at 61st Avenue NE.
OPEN	All year
DESCRIPTION	A 1930s-era one-story cedar shake guest cottage with simple decor and painted wood floors, located amongst tall firs on the Puget Sound waterfront next to the hosts' log home, and featuring expansive marine and mountain views.
NO. OF ROOMS	One room with a private bathroom.

RATES	Year-round rate is $99 for the cottage. There is no minimum stay and cancellation requires five days' notice.
CREDIT CARDS	MasterCard, Visa
BREAKFAST	Continental plus is served at the cottage door on a breakfast tray and includes pastry or quick bread, fruit, juice, and beverages. Choose the Romantic Upgrade and your table will be set with linen and silver.
AMENITIES	Barbecue on deck, refrigerator, microwave, canoe, beachside campfire, slippers, bird-watchers' paradise.
RESTRICTIONS	None. There is a $10 pet fee per night. Hunter is the resident cat and there are laying hens.
REVIEWED	*Best Places to Stay in the Pacific Northwest; Going Places: Family Getaways in the Pacific Northwest*

SWANTOWN INN

1431 11th Avenue SE, Olympia, WA 98501   *360-753-9123*
Lillian & Ed Peeples, Innkeepers
German spoken
EMAIL *swantown@olywa.net*
WEBSITE *www.olywa.net/swantown*

LOCATION	Located in Olympia's historic Eastside neighborhood, approximately one mile from the State Capitol and downtown shops and restaurants, with convenient access from I-5 via the Port of Olympia exit.
OPEN	All year
DESCRIPTION	An elegant 1893 three-story Queen Anne/Eastlake Victorian inn filled with antiques and decorated with distinctive trimwork, stained glass, and original oil chandeliers, with comfortable and elegant furnishings inspired by the 1890's Aesthetic Movement.
NO. OF ROOMS	Three rooms with private bathrooms. Try the Astoria Room.
RATES	April through September, rates are $85-115 for a single or double and $260 for a suite. October through March, rates are $75-105 for a room with a private bathroom and $230 for a suite. There is no minimum stay and cancellation requires seven days' notice.
CREDIT CARDS	MasterCard, Visa
BREAKFAST	Full gourmet breakfast is served in the dining room and features fresh-baked scones and muffins, seasonal homegrown produce, and

Swantown Inn, Olympia

	an entrée such as crepes Benedict, German pancakes, frittatas, or New Orleans French toast.
AMENITIES	Sunset views of the Capitol dome and the Black Hills beyond, half an acre of organic gardens and orchard, afternoon tea, croquet, gazebo, modem accessible workstation, air conditioning, fax.
RESTRICTIONS	No smoking, no pets, children over 12 are welcome.
MEMBER	Washington State Bed & Breakfast Guild

ORCAS ISLAND

Named not for the whales (the large cetaceans tend to congregate on the west side of San Juan Island and are rarely spotted here) but for a Spanish explorer, Orcas has a reputation as the most beautiful of the four main San Juan islands. It's also the biggest (geographically) and the hilliest, boasting 2,400-foot Mount Constitution as the centerpiece of Moran State Park. From the old stone tower on Mount Constitution, you can see Vancouver, Mount Rainier, and everything in between. The 4,800-acre Moran State Park has one lake for freshwater swimming, two more for boating, and five for fishing.

BUCK BAY FARM

Star Route Box 45, Olga, WA 98279   *360-376-2908*
Rick & Janet Bronkey, Resident Owners   *888-422-2825*
                                       FAX 360-376-2825

WEBSITE *www.rockisland.com/~paperjam/buckbay.html*

LOCATION	On Orcas Island. Take the ferry from Anacortes (80 miles north of Seattle). The inn is 17 miles from the ferry landing. Take Horseshoe Highway to Port Lawrence Road.
OPEN	All year
DESCRIPTION	A three-story farmhouse in a country setting on five acres.
NO. OF ROOMS	Four rooms with private bathrooms and two rooms with one shared bathroom. Rick and Janet recommend the Rose Room.
RATES	Year-round rates are $95-115 for a single or double with a private bathroom and $85 for a single or double with a shared bathroom. From October 16 through April 14, the second night is half price, except for holiday weekends. There is no minimum stay.
CREDIT CARDS	American Express, Discover, MasterCard, Visa
BREAKFAST	Full hearty, homestyle breakfast is served.
AMENITIES	Hot tub in the orchard, robes, down comforters and pillows, firepit, Ping-Pong.
RESTRICTIONS	No smoking, no pets. Brandy is the resident bassett hound, Bob is the cat, and there are several sheep on the property. All animals live outside.
MEMBER	Washington Bed & Breakfast Guild, Professional Association of Innkeepers International
RATED	AAA 2 Diamonds

Chestnut Hill Inn Bed & Breakfast, Orcas

CHESTNUT HILL INN BED & BREAKFAST

5157 Victorian Valley Road, Orcas, WA 98280   360-376-5157
Daniel & Marilyn Loewke, Resident Owners
EMAIL chestnut@pacificrim.net   FAX 360-376-5283
WEBSITE www.chestnuthillinn.com

LOCATION	Take the ferry to Orcas Island. Exit the ferry and turn right. Drive 0.8 mile and take the first left, onto La Porte. Stay to the left where La Porte splits. It becomes John Jones Drive. Take it for 0.25 mile until you come to the break in the trees.
OPEN	All year
DESCRIPTION	A 1960 two-story farmhouse with French country decor, resting high on a grassy knoll on 16 acres overlooking Victorian Valley.
NO. OF ROOMS	Five rooms with private bathrooms. Try the Chestnut Suite.
RATES	May through October, rates are $155 for a single or double, $195 for a suite, and $775 for the entire B&B. November through April, rates are $125 for a single or double, $175 for a suite, and $675 for

the entire B&B. There is a two-night minimum stay during weekends and major holidays for a single or double and year-round for a suite. Cancellation requires seven days' notice.

CREDIT CARDS	Discover, MasterCard, Visa
BREAKFAST	Full breakfast is served in the dining room and includes a fresh fruit starter or granola; fresh-squeezed orange juice; home-baked scones, muffins, or croissants; and a hot entrée such as apple pancakes with marionberry butter and sausage or artichoke, onion, and bacon frittatas with homemade chicken sausage. Dinner is available from November through April only.
AMENITIES	Veranda overlooking the valley and the barns and stables in the pasture; large rowing pond with a rowboat, dock, and island in the middle; quaint country chapel in the meadow; afternoon wine and cheese; robes; slippers; candies; cookies; soaps; lotions; loofahs; bottled water; champagne; Egyptian cotton linen; four-poster canopy feather beds; fireplaces; movies; games; picnic baskets; wedding packages; dinners in the fall, winter, and spring.
RESTRICTIONS	No smoking, no pets, no children. Josie is the resident golden retriever, and Opal and Rosie are the cats. The Appaloosa horse is named Rhum.
REVIEWED	*Northwest Best Places; The Best Places to Kiss in the Northwest; Best Places to Stay in the Pacific Northwest; Fodor's; Frommer's*
MEMBER	Professional Association of Innkeepers International
RATED	AAA 3 Diamonds, Best Places to Kiss 4 Lips, Northwest Best Places 4 Stars

---

DEER HARBOR INN

Deer Harbor Road, Deer Harbor, WA 98243   360-376-4110
Craig & Pam Carpenter, Innkeepers   FAX 360-376-2237
EMAIL carpecr@pacificrim.net
WEBSITE www.sanjuan.com/deerharborinn

LOCATION	Turn left off the ferry, drive 2.6 miles, and turn left on Deer Harbor Road. Then go 5.5 miles and turn left at the sign.
OPEN	All year
DESCRIPTION	A 1988 two-story log cabin lodge with handmade log furniture, located in the middle of a 90-year-old apple orchard with a lovely water view. There are also four private spa cottages.
NO. OF ROOMS	Eight rooms with private bathrooms. The Carpenters recommend room 7.

RATES	May through October, rates are $99-189 for a single or double. November through April, rates are $69-129. There is no minimum stay and cancellation requires 14 days' notice.
CREDIT CARDS	American Express, MasterCard, Visa
BREAKFAST	Continental plus, delivered to guestrooms in a picnic basket, includes homemade muffins, fresh fruits, and beverages. Dinner and special meals are also available.
AMENITIES	Hot tub, fireplace in cottages, apple orchard, turn-of-the-century fine restaurant serving tea and finger sandwiches in the afternoons, fresh seafood dinners in the evenings, lovely water views.
RESTRICTIONS	No smoking, no pets, children over 12 are welcome. Molly and Muffy are the resident dogs.
REVIEWED	*Northwest Best Places; Essential San Juan Islands Guide; Fodor's*

DOUBLE MOUNTAIN BED & BREAKFAST

PO Box 614, Eastsound, WA 98245   360-376-4570

THE GARDEN HOUSE

Star Route, Olga, WA 98279   360-376-4549

HAZELWOOD BED & BREAKFAST

1285 Victorian Valley Drive, Orcas, WA 98280   360-376-6300
Dan & Susan Smith, Innkeepers   888-360-6300
EMAIL *hazelwood@thesanjuans.com*   FAX 360-376-5249
WEBSITE *www.hazelwoodb&b.com*

LOCATION	Take the ferry from Anacortes to Orcas Island. Exit the ferry and turn right. Drive to the first country road (La Porte Road) and turn left. Go about 0.25 mile to Victorian Valley Road and turn left. Follow the signs to the B&B.
OPEN	All year
DESCRIPTION	A 1986 two-story geodesic dome on 12 acres of Douglas fir and madrona trees, with views of the Olympic Mountains and the islands.

NO. OF ROOMS	One room with a private bathroom and two rooms share one bathroom. Try the Orcas Room.
RATES	Year-round rates are $125-135 for a single or double with a private bathroom and $95-105 for a single or double with a shared bathroom. There is a two-night minimum stay. Ask about a cancellation policy.
CREDIT CARDS	MasterCard, Visa
BREAKFAST	Full breakfast is served in the dining room and includes fresh fruits; juices; coffee; tea; yogurt and grains; homemade breads, scones, or muffins; plus frittatas, omelets, or pancakes. Vegetarian and other diets are accommodated.
AMENITIES	Robes and flowers in rooms; seasonal organic fruits and vegetables; organic, free-range eggs; meeting room; massages by appointment; peaceful, quiet accommodations.
RESTRICTIONS	No smoking, no pets. Belle and Bo are the resident Labs.
REVIEWED	*Essential San Juans Islands Guide*

HOMESTEAD BED & BREAKFAST

RR 1 Box 66D, Eastsound, WA 98245 360-376-5284

KANGAROO HOUSE BED & BREAKFAST

North Beach Road, Eastsound, WA 98245 360-376-2175
Peter & Helen Allen, Innkeepers 888-371-2175
EMAIL kangaroo@thesanjuans.com *FAX 360-376-3604 (call first)*
WEBSITE www.pacificws.com/kangaroo

LOCATION	From the Orcas ferry landing, follow the signs to Eastsound, about 10 miles. In Eastsound, turn left at the second intersection, Prune Alley, which becomes North Beach Road. Continue north for one mile through two stop signs.
OPEN	All year
DESCRIPTION	A 1907 two-story Craftsman-style inn with an eclectic mix of period and traditional furnishings.
NO. OF ROOMS	Two rooms with private bathrooms and three rooms with one-and-a-half shared bathrooms. Peter and Helen suggest Kathleen's Suite.

Kangaroo House Bed & Breakfast, Eastsound

RATES	Year-round rates are $110 for a single or double with a private bathroom, $75-90 for a single or double with a shared bathroom, and $125 for a suite. There is no minimum stay and cancellation requires 10 days' notice.
CREDIT CARDS	American Express, Discover, MasterCard, Visa
BREAKFAST	Full three-course breakfast is made from scratch using the freshest ingredients. Breakfast includes seasonal fruits and vegetables, garden herbs, and local specialties. All breads, pastries, and muffins are homemade. Dinner is also available by special arrangement during the "quiet season."
AMENITIES	Robes, hair dryers, garden hot tub.
RESTRICTIONS	No smoking, no pets. Children are welcome. Yukon is the resident Samoyed, Li'l Bit is the calico, and Boomerang is the Maine coon cat.
REVIEWED	*Northwest Best Places; Fodor's Bed & Breakfasts, Country Inns, and Other Weekend Pleasures: The Pacific Northwest; Essential San Juans Islands Guide; Lonely Planet; The Non-Smokers Guide to Bed & Breakfasts; Inspected, Rated, & Approved Bed & Breakfasts & Country Inns*
MEMBER	Washington Bed & Breakfast Guild, Professional Association of Innkeepers International
RATED	AAA 2 Diamonds
KUDOS/COMMENTS	"Very clean and well run. Close to town. Allows children." "A comfortable, family-centered B&B."

L'AERIE BED & BREAKFAST

Rosario Road, Eastsound, WA 98245   *360-376-4647*

LIBERTY CALL BED & BREAKFAST

Lake Killebrew City Road, Orcas, WA 98280   *360-376-5246*
Margaret & Michael Jonas, Resident Owners
Italian spoken

LOCATION	Turn right as you exit the ferry, go approximately 200 yards, and turn left at the driftwood sign; take the diagonal dirt road up to the B&B.
OPEN	Generally May through September
DESCRIPTION	A 1904 two-story "European inspired" island host home decorated in nautical and aviation themes.
NO. OF ROOMS	Two rooms with private bathrooms.
RATES	Rate is $85 for a double, singles are $10 less. There is no minimum stay.
CREDIT CARDS	No
BREAKFAST	Full breakfast, served in the dining room, varies daily but includes juices, cereals, fruit dishes, a main course, baked goodies, and beverages.
AMENITIES	Flowers from the garden.
RESTRICTIONS	No smoking, no pets, children are welcome. The resident dogs are Hannah and Jolley; Kitty-coo is the resident cat. There are also three pygmy goats.

NORTHSHORE COTTAGES

PO Box 1273, Eastsound, WA 98245   *360-376-5131*
WEBSITE *www.northshore4tif.com*

THE OLD TROUT INN

Horseshoe Highway, Route 1, Eastsound, WA 98245   *360-376-8286*
Sandra Bronson, Resident Owner   *FAX 360-376-8283*
Some Spanish and Italian spoken
EMAIL sandrab@rockisland.com   *WEBSITE www.oldtroutinn.com*

LOCATION	Take the Anacortes ferry to Orcas Island and drive 2.5 miles from the ferry going toward Eastsound Village; the inn is on the left side.
OPEN	All year
DESCRIPTION	A rambling 1972 three-story contemporary lodge-style inn with wide-plank hardwood floors, exposed wood beams, and antiques, overlooking a pond.
NO. OF ROOMS	All rooms with private bathrooms. Try the Pond Suite.
RATES	June through October, rates are $125-175 for a single or double. November through May, rates are $120. There is a minimum stay from June through October and cancellation requires 14 days' notice.
CREDIT CARDS	Discover, MasterCard, Visa
BREAKFAST	Full breakfast, served in the dining room or on the decks, includes granola and other dry cereals with nuts, fruit, homemade breads and muffins, sourdough pancakes, entrée with meat, sorbet or fruit ices, and beverages. Special meals are also available.
AMENITIES	Flowers; robes; port; cheese, wine, and fruit in evenings; shampoo, conditioner, body wash, hair dryers, hand lotion, spa towels; three hot tubs on pond.
RESTRICTIONS	No smoking, no pets, children over 14 are welcome. Muck, Tuck, and Cosmo are the resident cats and Lucy is the goose.
REVIEWED	*The Best Places to Kiss in the Northwest; Frommer's; Fodor's*
MEMBER	Professional Association of Innkeepers International

ORCAS HOTEL

PO Box 155, Orcas, WA 98280   *360-376-4300*
                                       FAX 360-376-4399

KUDOS/COMMENTS	"Lovely gardens, thoughtful innkeepers, convenient to ferry." (1996)

Otters Pond Bed & Breakfast of Orcas Island, Eastound

OTTERS POND BED & BREAKFAST OF ORCAS ISLAND

6 Pond Road, Eastsound, WA 98245
Carl & Susan Silvernail, Innkeepers
Spanish spoken
EMAIL otterbehere@otterspond.com

360-376-8844
888-893-9680
FAX 360-376-8847
WEBSITE www.otterspond.com

LOCATION | Take the San Juan Islands ferry from Anacortes, exit the ferry, and follow Horseshoe Highway to the left for about 10 miles. Go right at the signpost pointing toward Eastsound village. Pass through Eastsound along the waterfront for approximately one mile and turn right at the stop sign. Continue for about 2.9 miles, looking for a group of mailboxes on the right, one with its post showing three blue reflectors and the Pond Road sign. Turn here onto the narrow gravel road and go 300 feet, turning right at the second driveway.

OPEN | All year

DESCRIPTION | A 1992 two-story French country host home, "built to reflect Northwest living at its finest," with an upscale eclectic interior of Northwest, French, and Asian decor, and with views of the woodlands and pond.

NO. OF ROOMS | Four rooms with private bathrooms and one room with one shared bathroom. Carl and Susan suggest the Swan Room.

RATES	April through September, rates are $100-150 for a single or double with a private bathroom, $75 for a single or double with the shared bathroom, and $75-150 for a suite. October through March, rates are $100-135 for a single or double with a private bathroom, $75 for a single or double with the shared bathroom, and $75-135 for a suite. There is a minimum stay during June, July, and August. Cancellation requires 10 days' notice.
CREDIT CARDS	Discover, MasterCard, Visa
BREAKFAST	Full five-course gourmet breakfast is served in the dining room or on the large front and rear decks, featuring island-grown produce and ingredients. A sample menu: white grape and champagne sorbet, apricots *honfleur*, Swiss muesli, smoked salmon eggpuff or bananas Foster French toast, island coffee, and selected teas.
AMENITIES	Picnic lunches; therapeutic hot tub overlooking the 20-acre pond and wetland; skylights in most rooms; large deck overlooking the pond, creek, and wooded areas; large wraparound front porch; quiet library; fabulous bird-watching; fresh flowers in rooms; luxurious robes; afternoon refreshments; evening turndown; island art and music; massage and exercise facilities nearby; nature-focused activities such as natural history tours, whale-watching, and kayaking.
RESTRICTIONS	No smoking, no pets, no children. Rusty and Bubby are the resident Pomeranians.
REVIEWED	*The Best Places to Kiss in the Northwest; Fodor's Northwest Guide; Northwest Best Places*
MEMBER	Professional Association of Innkeepers International, Washington State Bed & Breakfast Guild
RATED	AAA 2 Diamonds

SAND DOLLAR INN

Star Route Box 10, Olga, WA 98279   *360-376-5696*
WEBSITE *www.sdollar.com*   *FAX 360-376-2193*

AWARDS	"Good view, great breakfasts, very clean."

Sandcastle Guest House, Eastsound

SANDCASTLE GUEST HOUSE

991 Andersen Street, Eastsound, WA 98245   360-376-2337
Peppe & Helene Picone, Innkeepers   FAX 360-376-2337
EMAIL *ppicone@rockisland.com*
WEBSITE *www.rockisland.com/~ppicone*

LOCATION	From the village of Eastsound, go north on North Beach Road. Turn right (east) on Mount Baker Road and travel east for approximately 1.25 miles. Turn left on Terrills Beach Road, go 0.8 mile, and turn left onto Andersen Street. The guesthouse is the first place on the right.
OPEN	All year
DESCRIPTION	A 1994 waterfront two-story Pacific Northwest gray shingled guesthouse with lots of windows and contemporary wood furnishings.
NO. OF ROOMS	One room with a private bathroom.

RATES	June through October, rates are $95-105 for a single or double. November through May, rates are $75-85. There is a two-night minimum stay and cancellation requires 14 days' notice for a refund (less 10 percent) if guesthouse is rebooked.
CREDIT CARDS	No
BREAKFAST	Continental breakfast is served in the dining room and includes fresh orange juice, gourmet coffee, seasonal fruit, and homemade muffins.
AMENITIES	Fully equipped kitchen; cable TV/VCR; CD player; phone; gas barbecue; flower gardens and landscaping designed for bird-watching; boardwalk path through a wetlands to a private beach, perfect for launching kayaks or canoes; wildlife library and binoculars in the guesthouse.
RESTRICTIONS	No smoking, no pets. Tess is the resident Brittany, Spence is the cat, and Chloe is the beagle. "Two of our dogs were rescued from the pound and are shy of strangers. Our Beagle is a friendly dog who loves kids and treats."
REVIEWED	*Washington Handbook; San Juan County Visitors Guide.*

SMALL ISLAND FARM & INN

Route 1 Box 76, Eastsound, WA 98245   *360-376-4292*

SPRING BAY INN ON ORCAS ISLAND

Obstruction Pass Trailhead Road, Olga, WA 98279   *360-376-5531*
Carl Burger & Sandy Playa, Resident Owners   *FAX 360-376-2193*
German spoken
EMAIL info@springbayinn.com
WEBSITE springbayinn.com

LOCATION	Twenty miles from the Orcas Island ferry landing via the Horseshoe Highway. Turn left in Olga on Port Lawrence Road, then turn right onto Obstruction Pass Road.
OPEN	All year
DESCRIPTION	A 1991 two-story contemporary version of a New England farmhouse with an interior of natural woods and some antiques—a waterfront lodge surrounded by forest land.
NO. OF ROOMS	Five rooms with private bathrooms. Carl and Sandy recommend the Ranger Room.

RATES	Year-round rates are $195-235 for a single or double, and the entire B&B rents for $1,055. There is a minimum stay of two nights from April through October and cancellation requires 14 days' notice with a $25 charge.
CREDIT CARDS	American Express, Discover, MasterCard, Visa
BREAKFAST	Full healthy gourmet or continental is served in the dining room or in the guestrooms and includes an entrée accompanied by a fruit smoothie, fresh-pressed/squeezed juice, fruit soup or salad. Entrées include granola/oat-bran pancakes, spinach Jarlsberg quiche, and broccoli walnut crepes. Granola and dessert are often included. Special meals are also available by prior arrangement.
AMENITIES	Robes, wood-burning fireplaces, and fresh flowers in rooms; afternoon tea, evening samplings of Northwest wines; kayak tour included in stay (complete with instruction, guide, and necessary gear); hot tub at water's edge; trails through the surrounding 137 acres of parkland.
RESTRICTIONS	No smoking, no pets, no more than two people per room. Carson and Radcliff are the resident golden retrievers. They are "career-change guide dogs" from San Rafael Guide Dogs for the Blind. They do not bark and are not allowed in guestrooms.
REVIEWED	*Northwest Best Places; Fodor's Seattle to Vancouver; Fodor's Pacific Northwest's Best Bed & Breakfasts; Frommer's Outside Adventure Guide to the Pacific Northwest; The Best Places to Kiss in the Northwest; Essential San Jaun Islands Guide; Lonely Planet Guide; Best Places to Stay in the Pacific Northwest*
MEMBER	Professional Association of Innkeepers International
RATED	AAA 3 Diamonds, Best Places to Kiss 4 Lips, Northwest Best Places 3 Stars

---

TURTLEBACK FARM INN

Route 1, Crow Valley Road, Eastsound, WA 98245   *360-376-4914*
William & Susan Fletcher, Resident Owners   *800-376-4914*
Spanish spoken   *FAX 360-376-5329*
WEBSITE *www.turtlebackinn.com*

LOCATION	Six miles northwest of the Orcas ferry landing and four miles southwest of the main town of Eastsound. Turn left as you depart the ferry, drive 2.8 miles north on Horseshoe Highway, and turn left on Deer Harbor Road. Drive 0.9 mile, take the first right, then drive 2.4 miles to the inn.
OPEN	All year

Turtleback Farm Inn, Eastsound

DESCRIPTION	A restored 1895 two-story "folk national" farmhouse and a cedar-sided, shaker-style orchard house, furnished with a mix of traditional antiques and comfortable contemporary decor, overlooking Crow Valley with Mount Constitution as a backdrop.
NO. OF ROOMS	Eleven rooms with private bathrooms.
RATES	May through October and holidays, rates are $80-210 for a single or double. November through April (excluding holidays), rates are slightly less. There is a minimum stay from April through October and cancellation requires 10 days' notice.
CREDIT CARDS	Discover, MasterCard, Visa
BREAKFAST	Full breakfast is served in the dining room or guestrooms, or on the deck (weather permitting). Breakfast includes fresh fruit, fresh orange juice or apple juice, homemade granola with yogurt and raisins, a main course that changes daily, and meats. Lunch, dinner, and special meals can be accommodated.
AMENITIES	Fresh flowers, candies, cookies, sherry, fruit; complimentary self-service beverage bar with wide assortment of coffee, tea, and chocolate; one room in Orchard House with full handicapped access; farm with meadows, ponds, and woodlands available for exploring.
RESTRICTIONS	No smoking, no pets, children over eight are welcome. Shardik and Spud are the resident dogs, and there are sheep, geese, and chickens on the property.

REVIEWED	*Special Places for the Discerning Traveler; Weekends for Two in the Pacific Northwest; Fodor's; The Best Places to Kiss in the Northwest; America's Wonderful Little Hotels & Inns; Recommended Country Inns*
MEMBER	Independent Innkeepers Association
RATED	AAA 3 Diamonds, Mobil 3 Stars
KUDOS/COMMENTS	"Elegant farmhouse, country experience at its best, cozy rooms, delicious breakfast." "Beautiful setting, attention to detail."

WINDSONG BED & BREAKFAST INN

Deer Harbor Road, Orcas, WA 98280   360-376-2500
Sam & Kim Haines, Innkeepers   800-669-3948
Spanish spoken   FAX 360-376-4453
EMAIL *windsong@pacificrim.net*   WEBSITE *www.pacificws.com/windsong*

LOCATION	From Seattle, take I-5 north to exit 230 and go west on Route 20 for 20 miles through Anacortes to the San Juan Ferry Terminal. Take the ferry to Orcas, turn left from the ferry dock, go north for 2.5 miles on Horseshoe Highway, and take a left (west) onto Deer Harbor Road.
OPEN	All year
DESCRIPTION	A historic 1917 two-story Craftsman schoolhouse on four pastoral acres with ponds and a brook near Puget Sound and far from the world.
NO. OF ROOMS	Four rooms with private bathrooms. Sam and Kim suggest the Nocturne or Concerto Rooms.
RATES	High-season rates are $110-150 for a single or double. Regular rates are $90-120 for a single or double. There is a minimum stay during July and August, and cancellation requires seven days' notice.
CREDIT CARDS	MasterCard, Visa
BREAKFAST	Full multicourse breakfast is served in the dining room and includes beverages, sorbet, cereal, fruit, an entrée, breads, and meat. Dinner is also available.
AMENITIES	Robes, hair dryers, mouthwash, Q-Tips, soaps, shampoo, and conditioner; bathrooms and bedrooms individually heat-controlled; concierge service; down comforters; three en suite fireplaces; en suite sitting areas; guest living room with entertainment center (cable TV/VCR, CD player, and tape deck); luggage service, nightly turndown service; room TV/VCR, subject to availability; pick-up and drop-off at ferry and airport; spa/hot tub in Moon Room;

special occasions recognized with balloons and gratis champagne or fruit basket; video, book, magazine, and board game library.

RESTRICTIONS	No smoking, no pets, children over 12 are welcome. Suzi is the resident poodle, Maggie is the Lhasa apso, Manx is the outdoor cat.
REVIEWED	*Northwest Best Places; Essential San Juan Islands Guide; Frommer's Washington and Oregon; Sweethearts' Getaway Guide to the Northwest; Fodor's Bed & Breakfasts, Country Inns; Fodor's Gay Guide to the Pacific Northwest; Damron Accommodations; The Best Places to Kiss in the Northwest; Pacific Northwest's Best Bed & Breakfasts*
MEMBER	Washington Bed & Breakfast Guild, Professional Association of Innkeepers International
RATED	AAA 3 Diamonds, ABBA 3 Crowns, Mobil 3 Stars
KUDOS/COMMENTS	"Airy and elegant restored schoolhouse. Hot tub, gourmet breakfast." "Beautifully decorated interior."

PATEROS

Pateros is very rural; the nearest town, very small. The draws here are the seclusion, the scenery, the fine Nordic skiing, river rafting, bird-watching, and hiking. About 20 miles north of the southern tip of snaky Lake Chelan.

AMY'S MANOR BED & BREAKFAST

435 Highway 153, Pateros, WA 98846   509-923-2334
Pam Miller, Innkeeper   888-923-2334
WEBSITE *www.amysmanor.com*   FAX 509-923-2691

LOCATION	Four and a half miles north of Pateros on Highway 153 along the Methow River. Go left just after the metal bridge.
OPEN	All year
DESCRIPTION	A 1928 two-story French Provençal country inn with country French decor, nestled into the foothills of the Cascade Mountains overlooking the Methow River.
NO. OF ROOMS	One room with a private bathroom and two rooms with two shared bathrooms.
RATES	Year-round rates are $100 for a single or double with a private bathroom and $80-90 for a single or double with a shared bathroom. There is a minimum stay and cancellation requires five days' notice for weekday stays, 10 days for weekend stays.

CREDIT CARDS	MasterCard, Visa
BREAKFAST	Full breakfast is served in the dining room and includes egg soufflé with potatoes and chives, oatmeal buttermilk pancakes, pear and apple salad, bacon, coffee, and fresh-pressed cider. Dinner and special meals are available.
AMENITIES	Robes, flowers, hiking on property, air conditioning, wedding facilities. Chef Pamela Miller teaches cooking classes and serves dinner throughout the year.
˹ ˻TRICTIONS	No smoking inside, no pets, children over 12 are welcome. There are a draft horse, a thoroughbred, and a number of ducks and chickens on the property.
REVIEWED	*Northwest Best Places; The Best Places to Kiss in the Northwest*

VALLEY VIEW BED & BREAKFAST

28 Buckhorn Mountain Road, Pateros, WA 98846   *509-923-9636*

PESHASTIN

You'll find Peshastin just three miles east of Leavenworth on Highway 2.

LIETZ BED & BREAKFAST

8305 Lynn Street, Peshastin, WA 98847   *509-548-7504*
Verne & Helen Lietz, Resident Owners
German and French spoken

LOCATION	Turn north off Highway 2 at the Peshastin exit, drive over the Wenatchee River Bridge and take the first right onto School Street, then drive two blocks to Lynn Street and turn right.
OPEN	All year
DESCRIPTION	A 1957 ranch home with country and antique decor on the bank of the Wenatchee River.
NO. OF ROOMS	Three rooms share two bathrooms.
RATES	May to January, a single or double is $65; February to May, rooms are $55. There is a two-night minimum stay during festivals and cancellation requires 48 hours' notice.

CREDIT CARDS	No
BREAKFAST	Full hearty breakfast is served in the dining room and includes blueberry French toast; sausage, ham, or bacon; egg dishes and omelets; potatoes, muffins, coffeecake, and cereal.
AMENITIES	Fresh flowers, baskets of fresh fruit in rooms, organ and piano in the living room, handicapped access, views of the Wenatchee River.
RESTRICTIONS	No smoking, no pets. Shadow is the resident German shepherd.
MEMBER	Northwest Bed & Breakfast Association, Retreat & Reveille, Inns & Outs International

POINT ROBERTS

CEDAR HOUSE INN BED & BREAKFAST

1534 Gulf Road, Point Roberts, WA 98281　　　　　*360-945-0284*

PORT ANGELES

The north shore of the Olympic Peninsula was home to several thriving Native American tribes long before outside explorers laid claim to the area. Today this blue-collar mill town is known as Port Angeles, "where the Olympics greet the sea." Port Angeles Harbor, protected against wind and waves by Ediz Hook sand spit, is the largest natural deep-water harbor north of San Francisco. It is also a jumping-off point to Victoria, 17 miles across the strait on Canada's Vancouver Island. Port Angeles is also at the northern (and most popular) end of the Olympic National Park. The park, as big as Rhode Island, with a buffer zone of national forest surrounding it, contains the largest remaining herd of the huge Roosevelt elk. Drive along winding precipices to mile-high Hurricane Ridge and breathtaking views that mountains with twice the altitude seldom offer.

A NICE TOUCH BED & BREAKFAST

1665 Black Diamond Road, Port Angeles, WA 98362　　　*360-457-1938*
Lester West, Resident Owner　　　　　　　　　　　　*800-605-6296*

ANGELES INN BED & BREAKFAST

1203 East 7th Street, Port Angeles, WA 98362   360-457-4269
Al & June James, Resident Owners   888-552-4263
EMAIL james@olypen.com   FAX 360-457-4269 *(call first)*
WEBSITE www.northolympic.com/angeles

LOCATION	From Race Street (the road to Olympic National Park and Hurricane Ridge), turn east and go three blocks to the inn.
OPEN	All year
DESCRIPTION	A 1976 two-story contemporary inn with modern decor.
NO. OF ROOMS	Two rooms with private bathrooms and two rooms with one shared bathroom. Try the Master Bedroom.
RATES	Year-round rates are $75-95 for a single or double with a private bathroom and $60-75 for a single or double with a shared bathroom. There is a minimum stay during weekends and holidays, and cancellation requires five days' notice.
CREDIT CARDS	MasterCard, Visa
BREAKFAST	Full breakfast is served in the dining room and includes coffee, tea, juice, fruit, entrée, and pastries.
RESTRICTIONS	No smoking, no pets, children over five are welcome.
MEMBER	Washington Bed & Breakfast Guild, Olympic Peninsula Bed & Breakfast Association
RATED	AAA 2 Diamonds

BAVARIAN INN BED & BREAKFAST

1126 East Seventh Street, Port Angeles, WA 98362   360-457-4098

BAYTONS' ON-THE-BLUFF BED & BREAKFAST

824 West Fourth Street, Port Angeles, WA 98363   360-457-5569
Ron & Zoe Bayton, Resident Owners

KUDOS/COMMENTS	"Spectacular, panoramic view of the Strait of Juan De Fuca and Vancouver Island, Canada. Generous hospitality."

THE BEACH HOUSE

1922 Place Road, Port Angeles, WA 98363   *360-452-3245*
Monell & Gus Ormbrek, Resident Owners
EMAIL *Monell@olypen.com*
WEBSITE *www.northolympic.com/beachhouse/index.html*

LOCATION	Follow Highway 101 through Port Angeles and turn right onto Highway 112. Go three miles to Place Road, turn right again, and go two miles to the bottom of the hill, straight into the Beach House driveway.
OPEN	All year
DESCRIPTION	A 1995 contemporary guesthouse that rents as a private unit (two bedrooms plus pull-out couch, accommodates up to six people).
NO. OF ROOMS	Two rooms with a shared bathroom.
RATES	Call for year-round rates. There is no minimum stay.
CREDIT CARDS	None
BREAKFAST	Continental breakfast is served in the guesthouse kitchen and includes cereal, fruit, pastry, smoked salmon, bagels, ham, cheese, eggs, orange juice, milk, breads, crumpets, and coffee.
AMENITIES	Billiards, Ping-Pong table, electronic darts, satellite TV/VCR.
RESTRICTIONS	No smoking, no pets. Sadie is the resident basset hound.

BJ'S GARDEN GATE

397 Monterra Drive, Port Angeles, WA 98362   *360-452-2322*
BJ & Frank Paton, Innkeepers   *800-880-1332*
                                                      FAX 360-417-5098
EMAIL *bjgarden@olypen.com*   WEBSITE *www.bjgarden.com*

LOCATION	Seven miles east of Port Angeles on Highway 101, exit left onto Old Olympic Highway. Take a left onto Gunn Road and left onto Monterra Drive.
OPEN	All year
DESCRIPTION	A 1998 two-story gingerbread Victorian country inn with Victorian decor and antiques and extensive picture windows overlooking dramatic water views.
NO. OF ROOMS	Five rooms with private bathrooms. Try the Maria Theresa Suite.

BJ's Garden Gate, Port Angeles

RATES	High-season rates are $145-180 for a single or double. Regular rates are $130-165 for a single or double. There is no minimum stay and cancellation requires seven days' notice.
CREDIT CARDS	American Express, MasterCard, Visa
BREAKFAST	Full breakfast is served in the dining room and includes coffee, tea, cocoa, juices, fresh-baked muffins and scones, a fruit plate or chilled fruit soups, and a main entrée (such as baked stuffed French toast or quiches and chicken sausage stuffed with apples) with breakfast meats, ending with a light dessert.
AMENITIES	Evening dessert; ice water and early morning coffee in rooms; dramatic water views; Jacuzzi for two; in-room massage; TV/VCR and CD player with video and CD libraries; private fireplace with sitting areas; antiques throughout, including king- or queen-size beds; air conditioning; fresh flowers.
RESTRICTIONS	No smoking, no pets, no children
REVIEWED	*America's Favorite Inns, B&Bs & Small Hotels; Sweethearts' Getaway Guide*
MEMBER	Olympic Peninsula Bed & Breakfast Association
RATED	AAA 3 Diamonds

BLUE MOUNTAIN LODGE

380 *Lewis Road, Port Angeles, WA 98362*   *360-457-8540*
James & Carolyn Shurvinton, Resident Owners

KUDOS/COMMENTS "Lovely private cottage in the country with nice hosts."

CLARKS' HARBORVIEW BED & BREAKFAST

126 *West 4th Street, Port Angeles, WA 98363*   *360-457-9891*
Earl & Maxine Clark, Innkeepers
WEBSITE *www.bbchannel.com/bbc/p215392.htm*

LOCATION	From the center of town, go west on Front Street (one block south of the ferry dock), which will angle to the left and become Marine Drive. Go one block beyond the traffic light (Tumwater truck route) to Tumwater Street, which goes uphill and curves right to 5th Street. Then go west to G Street and take a right to 4th Street.
OPEN	All year
DESCRIPTION	A 1981 one-and-a-half-story split-level host home with unobstructed views of the harbor, the Strait of Juan de Fuca, Victoria, the San Juan Islands, and Mount Baker.
NO. OF ROOMS	One room with a private bathroom.
RATES	Year-round rates are $60-65 for a single or double. There is no minimum stay and cancellation requires 24 hours' notice less a $10 fee.
CREDIT CARDS	No
BREAKFAST	Full breakfast is served in the dining room and includes a fresh fruit dish, an entrée such as scrambled eggs with hashbrowns and sausage, homemade pastries and cookies, and coffee or tea.
AMENITIES	Complimentary sherry, pool table in rec room, courtesy transportation to the ferry and airport.
RESTRICTIONS	No smoking, no pets, children are welcome. No charge for children under two; $10 for children ages two through nine; and $25 for children over nine.
MEMBER	Olympic Peninsula Bed & Breakfast Association, Washington Bed & Breakfast Guild

COLETTE'S BED & BREAKFAST

339 Finn Hall Road, Port Angeles, WA 98362
Peter & Lynda Clark, Innkeepers
WEBSITE *www.colettes.com*

360-457-9197
FAX 360-452-0711

LOCATION	Two hours from Seattle via the Bainbridge ferry. Take Highway 305 to Highway 3 to Highway 104 to Highway 101 through Sequim. Go three miles past Sequim and turn right onto Carlsborg (at signal). Go 1.8 miles, turn left onto Old Olympic Highway and drive 3.7 miles, then turn right onto Matson and continue for 0.8 mile. Turn left onto Finn Hall. Drive one mile to the B&B sign.
OPEN	All year
DESCRIPTION	A 1950 contemporary inn, fully remodeled in 1996, on 10 acres of waterfront property nestled between the Olympic Mountains and the Strait of Juan de Fuca.
NO. OF ROOMS	Two rooms with private bathrooms. Try the Burgandy Suite.
RATES	High-season rates are $155-175 for a single or double. Regular rates are $110-175 for a single or double. There is no minimum stay.
CREDIT CARDS	MasterCard, Visa
BREAKFAST	Multicourse gourmet breakfast is served in the dining room or in the guestrooms and includes fresh-baked breads, custom-blended coffee or fine teas, and an entrée such as cream puffs with homemade caramel sauce.
AMENITIES	Private 10-acre waterfront estate; all rooms with two-person jetted tubs; gas fireplace; stereo, cable TV/VCR, and extensive video and classical CD collections; library; robes; fresh fruit basket; afternoon tea and treats.
RESTRICTIONS	No smoking, no pets
MEMBER	Olympic Peninsula Bed & Breakfast Association, Washington State Bed & Breakfast Guild, Olympic Peninsula Travel Association, Professional Association of Innkeepers International

COUNTRY COTTAGE

624 Billy Smith Road, Port Angeles, WA 98362
Victoria Richmond, Resident Owner

360-452-7974

DOMAINE MADELEINE BED & BREAKFAST

146 Wildflower Lane, Port Angeles, WA 98362   *360-457-4174*
Madeleine & John Chambers, Resident Innkeeper
French, Spanish Fersi, and German spoken   *FAX 360-457-3037*
EMAIL romance@domainemadeleine
WEBSITE www.domainemadeleine.com/ab

LOCATION	From downtown Port Angeles, take Highway 101 east for seven miles, turn left on Old Olympic Highway, drive 1.4 miles, and turn left on Gehrke. Drive 0.3 mile and turn right on Finn Hall, drive 0.2 mile and look for the sign.
OPEN	All year
DESCRIPTION	A 1947 two-story contemporary inn featuring an eclectic interior and exotic antiques, on 5 acres with Monet gardens and panoramic views of the Strait of Juan de Fuca, the Olympic Mountains, and Mount Baker.
NO. OF ROOMS	Five rooms with private bathrooms.
RATES	April 15 through October 15, rates are $145-175 for a double. Low-season rates are $10 less. There is a minimum stay during high-season weekends and during holidays, and cancellation requires seven days' notice.
CREDIT CARDS	American Express, Discover, MasterCard, Visa
BREAKFAST	Full gourmet breakfast, served in the dining room, includes four or five courses such as ratatouille omelet, spanakopita, apple soufflé, and fresh-baked French bread dessert.
AMENITIES	Fresh flowers in every room; designer robes; courtesy basket; French perfumes; games; imported chocolate truffles; CD player, TV/VCR (with 150 movies), and telephone in each room; four rooms have private Jacuzzis for two; all rooms with fireplaces; four waterfront rooms and one cottage with mountain views; tea/coffee and bar with snacks available all day.
RESTRICTIONS	No smoking indoors, children over 12 are welcome.
REVIEWED	*Northwest Best Places; The Best Places to Kiss in the Northwest; Fodor's Best B&Bs in the Northwest; America's Wonderful Little Inns & Hotels*
MEMBER	Professional Association of Innkeepers International, North Olympic Bed & Breakfast Association
RATED	AAA 3 Diamonds, Mobil 4 Stars, Best Places to Kiss 4 Lips
KUDOS/COMMENTS	"Waterfront estate with panoramic views of the Strait of Juan de Fuca and the Olympics, wonderful breakfast, great hosts." "Deluxe rooms, gourmet breakfasts, artistic decor."

ELWHA RANCH BED & BREAKFAST

905 Herrick Road, Port Angeles, WA 98362   360-457-6540
Margaret Mitchell, Resident Owner

KUDOS/COMMENTS   "A beautiful setting on the side of the Elwha Canyon in the
Olympic Mountains. Excellent service."

GLIMBERG HOUSE BED & BREAKFAST

2652 Black Diamond Road, Port Angeles, WA 98362   360-457-6579
Jane Glimberg, Resident Owner

THE HAVEN BED & BREAKFAST

1206 West 10th Street, Port Angeles, WA 98362   360-452-6373
WEBSITE www.northolympic.com/thehaven

THE INN TRANSIT BED & BREAKFAST

1405 West 5th Street, Port Angeles, WA 98363   360-452-1207
WEBSITE www.northolympic.com/inntransit

LAKE SUTHERLAND LODGE BED & BREAKFAST

430 South Shore Road, Port Angeles, WA 98363   360-928-2111
Paul Smith, Innkeeper   888-231-1444
Norwegian spoken   FAX 360-928-3603
EMAIL lakesutherland@tenforward.com
WEBSITE www.hotserv.com/lakesutherland

LOCATION   West on Highway 101 to Southshore Road (at the east end of Lake
                  Sutherland), turn south, and go 0.5 mile. The lodge is on the right.

OPEN   All year

DESCRIPTION	A 1995 three-story log and brick host home filled with mementos of the innkeepers' travels.
NO. OF ROOMS	Two rooms with private bathrooms and two rooms with one shared bathroom. Paul suggests the Scandinavian Room.
RATES	June through September 15, rates are $90 for a single or double with a private bathroom, $65 for a single or double with a shared bathroom, and $300 for the entire lodge. Mid-September through May, rates are $75 for a single or double with a private bathroom, $65 for a single or double with a shared bathroom, and $270 for the entire lodge. There is no minimum stay and cancellation requires 48 hours' notice.
CREDIT CARDS	American Express, Discover, MasterCard, Visa
BREAKFAST	Full breakfast is served in the dining room and includes orange juice, fruit, eggs, waffles or French toast, coffee, tea, and milk.
AMENITIES	Porch swing with view of the lake; robes upon request; parking for boat trailers (boat ramp one mile up the road); large library with chess, games, magazines, puzzles, and books. No TV.
RESTRICTIONS	No smoking, no pets, no alcohol
MEMBER	Olympic Peninsula Bed & Breakfast Association

MAPLE ROSE INN

112 Reservoir Road, Port Angeles, WA 98363   360-457-7673
Darryl Hayes & Geoff Shelton, Innkeepers   800-570-2007
EMAIL *maplerose@tenforward.com*   FAX 360-457-0176
WEBSITE *www.northolympic.com/maplerose*

LOCATION	Two miles south of the downtown ferry dock, exactly 0.5 mile outside the city limits.
OPEN	All year
DESCRIPTION	A 1992 four-story country inn with eclectic and transitional decor.
NO. OF ROOMS	Five rooms with private bathrooms. Try the Master Suite.
RATES	May through September, rates are $79-98 for a single or double, $127-167 for a suite, and $600 for the entire B&B. October through April, rates are $69-89 for a single or double, $98-127 for a suite, and $491 for the entire B&B. There is a two-night minimum stay during holiday weekends and cancellation requires seven days' notice.
CREDIT CARDS	American Express, Discover, MasterCard, Visa
BREAKFAST	Full breakfast is served in the dining room and includes a fruit dish and a main entrée such as quiche, eggs, or pancakes.

AMENITIES	Robes; toiletries; cable TV; telephones; two rooms with whirlpool tubs; hot tub; exercise room; library, activity area; kitchenettes in suites; decks; birthday balloons, anniversary cakes, roses, and champagne.
RESTRICTIONS	No smoking. Children are welcome with prior approval. Peajoe is the resident golden retriever, Niki is the silver tabby, and Zelda and Herman are the finches. "Peajoe likes to try her hand at opera when guests arrive—she doesn't bark or howl, she sings."
MEMBER	Olympic Peninsula Bed & Breakfast Association, Olympic Peninsula Travel Association
RATED	AAA 3 Diamonds, Mobil 2 Stars

THE SEASUNS BED & BREAKFAST INN

1006 South Lincoln Street, Port Angeles, WA 98362   *360-452-8248*
Bob & Jan Harbick, Innkeepers   *888-291-5066 (code: 3959)*
EMAIL *seasuns@olypen.com*   *FAX 360-417-0465*
WEBSITE *www.northolympic.com/seasuns*

LOCATION	Ten blocks from downtown Port Angeles and 12 blocks from the ferry terminal.
OPEN	All year
DESCRIPTION	A 1926 two-story Dutch colonial inn—a country estate in the city—decorated with period furnishings from the 1920s, surrounded by glorious mountain and water views, gardens, and waterfalls.
NO. OF ROOMS	Five rooms with private bathrooms. Try the Winter Room.
RATES	May 15 through October 15, rates are $90-125 for a single or double and $110-125 for a suite. October 16 through May 14, rates are $80-110 for a single or double and $95-110 for a suite. There is no minimum stay. Ask about a cancellation policy.
CREDIT CARDS	MasterCard, Visa
BREAKFAST	Full breakfast is served in the dining room and includes a variety of Pacific Northwest specialty foods such as smoked salmon frittata and halibut filet, always served with fresh fruit, juice, and fresh-baked breads. Lunch and dinner are available from October 16 through May 14 with prior arrangement.
AMENITIES	Coffee delivered to guestrooms in antique silver urns before breakfast; flowers; robes; chocolates; gardens for romantic strolls and relaxation; tea and fresh-from-the-oven baked goodies in the afternoon.
RESTRICTIONS	No smoking, no pets, children over 12 are welcome. Max is the resident golden retriever.

REVIEWED	*The Best Places to Kiss in the Northwest; Short Trips in the Pacific Northwest; Best Places to Stay in the Pacific Northwest; Unofficial Guide to B&Bs and Small Inns in the Pacific Northwest*
MEMBER	North Olympic Peninsula Bed & Breakfast Association, Washington State Bed & Breakfast Guild, Professional Association of Innkeepers International
RATED	AAA 2 Diamonds, Mobil 3 Stars

TUDOR INN

1108 South Oak, Port Angeles, WA 98362   *360-452-3138*
Jane Glass, Innkeeper
WEBSITE *www.tudorinn.com*

LOCATION	Take Highway 101 into the center of town to Lincoln Street, turn left (south) and continue to 11th Street, turn right and drive two blocks to Oak; the inn is on the corner of 11th and Oak Streets.
OPEN	All year
DESCRIPTION	A 1910 three-story Tudor inn decorated with various antiques.
NO. OF ROOMS	Five rooms with private bathrooms. Jane recommends the Country Room.
RATES	May 15 through October 15, rates are $85-125 for a double and $490 for the entire B&B. Mid-October through mid-May, rates are

Tudor Inn, Port Angeles

$75-110 for the rooms and $425 for the entire B&B. There is a minimum stay on weekends and cancellation requires five days' notice.

CREDIT CARDS	American Express, Discover, MasterCard, Visa
BREAKFAST	Full breakfast, served in the dining room, includes coffee, tea, or hot chocolate; fresh fruit compote and juice; an entrée such as homemade waffles, blueberry pancakes, eggs Florentine, apple caramel French toast; plus bacon; breads; muffins; and beverages. Picnic breakfast is also available with granola, fruit, muffins, bread, and beverages.
AMENITIES	Robes, fresh flowers, afternoon tea with fresh-baked cookies, lemonade in the summer.
RESTRICTIONS	No smoking, no pets, children over 12 are welcome. Stanley, the Persian cat, "loves attention and being stroked under the chin."
REVIEWED	*Northwest Best Places; Frommer's; The Best Places to Kiss in the Northwest; Lonely Planet; Fodor's; American's Wonderful Little Hotels & Inns; Non-Smokers Guide to Bed & Breakfasts*
MEMBER	Olympic Peninsula Bed & Breakfast Association, Washington Bed & Breakfast Guild
RATED	AAA 3 Diamonds, Mobil 3 Stars, *Best Places* 2 Stars
AWARDS	*Pacific Northwest* magazine's Preferred Establishment Award
KUDOS/COMMENTS	"Impeccably clean, beautifully furnished, friendly hosts, great breakfast!" "European-style English gardens, very comfortable, innkeepers always warm and friendly. Great B&B."

PORT HADLOCK

The false-front, Old West-style buildings in Hadlock have been painted with the same hot pinks, blues, and purples that some supermarkets use to ice cakes—a new take on "local color."

OAK BAY COTTAGES

3659 Oak Bay Road, Port Hadlock, WA 98339   *360-437-0380*

PORT LUDLOW

Off Highway 104, on the way to Olympic National Park and Port Townsend.
Nearby is Anderson Lake State Recreation Area.

NANTUCKET MANOR BED & BREAKFAST

941 Shine Road, Port Ludlow, WA 98365　　　　360-437-2676
Peggy & Peter Conrardy, Innkeepers　　　　FAX 360-437-2791
WEBSITE *www.olympus.net/nantucket/*

LOCATION	From Seattle, take the Bainbridge Island ferry. Go north on Highway 305 for 13.5 miles, then right on Highway 3 north for seven miles to the Hood Canal Bridge. One hundred yards past the west end of the bridge, turn left onto Shine Road and travel 1.4 miles to the manor. From Port Townsend, travel south out of town for about 20 miles to Highway 104. Turn left and travel 2.4 miles to Shine Road. Turn right and travel one mile to the manor.
OPEN	All year
DESCRIPTION	A 1991 grand two-story Nantucket Island-style inn with expansive gardens, a sweeping veranda, balconies, gazebo, and panoramic water and mountain views.
NO. OF ROOMS	Five rooms with private bathrooms. Try the Nantucket Room.
RATES	High-season rates are $155-180 for a single or double. Regular rates are $145-170 for a single or double. There is a minimum stay during festivals and cancellation requires seven days' notice.
CREDIT CARDS	Discover, MasterCard, Visa
BREAKFAST	Four-course gourmet breakfast is served in the dining room and includes coffee, tea, juice, an individual fruit plate with seven seasonal fruits, homemade muffins, an entrée such as quiche with smoked salmon, rosemary potatoes, and a dessert of blackberry cobbler. "Our guests always ask for our recipes."
AMENITIES	All rooms feature down comforters and terry robes, wine and tea are served in the afternoon, choice of champagne or sparkling cider for honeymoon and anniversary couples, nightly turndown service.
RESTRICTIONS	No smoking, no pets, children over 12 are welcome. Heidi is the schnauzer. She stays in the owners' living area.
REVIEWED	*Northwest Best Places; The Best Places to Kiss in the Northwest; Olympic Peninsula Best Places*
MEMBER	Professional Association of Innkeepers International, Olympic Peninsula Bed & Breakfast Association
RATED	AAA 3 Diamonds

PORT ORCHARD

The center of this small town hugs the southern shoreline of one of Puget Sound's many fingers of water—Sinclair Inlet. With its boardwalk and beach access, the waterfront area is a true gathering place. On Saturdays, from the end of April through October, the Port Orchard Farmers Market (Marina Park, one block from Bay Street) offers a tantalizing selection of cut flowers, fresh vegetables, baked goods, and crafts. Take home some Hood Canal oysters or ask the oyster lady to cook a few on her grill. There are numerous antique shops, and the Sidney Art Gallery and Museum displays Northwest art on the first floor of the Masonic Lodge Building.

LAUREL INN

7914 Beach Drive East, Manchester, WA 98353   *360-769-9544*
Judy McQueen, Innkeeper   *888-888-9661*

LOCATION	Eight miles northeast of downtown Port Orchard, two blocks north of the Manchester shopping area, and ten minutes from the Southworth ferry. Accessible by car or ferry.
OPEN	All year
DESCRIPTION	A 1990 two-story contemporary host home furnished with family heirlooms, needlework, and collectibles from around the world, with water views.
NO. OF ROOMS	One room with a private bathroom and two rooms with one bathroom. Judy recommends the Rainier Room.
RATES	Year-round rates are $83-88 for a single or double with a private bathroom and $53-68 for a single or double with a shared bathroom. There is no minimum stay; the first night must be guaranteed with payment or credit card; cancellation requires seven days' notice.
CREDIT CARDS	Discover, MasterCard, Visa
BREAKFAST	Full breakfast is served in the dining room—or guestrooms (honeymooners only)—and includes fresh or baked fruit, juice, coffee and tea, homemade muffins and breads, and entrées such as Hawaiian French toast with bananas and coconut syrup, salmon patties with poached eggs and lemon sauce, and gingerbread pancakes with pears. Vegetarian and other dietary needs are accommodated.
AMENITIES	Fresh flowers in season, robes, CD player, TV/VCR, large selection of videos, late afternoon snacks, guest refrigerator, soft drinks, magazines, parlor games, rooms decorated for special occasions.
RESTRICTIONS	No smoking inside, no pets, children over 12 are welcome. Children of all ages are welcome when the family occupies all three rooms.

NORTHWEST INTERLUDE BED & BREAKFAST

3377 Sarann Avenue East, Port Orchard, WA 98366   360-871-4676
Barbara Cozad & Frances Scott, Resident Innkeepers

REFLECTIONS—A BED & BREAKFAST INN

3878 Reflection Lane East, Port Orchard, WA 98366   360-871-5582
Jim & Cathy Hall, Resident Owners

LOCATION	In downtown Port Orchard, turn left (east) at the light by the B.P. gas station, go 3.2 miles on Beach Drive to Reflection Lane, and turn right, up the hill.
OPEN	All year
DESCRIPTION	A 1980 two-story colonial furnished with New England antiques from the mid-1800s.
NO. OF ROOMS	Two rooms with private bathrooms and two rooms share one bathroom. The Annette Room is the best.
RATES	Please call for current rates and cancellation information.
CREDIT CARDS	MasterCard, Visa
BREAKFAST	Full breakfast is served in the dining room.
AMENITIES	Wine or tea on arrival; flowers in room; terry robes; hot tub on deck; bayberry soap; tray with fresh fruit, nuts, and chocolate in each room with turndown service; wedding, small meeting, and retreat facility; coffee available half an hour before breakfast; fireplace in living room; newspaper at breakfast table.
RESTRICTIONS	No smoking inside, no pets, children over 15 are welcome. Maggie, the resident golden retriever, "thinks God created humans to give her loving attention."
REVIEWED	*Northwest Best Places*
MEMBER	Washington State Bed & Breakfast Guild, Bed & Breakfasts of Kitsap Peninsula
KUDOS/COMMENTS	"Scenic hilltop view of water, a wonderful place to host a wedding." "Beautiful rooms, friendly hosts, hearty breakfasts." "Cathy is a great cook and a gracious hostess."

PORT TOWNSEND

During the early days of the clipper ships, Port Townsend was the official point of entry to Puget Sound. Vessels from around the globe landed, and the foreign consuls added a cosmopolitan flavor to the social life of the wealthy folk who settled here. This early prosperity gave rise to the construction of more than 200 Victorian homes, reflecting the reign of Queen you-know-who. Overlooking Admiralty Inlet, Fort Worden was part of the defense system established to protect Puget Sound a century ago. Check out the Marine Science Center, the Centrum Summer Arts Festival (one of the most successful cultural programs in the state, with dance, fiddle tunes, chamber music, a writers conference, jazz, blues, and theater), the Rhododendron Festival in May, and the Wooden Boat Festival at Point Hudson Marina the weekend after Labor Day.

ANN STARRETT MANSION
VICTORIAN BED & BREAKFAST

744 Clay Street, Port Townsend, WA 98368
Edel Sokol, Innkeeper
German spoken
EMAIL *starrett@olympus.net*

360-385-3205
888-385-3205
FAX 360-385-2976
WEBSITE *www.olympus.net/starrett*

LOCATION	Driving into Port Townsend on State Route 20 or arriving via state ferry, drive through the business district and turn left on Monroe. Take the second left onto Clay, and drive three blocks to the intersection of Clay and Adams.
OPEN	All year
DESCRIPTION	An 1889 four-story Victorian stick-style inn decorated with colorful Victorian furnishings and detailed throughout with elaborate moldings and authentic Victorian colors and antiques. Listed on the National and State Historic Registers.
NO. OF ROOMS	Eleven rooms with private bathrooms. Try the Master Suite.
RATES	High-season rates are $89-225 for a single or double, $175-225 for a cottage, and $1,430 for the entire inn. Regular rates are $85-145 for a single or double, $129-145 for a cottage, and $1,227 for the entire inn. There is no minimum stay and cancellation requires 14 days' notice.
CREDIT CARDS	American Express, Discover, MasterCard, Visa
BREAKFAST	Full breakfast is served in the dining room and includes coffeecake, fresh fruit, orange juice, our homemade "cran-ola," coffee, tea, or cocoa, plus an entrée such as Viennese eggs and cheese puffs, New Orleans French Quarter toast (French toast filled with cream, berries, and chocolates, topped with a spirited berry sauce), or

German griddle cakes stuffed with fresh apples. The breakfast menu varies daily. A take-out sack breakfast is available for guests departing early. Lunch, dinner, and catered meals are also available.

AMENITIES	Concierge service; robes; hair dryers; wine for special occasions and repeat guests; private meeting rooms; tea and cake; early coffee and the *Wall Street Journal*; complimentary books ("If you can't finish reading it, please take it with you"); relax, read, or watch a video in one of two Victorian-appointed parlors.
RESTRICTIONS	No smoking, children are accommodated in the cottages.
REVIEWED	*The Best Places to Kiss in the Northwest; Quick Escapes; Northwest Best Places; Fodor's; Best Places to Stay in the Pacific Northwest; Guide to Historic Inns; Non-Smokers Guide to B&Bs; America's Wonderful Little Hotels & Inns*
RATED	AAA 3 Diamonds, Mobil 3 Stars
AWARDS	1996, Great American Home Award, National Trust for Historic Preservation

ANNAPURNA INN

538 Adams, Port Townsend, WA 98368　　　　360-385-2909
Robin Shoulberg, Resident Owner　　　　800-868-2662

KUDOS/COMMENTS	"Cozy, friendly, caring, vegetarian breakfasts only, massages, steam room and sauna."

BAKER HOUSE BED & BREAKFAST

905 Franklin, Port Townsend, WA 98368　　　　360-385-6673
Herb & Jean Herrington, Resident Owners　　　　800-240-0725
FAX 360-385-6673 (call first)

LOCATION	On the corner of Franklin and Taylor, two blocks above downtown Port Townsend in the historic district.
OPEN	All year
DESCRIPTION	An 1898 three-story Victorian with traditional, comfortable furnishings.
NO. OF ROOMS	Three rooms with private bathrooms.
RATES	Year-round rates are $75-85 for a single or double. Cancellation requires 24 hours' notice.

Baker House Bed & Breakfast, Port Townsend

CREDIT CARDS	MasterCard, Visa
BREAKFAST	Full three-course breakfast is served.
AMENITIES	A veranda on the second floor offers views of Puget Sound, Port Townsend, and the garden; tea and cookies in the living room.
RESTRICTIONS	No pets, children over 12 are welcome. Patches is the resident cat.
REVIEWED	*Inns & Outs*
MEMBER	Olympic Peninsula Bed & Breakfast Association
KUDOS/COMMENTS	"Beautiful, with verandas that offer fabulous views of Puget Sound." (1996)

BAY COTTAGE

4346 South Discovery Road, Port Townsend, WA 98368   *360-385-2035*
WEBSITE www.olympus.net/biz/getaways/bc/index.htm

BISHOP VICTORIAN SUITES

714 Washington Street, Port Townsend, WA 98368   *800-824-4738*

Bowen's Inn Bed & Breakfast

110 Jackman, Port Townsend, WA 98386   360-379-1999

Chanticleer Inn

1208 Franklin Street, Port Townsend, WA 98368   360-385-6239
Pattye O'Connor & Shirley O'Connor, Innkeepers   800-858-9421
EMAIL chntclr@olypen.com   FAX 360-385-3377
WEBSITE www.northolympic.com/chanticleer/

LOCATION	Upon entering Port Townsend on Highway 20, you will drive past a Safeway on the left. About 0.25 mile directly in front of you, you will see a white lighthouse on the hill. Turn left on Washington Street, just in front of the lighthouse. Go eight blocks, then turn left on Fillmore Street. The inn is two blocks ahead on the left at the corner of Fillmore and Franklin Streets.
OPEN	All year
DESCRIPTION	An 1876 two-story Victorian stick-style inn, painted a cream color with evergreen trim, with bay windows flanking a brick chimney covered by red climbing roses; a light, airy interior with comfortable, eclectic furnishings, and some antiques. Listed on the National and State Historic Registers.
NO. OF ROOMS	Four rooms with private bathrooms. The O'Connors recommend the Springfield Suite.
RATES	Year-round rates are $95-115 for a single or double, $145 for a suite ($125 with a four-night minimum stay), and the entire B&B rents for $600 a night. There is a minimum stay during holidays and festival weekends, and cancellation requires seven days' notice with a $25 fee. "We will try to re-rent the room; however, the full rate will be charged if we are unable to rent."
CREDIT CARDS	Diners Club, MasterCard, Visa
BREAKFAST	Full three-course gourmet breakfast is served in the dining room and includes juice and coffee, homemade granola, homemade muffins or bread, and an egg dish (sherry eggs, savory egg soufflé, etc.) with meat, or blueberry French toast with cream cheese. Holiday meals are included in special packages; sack lunches are available in the summer.
AMENITIES	Fresh flowers and complimentary cream sherry in all rooms; feather beds; Virginia Room has Jacuzzi tub; Springfield Suite has private deck with 180-degree view of Port Townsend Harbor and

the snow-covered Olympic and Cascade mountain ranges; air-conditioned; Saturday evening wine social; one room available on main floor for those who have difficulty with stairs; owners will arrange flowers, cake, surprises for special occasions.

RESTRICTIONS	No smoking, no pets, children over 16 are welcome.
REVIEWED	*The Best Places to Kiss in the Northwest; Destination Washington*
RATED	AAA 3 Diamonds
KUDOS/COMMENTS	"Wonderfully appointed rooms, fabulous breakfast, owner played harp for us at breakfast, immaculately clean."

THE ENGLISH INN

718 "F" Street, Port Townsend, WA 98368
WEBSITE www.English-Inn.com

360-385-5302
800-254-5302
FAX 360-385-6562

FW HASTINGS HOUSE—OLD CONSULATE INN

313 Walker at Washington, Port Townsend, WA 98368
WEBSITE www.oldconsulateinn.com

360-385-6753
800-300-6753
FAX 360-385-2097

KUDOS/COMMENTS "Nicely furnished, great breakfast."

HOLLY HILL HOUSE

611 Polk, Port Townsend, WA 98368
Lynne Sterling, Resident Owner

360-385-5619
800-435-1454

THE JAMES HOUSE

1238 Washington Street, Port Townsend, WA 98368
Carol McGough, Innkeeper
EMAIL info@jameshouse.com

360-385-1238
800-385-1238
FAX 360-379-5551

LOCATION	Sits on the bluff overlooking the Whidbey Island ferry dock in the historic district of Port Townsend.
OPEN	All year
DESCRIPTION	An 1889 three-story Queen Anne Victorian inn that is listed on the National and State Historic Registers.
NO. OF ROOMS	Eleven rooms with private bathrooms and two rooms with two shared bathrooms.
RATES	Year-round rates are $110-135 for a single or double with a private bathroom and $75-85 for a single or double with a shared bathroom. Suites and the guesthouse are $175 a night. There is no minimum stay and cancellation requires five days' notice.
CREDIT CARDS	American Express, MasterCard, Visa
BREAKFAST	Full breakfast is served in the dining room and includes coffee, tea, juice, fresh fruit dish, entrée, and fresh-baked bread.
AMENITIES	Fresh-baked cookies in the afternoon, sherry in the evening, fresh flowers.
RESTRICTIONS	No smoking, no pets, children over 12 are welcome.
REVIEWED	*Northwest Best Places; Best Places to Stay in the Pacific Northwest; The Best Places to Kiss in the Pacific Northwest; Fodor's Guide to the Pacific Northwest; The Complete Guide to Bed & Breakfast Inns & Guesthouses*
MEMBER	Unique Northwest Country Inns, Professional Association of Innkeepers International
RATED	AAA 3 Diamonds, Mobil 3 Stars, Northwest Best Places 3 Stars

LIZZIE'S VICTORIAN BED & BREAKFAST

731 Pierce, Port Townsend, WA 98368

360-385-4168
800-700-4168
FAX 360-385-9467

KUDOS/COMMENTS	"Charming, fun hosts, beautiful decorating in all rooms." "Wonderful Victorian house, lovely furnishings, beautiful grounds, great hostess, good breakfast." "Classic, old-world charm. One of the finest B&Bs in Port Townsend."

Manresa Castle, Port Townsend

MANRESA CASTLE

7th & Sheridan, Port Townsend, WA 98368   360-385-5750
Robert O'Conner, Innkeeper   800-732-1281
WEBSITE *www.olympus.net/manresa*   FAX 360-385-5883

LOCATION	On top of Castle Hill next to the hospital.
OPEN	All year
DESCRIPTION	An 1892 three-story German castle with Victorian decor. Listed on the National Historic Register. The castle was a private residence from 1892 to 1928, then became a Jesuit training college until 1968, when it was converted into a country inn.
NO. OF ROOMS	Forty rooms with private bathrooms. Try room 200.
RATES	May through mid-October, rates are $65-85 for a single or double and $85-175 for a suite. Mid-October through April, rates are $60-80 for a single or double and $80-130 for a suite. There is no minimum stay and cancellation requires 72 hours' notice.
CREDIT CARDS	Discover, MasterCard, Visa
BREAKFAST	Continental breakfast is served in the breakfast room and includes croissants, muffins, cake, toast, juice, and coffee. Dinner is also available.
AMENITIES	Restaurant and cocktail lounge, banquet and meeting facilities, cable TV with free Showtime and telephone in every room.
RESTRICTIONS	No pets

MORGAN HILL GUEST COTTAGE

608 Roosevelt, Port Townsend, WA 98368   *360-385-2536*

QUIMPER INN

1306 Franklin Street, Port Townsend, WA 98368   *360-385-1060*
                                                           800-557-1060

RAVENSCROFT INN

533 Quincy Street, Port Townsend, WA 98368   *360-385-2784*
Leah Hammer, Innkeeper   *800-782-2691*
EMAIL ravenscroft@olympus.net   *FAX 360-285-6724*
WEBSITE www.ravenscroftinn.com

LOCATION   Downtown Port Townsend is located on Water Street. Head
                    northeast to Monroe and turn left. Go up Monroe, turn left on Clay
                    Street (the second left), go two blocks, and turn left again onto
                    Quincy. Take an immediate right into the driveway.

OPEN   All year

DESCRIPTION   A 1989 three-story colonial "Charleston Single House" replicate
                    with an interior that features a blend of old and new, keeping true
                    to the spirit of the colonial era while offering the most modern
                    amenities.

NO. OF ROOMS   Eight rooms with private bathrooms.

RATES   High-season rates are $67-175 for a single or double, $165-175 for
                    a suite, and $956 for the entire B&B. Regular rates are $65-160 for
                    a single or double, $150-160 for a suite, and $885 for the entire
                    B&B. There is a minimum stay during weekends, holidays, and
                    special events. Cancellation requires seven days' notice.

CREDIT CARDS   American Express, Discover, MasterCard, Visa

BREAKFAST	Full gourmet breakfast is served in the dining room and includes fresh fruit frappe, and a variety of special entrées, followed by fresh-baked coffeecakes or pastries. All dietary needs are met.
AMENITIES	Afternoon refreshments; special treats for anniversaries, honeymoons, and birthdays; facilities for small meetings and weddings; Sunday concerts once a month.
RESTRICTIONS	No smoking, no pets, children over 12 are welcome.
REVIEWED	*Weekends for Two in the Pacific Northwest; The Best Places to Kiss in the Northwest; Inn Places, Women's Travel; Northwest Best Places; Complete Guide to Bed & Breakfast and Inns and Guesthouses; Recommended Country Inns; America's Wonderful little Hotels and Inns; Fodor's; Frommer's*
MEMBER	Professional Association of Innkeepers International, Washington Bed & Breakfast Association, Washington Hotel and Motel Association
RATED	AAA 3 Diamonds, Mobil 3 Stars, Best Places to Kiss 3.5 Lips
AWARDS	1988, Outstanding New Inn of the Year, Inn Marketing; 1996, Skookum Award of Appreciation, given for using handicapped workers
KUDOS/COMMENTS	"Very lovely, custom-decorated rooms, great hosts and breakfast, comfortable and cozy, breakfast with world-class pianist playing!" "Wonderful new Victorian house, in-room soaking tubs, beautifully decorated, great hostess."

SALMONBERRY FARM

2404 35th Street, Port Townsend, WA 98368   *360-385-1517*
Meg & Doug Mason, Innkeepers   *FAX 360-385-1517*
EMAIL seahorse@olympus.net
WEBSITE www.olympus.net/biz/getaways/

LOCATION	Near the western city limits of Port Townsend. From State Highway 20 (the main road into Port Townsend), go left (north) onto Jacob Miller Road. Go straight for two miles and turn right (east) onto Hastings Avenue. Head east for 0.9 mile, turn left (north) onto Howard Street, and take the second right onto 35th Street. Look for the large carved sign.
OPEN	All year
DESCRIPTION	A 1987 two-story carriage house located on acres of open space in a relatively undeveloped part of Port Townsend. The upper level of the carriage house accommodates humans—three horses occupy the first level of the home.

NO. OF ROOMS	One room with a private bathroom.
RATES	Year-round rate is $90 for a double ($10 for each additional guest over two). There is a two-night minimum stay on three-day weekends and weekends during the Centrum Festival. "We trust people to give adequate notice of cancellations."
CREDIT CARDS	No
BREAKFAST	Breakfast is available in the guestrooms. The refrigerator is stocked with breakfast foods, and fresh-baked bread or muffins are delivered hot from the oven at a time designated by the guest.
AMENITIES	Fully equipped kitchen; fresh-cut flowers, chocolates, and liqueur; roses and champagne upon request; horse boarding always available and encouraged; great rail rides on miles of trails directly accessible from property; beautiful view of the Olympic Mountains from the balcony; bald eagles overhead.
RESTRICTIONS	No smoking, all children and pets are welcome! Stetson is the resident Jack Russell terrier, and Mr. Magoo, Tigger, Rumpole, Aphrodite are the cats. The thoroughbred horses, who live downstairs, are Swindler, Tequi and Ziggy. "The horses are used for combined training competitions, but can be made available for riding at owners' discretion. Many kids have had their first riding experience at SalmonBerry Farm."

POULSBO

Poulsbo was once a community of fishermen and loggers, primarily Scandinavian. Today, it's full of gift shops and its snug harbor is full of yachts. It's Scandinavian heritage, however, is still going strong—Front Street sports its "Velkommen til Poulsbo" signs, and the architecture is a dolled-up version of the fjord villages of Norway. Once you've seen the town, be sure to stroll the boardwalk along Liberty Bay. Local celebrations include the Viking Jazz Festival in February, Viking Fest in March, Strawberry Festival and Skandia Midsommarfest in June, Fireworks on the Fjord in July, Arts by the Bay in August, Paddlepalooza in August, and Yule Fest and Gud Yul in December.

FOXBRIDGE BED & BREAKFAST

30680 Highway 3 NE, Poulsbo, WA 98370 360-598-5599
Beverly & Chuck Higgins, Resident Owners *FAX 360-598-3588*
EMAIL *foxbridge@sprintmail.com* WEBSITE *www.sfox.com/foxbridge*

LOCATION	Heading north on Highway 3, follow the signs leading to the Hood Canal Bridge. The B&B is 0.1 mile north of milepost 59 on your right.

OPEN	All year
DESCRIPTION	A 1993 two-story Georgian manor with traditional interior, on 5 wooded acres.
NO. OF ROOMS	Three rooms with private bathrooms. The Old World Room's sleigh bed is very popular.
RATES	Year-round rate is $85 for a single or double. There is a two-night minimum stay during holiday weekends and cancellation requires seven days' notice for a full refund.
CREDIT CARDS	MasterCard, Visa
BREAKFAST	Full breakfast is served in the dining room and includes varying entrées such as heart-shaped waffles topped with blueberries and whipped cream, eggs Benedict, or smoked-salmon quiche, preceded by seasonal fruits and berries, cereals, fruit juices, and a special starter (perhaps an apple crisp with maple cream sauce).
AMENITIES	Fruit orchard, private trout pond, gazebo, library, evening refreshments.
RESTRICTIONS	No smoking, no pets, children over 16 are welcome.
REVIEWED	*Best Places to Stay in the Pacific Northwest; Bed & Breakfasts and Country Inns; Washington State Travelers: Affordable Accommodations*
MEMBER	Washington Bed & Breakfast Guild, Kitsap County Lodging Association

LOMAS' MURPHY HOUSE BED & BREAKFAST

425 NE Hostmark Street, Poulsbo, WA 98370   360-779-1600
Bob & Barbara Lomas, Resident Owners   800-779-1606
WEBSITE *www.bbonline.com*   FAX 360-779-3832

LOCATION	From Seattle, take the Bainbridge ferry from downtown and follow Route 305 to Poulsbo, turning left after 12 miles onto Hostmark Street. From the north, take the Kingston ferry and follow the signs on Bond Road to Poulsbo. From the south, take Highway 16 from Tacoma across the Tacoma Narrows Bridge, go past Bremerton, and then north on Highway 3 to Poulsbo.
OPEN	All year
DESCRIPTION	A 1957 two-story plantation-style host home in which each bedroom is uniquely decorated.
NO. OF ROOMS	Five rooms with private bathrooms. Pick room 3.
RATES	May through October, rates are $89-98 for a single or double, $150 for a suite, and $550 for the entire B&B. November through April, rates are $79-89 for a single or double, $140 for a suite, and $500

for the entire B&B. There is no minimum stay and cancellation requires 72 hours' notice.

CREDIT CARDS	American Express, MasterCard, Visa
BREAKFAST	Full breakfast, served in the dining room or guestrooms, includes a hot entrée such as quiche or French toast, plus meats, a potato dish, various breads, homemade granola, fruit, yogurt, specialty jams, and beverages.
AMENITIES	Homemade cookies are always available, hot drinks in the afternoon, champagne and sparkling cider to celebrate special events, common room with fireplace, quiet library, game table.
RESTRICTIONS	No smoking, no pets, children over 16 are welcome.
REVIEWED	*The Best Places to Kiss in the Northwest*
MEMBER	Professional Association of Innkeepers International, Kitsap Peninsula Bed & Breakfast Association

THE MANOR FARM INN

26069 Big Valley Road NE, Poulsbo, WA 98370   360-779-4628

ONCE IN A WHILE

18956 Harris, Poulsbo, WA 98370   360-598-2212

PROSSER

Cherries have always grown well in the Yakima Valley, except when the weather doesn't cooperate. Too much rain cracks cherries; too little leaves them small. Chukar Cherries turns imperfect cherries into a year-round delicacy—dried cherries. In the showroom of their production center you'll also see chocolate-covered cherries, cherry poultry sauce, and even cherry waffle mix.

WINE COUNTRY INN

1106 Wine Country Road, Prosser, WA 99350   509-786-2855

PULLMAN

The largest of the Palouse towns, Pullman retains some of its cowpoke image, but covets an international reputation as a university town. Kamiak Butte, 13 miles north on Route 24, offers a good place for a picnic and nice overlooks of the rolling wheat country. About 30 miles north of Pullman on Highway 195, Steptoe Butte towers above the Palouse and affords an impressive panoramic view as well as unobstructed stargazing. History buffs will find Steptoe Battlefield near Rosalia interesting; as at Little Bighorn, the U.S. Cavalry lost this one, too. Just north of its confluence with the Snake River, the Palouse River gushes over a basalt cliff higher than Niagara Falls and drops 198 feet into a steep-walled basin. Hiking trails lead to an overlook above the falls and to streamside below the falls. Just downstream from the falls is the Marmes Rock Shelter, where remains of the earliest known inhabitants of North America, dating back 10,000 years, were discovered by archaeologists.

ASH STREET HOUSE

NE 315 Ash Street, Pullman, WA 99163   *509-332-3638*

COUNTRY BED & BREAKFAST

Route 2, Box 666, Pullman, WA 99163   *509-334-4453*
Bruce & Mary Lee Tenwick, Resident Owners

PUYALLUP

At the head of the fertile Puyallup Valley, this frontier farm town serves as a major gateway to Mount Rainier. Much of the bulb, rhubarb, and berry farmland continues to be cultivated, but a great part of it has been strip-malled and auto-row-ravaged around the edges. Avoid the fast-food strip to the south and head east up the valley to Sumner, White River, Orting, Wilkeson, and Carbonado. The Ezra Meeker Mansion, a lavish 17-room Italianate house (circa 1890), is the finest original pioneer mansion left in Washington. Its builder and first occupant, Ezra Meeker, introduced hops to the Puyallup Valley. Puyallup is big on old-time seasonal celebrations, and it's home to two of the biggest in the Northwest: the Daffodil Festival and Parade in early April and the Western Washington Fair, better known as the Puyallup Fair, in September.

HART'S TAYBERRY HOUSE BED & BREAKFAST

7406 80th Street East, Puyallup, WA 98371   *253-848-4594*
EMAIL tayberrybb@aol.com   WEBSITE www.bbonline.com/wa/tayberry/

RAINIER

7 C's (Seven Seas) Guest Ranch

11123 128th SE, Rainier, WA 98576   360-446-7957
Evelyn Cissna, Resident Owner

RAYMOND

Brackett's Log Cabin Bed & Breakfast

Route 1, Box 140 C, Raymond, WA 98577   360-942-6111
Mac & Nancy Brackett, Resident Owners

REDMOND

Once a bucolic suburban destination, now known worldwide as the headquarters for mighty Microsoft, this city at the north end of Lake Sammamish is also the hub of a lot of local (and national) cycling activity. The Marymoor Velodrome in Marymoor Park, a 400-meter concrete track built for the 1976 Olympic trials, draws world-class bicyclists for twice-weekly races from mid-May to September. The park itself, on the north shore of Lake Sammamish, is a huge expanse of ball fields and semiwild grassland that makes for great bird-watching. Less-ambitious bicyclers enjoy the Sammamish River Trail, which runs north along the river.

Lilac Lea Christian Bed & Breakfast

21008 Northeast 117th Street, Redmond, WA 98053   425-861-1898
Chandler & Ruthanne Haight, Resident Owners

LOCATION   Take Route 520 east from Seattle to Avondale Road, go north to the
                 Texaco station on the corner of 116th, go right to the end at 209th,
                 turn left, and then take the first right on NE 117th.

OPEN   All year

Lilac Lea Christian Bed & Breakfast, Redmond

DESCRIPTION	A 1990 two-story Dutch colonial with French provincial and early American interior decor and a separate guest entrance.
NO. OF ROOMS	One suite with a private bathroom.
RATES	Year-round rates are $75-85 for a suite. There is a minimum stay during the weekends in July and August, and cancellation requires seven days' notice less $20 processing fee.
CREDIT CARDS	No
BREAKFAST	Continental breakfast includes cereal, fruits, juice, muffins or fruit bread, and beverages.
AMENITIES	Feather beds and pillows, antique-furnished suite with TV, robes, study area, very private, large deck, picnic area, allergy-friendly environment (no indoor pets), bike rental and trails, next to an 800-acre wilderness area.
RESTRICTIONS	No smoking, no pets, no children, no alcohol
REVIEWED	*Inns & Outs International*
MEMBER	Suburban Eastside Bed & Breakfast Association

RENTON

At the southern tip of Lake Washington, sometimes 15 minutes, sometimes an hour from Seattle, depending on the traffic. Renton features the Spirit of Washington Dinner Train and in August, Renton River Days.

HOLLY HEDGE HOUSE

908 Grant Avenue South, Renton, WA 98055 206-226-2555
Lynn & Marian Thrasher, Resident Owners FAX 206-226-2555
Italian spoken

LOCATION	Four miles east on I-405 from Sea-Tac Airport. Take exit 4 onto Bronson Way north, left on Mill Avenue south to the Renton Hill entrance, continue 0.5 mile to South 7th, turn left and go one block to Grant, and turn right.
OPEN	All year
DESCRIPTION	A 1901 two-story English Tudor guesthouse with Waverly prints, wainscoting, and English country garden interior.
NO. OF ROOMS	"The entire guesthouse reserves for one couple at a time."
RATES	During high season (April through October) the guesthouse rents for $110-125. During low season it rents for $98-125. There is a two-night minimum stay on weekends and cancellation requires 14 days' notice (less $15 processing fee).
CREDIT CARDS	MasterCard, Visa
BREAKFAST	Full breakfast includes a varying menu of French toast supreme, ham and egg strata, eggs, bacon, hot and cold cereals, and pancakes, plus seasonal fruits, assorted muffins, and beverages.
AMENITIES	Plush terry robes; fresh flowers; private hot tub; private swimming pool; gas fireplace; extensive video, CD, and reading libraries; board games; bikes; tennis rackets and balls; extensive information about special attractions; croquet; swimming pool games.
RESTRICTIONS	No smoking, no pets, no children
REVIEWED	*Special Places for the Discerning Traveler; The Best Places to Kiss in the Northwest; America's Wonderful Little Hotels & Inns*
MEMBER	Bed & Breakfast Association of Suburban Seattle
AWARDS	1995, Waverly Room of the Year Award, *Country Inn Magazine*

REPUBLIC

An old mining town, Republic lies at the intersection of Highways 2 and 20, both scenic routes, near Sherman Pass. Fish the many mountain lakes around town. Check out the Stonerose Fossil and Interpretive Center.

K-DIAMOND-K CATTLE & GUEST RANCH

15661 Highway 21 South, Republic, WA 99166   509-775-3536
The Konz Family, Innkeepers   888-345-5355
EMAIL *kdiamond@televar.com*   FAX 509-775-3536 *(call first)*
WEBSITE *www.kdiamondk.com*

LOCATION	Four miles south of Republic on Highway 21 between mileposts 156 and 157.
OPEN	All year
DESCRIPTION	A 1980 two-story ranch-style lodge with an open-beam log ceiling, stone fireplace, and western interior.
NO. OF ROOMS	Four rooms with two shared bathrooms.
RATES	Year-round rate is $70 for a single or double with a shared bathroom. There is no minimum stay.
CREDIT CARDS	No
BREAKFAST	Full breakfast is served in the dining room and includes juice, coffee, pancakes or French toast, sausage, eggs, and coffeecake. Lunch and dinner are also available.
AMENITIES	Campfires; Old West atmosphere; cowboy boots and hats available; beautiful location amidst mountains, meadows, and forests. This is an operating cattle ranch.
RESTRICTIONS	No smoking. There are three dogs, three cats, and 30 horses; 100 cattle roam the property.

RITZVILLE

About 40 miles east of Moses Lake off I-90 in agricultural country, Ritzville celebrates the wheat harvest in mid-July. Check out the original art deco movie theater.

THE PORTICO BED & BREAKFAST

502 South Adams Street, Ritzville, WA 99169   509-659-0800
Mary Anne Phipps, Resident Owner

LOCATION	On the corner of 5th and Adams, right off I-90. Take either exit into town and follow the signs.
OPEN	All year
DESCRIPTION	A 1902 three-story Queen Anne/neocolonial home with Victorian interior, oak woodwork, antiques, and historic wallpaper.
NO. OF ROOMS	Two rooms with private bathrooms.
RATES	Year-round rates are $59-74 for a double. There is no minimum stay. Ask about a cancellation policy.
CREDIT CARDS	American Express, Discover, MasterCard, Visa
BREAKFAST	Full breakfast includes raspberries in summer, yeast-raised waffles, homemade cinnamon rolls, eggs, ham, sausage or bacon, plus beverages.
AMENITIES	Walking distance to town and golf course, wraparound porch and beautiful yard; very easy access to I-90.
RESTRICTIONS	No smoking, no pets, children are welcome with previous arrangement. Zeke, the resident golden Lab, is "large and friendly."
MEMBER	Washington State Bed & Breakast Guild
KUDOS/COMMENTS	"The most authentically restored turn-of-the-century mansion we've ever seen. Beautiful."

ROCHESTER

COUNTRY ROSE BED & BREAKFAST

18010 Anderson Road SW, Rochester, WA 98579   360-273-6213

ROSLYN

Modest turn-of-the-century homes in this former coal-mining town have become weekend places for city folk, and the former mortuary is now a video store and movie theater, but the main intersection (once the stage set for the hit TV series Northern Exposure) still offers a crosssection of the town's character: The historic Northwestern Improvement Company building (which once housed the company store) occupies one corner, while the old brick bank across the way still operates behind its original brass bars and oak counters.

HUMMINGBIRD INN

106 Pennsylvania Avenue East, Roslyn, WA 98941   *509-649-2758*
Roberta Spinazola, Innkeeper
WEBSITE *www.blueplanet-group/hummingbirdinn*

LOCATION   Take exit 80 off I-90 and go 2.8 miles north on Wooded Road. At the intersection with Highway 903, turn left and go one mile to Pennsylvania Avenue (main street). Turn left. The inn is the blue house with the white picket fence.

OPEN   All year

DESCRIPTION   An 1890s two-story farmhouse with country Victorian decor and lovely antiques.

Hummingbird Inn, Roslyn

NO. OF ROOMS	One room with a private bathroom and two rooms share two bathrooms. Roberta recommends the Pink Room.
RATES	Year-round rates are $70-95 for a single or double with a private bathroom and $60-65 for a single or double with a shared bathroom. The entire B&B rents for $150-180. There is no minimum stay and cancellation requires one weeks' notice.
CREDIT CARDS	Discover, MasterCard, Visa
BREAKFAST	Full breakfast is served in the dining room and includes juice, hot beverage, fruit salad, coffeecake or muffins, and a main entrée. No meat is served.
AMENITIES	Homemade cookies in the evening, fireplace, piano (in tune), lots of good books and games.
RESTRICTIONS	No smoking, no pets, children are welcome. Elsa is the resident German shepherd.
REVIEWED	*Hot Showers, Soft Beds, and Day Hikes in the North Cascades; Unofficial Guide to B&Bs and Small Inns of the Pacific Northwest*
MEMBER	Washington Bed & Breakfast Guild

ROSLYN BED & BREAKFAST

109 Arizona Avenue West, Roslyn, WA 98941   *509-649-2463*

SALKUM

THE SHEPHERD'S INN BED & BREAKFAST

168 Autumn Heights Drive, Salkum, WA 98582   *360-985-2434*
WEBSITE www.wbbg.com/ (look under Salkum)   *800-985-2434*

SEABECK

A tiny old logging town along the Hood Canal on the Kitsap Peninsula, about four miles southwest of Silverdale.

WILLCOX HOUSE COUNTRY INN

2390 Tekiu Road NW, Seabeck, WA 98380
Phillip & Cecilia Hughes, Innkeepers
WEBSITE *www.willcoxhouse.com*

360-830-4492
800-725-9477
FAX 360-830-0506

LOCATION	From Silverdale, at Highway 3 and Newberry Hill Road, go west about three miles to the stop sign at Seabeck Highway. Drive 13.2 miles and fork right at Old Holly Hill Road. Go 200 yards and turn right on Tekiu Road. Drive to the end (about 1.3 miles).
OPEN	All year
DESCRIPTION	A 1936 two-story country inn with traditional decor.
NO. OF ROOMS	Five rooms with private bathrooms. Phillip and Cecilia recommend the Constance Room.
RATES	Year-round rates are $129-199 for a single or double and $845 for the entire inn. There is a minimum stay during weekends and summer, and cancellation requires seven days' notice.
CREDIT CARDS	Discover, MasterCard, Visa
BREAKFAST	Full breakfast buffet is served in the dining room and includes granola, yogurt, fruit juice, milk, fruit platter, assorted pastries, and an entrée such as Belgian waffles with real maple syrup, crepes with homemade fruit syrups, *aebleskivers*, and croissant French toast. Lunch and dinner are also available.
AMENITIES	Wine and cheese social hour, hot beverage bar, robes, amenity baskets, clothes steamers, hair dryers.
RESTRICTIONS	No smoking, no pets, children over 15 are welcome.
REVIEWED	*The Best Places to Kiss in the Northwest; Northwest Best Places; Weekends for Two in the Pacific Northwest*
MEMBER	Professional Association of Innkeepers International
RATED	AAA 3 Diamonds
AWARDS	1993, One of the top 12 Inns in North America, *Country Inns* magazine; 1997, second place, dinner catagory, Jones Dairy Farm National recipe and cooking competition
KUDOS/COMMENTS	"Unique, romantic, secluded."

SEATTLE

Situated between sparkling Puget Sound and Lake Washington, and dotted with lakes, Seattle is nearly surrounded by water, with mountains just about everywhere you look. On clear days, Mount Rainier's distant snowcapped presence has even been known to halt commuter traffic—which has grown worse as the population grows and the city's bedroom communities spread farther afield. Rapid growth and international sophistication have brought to this city outstanding restaurants, thriving cultural organizations (such as the Seattle Symphony and Seattle Opera), and fabulous citywide festivals. Seattle is famous for its enduring relationships with Boeing and Bill Gates, for the Space Needle and Pike Place Market, and for coffee, always coffee, available in steaming cups from mobile espresso carts that sprout on street corners like mushrooms after a good rain.

THE BACON MANSION BED & BREAKFAST

959 Broadway East, Seattle, WA 98102
Daryl King, Innkeeper
EMAIL baconbandb@aol.com
WEBSITE www.site-works.com/bacon

206-329-1864
800-240-1864
FAX 206-860-9025

LOCATION	One mile north of downtown Seattle. Take exit 166 (Olive Way/Denny) from I-5, go east up the hill to Broadway East, turn left, and go five blocks. Veer right onto 10th Avenue East, go two blocks, then take a left on East Prospect and go one block.
OPEN	All year
DESCRIPTION	A 1909 split-beam Edwardian-style Tudor mansion with a grand staircase and stained glass. Listed on the National Historic Register.
NO. OF ROOMS	Eight rooms with private bathrooms and two rooms with one shared bathroom. Daryl suggests the Capitol Suite.
RATES	May through October and during holidays, rates are $104-144 for a single or double with a private bathroom and $79-94 for a single or double with a shared bathroom. November through April, rates are $84-124 for a single or double with a private bathroom and $69-79 for a single or double with a shared bathroom. There is a minimum stay during weekends, holidays, and from July through September 15. Cancellation requires seven days' notice—or guests are charged for each night the room is not rebooked.
CREDIT CARDS	American Express, Discover, MasterCard, Visa
BREAKFAST	Continental plus breakfast is served in the formal dining room and includes fresh fruit salad, yogurt, cereals, juices, freshly baked muffins, coffee, and tea.

AMENITIES	Phone with private voicemail, modem port, TV, and clock radio in each room; afternoon tea; one suite with handicapped access; meeting and reception facilities; patio with fountain and rose garden; turn-of-the-century library; two blocks off the Broadway shopping district.
RESTRICTIONS	No smoking, no pets, children of all ages are welcome (with restrictions).
REVIEWED	*Northwest Best Places; Fodor's Best Bed & Breakfasts of the Pacific Northwest; The Best Places to Kiss in the Northwest; Seattle Best Places; Lonely Planet; Fodor's Gay USA*
MEMBER	Bed & Breakfast Association of Seattle, Washington State Hotel & Motel Association
KUDOS/COMMENTS	"Grand old mansion near downtown Seattle. Tastefully decorated. Has several sitting areas for guests."

BED & BREAKFAST ON BROADWAY

722 Broadway East, Seattle, WA 98102
Russel Lyons & Don Fabian, Innkeepers
EMAIL *bbonbroadway@chcs.com*
WEBSITE *www.chcs.com/bbonbroadway*

206-329-8933
888-329-8933
FAX 206-726-0918

LOCATION	Near Volunteer Park, 1.5 miles from downtown Seattle on Capitol Hill.
OPEN	All year
DESCRIPTION	A 1901 four-story Northwest Craftsman inn with gleaming chandeliers, antiques, art collections, and Northwest decor.
NO. OF ROOMS	Four rooms with private bathrooms.
RATES	March through October, rates are $85-125 for a single or double; November through February, rates are $85-115. There is a minimum stay during summer and cancellations incur a $25 fee.
CREDIT CARDS	American Express, Diners Club, Discover, MasterCard, Visa
BREAKFAST	Continental plus is served in the dining room.
RESTRICTIONS	No smoking, no pets, no children

BEECH TREE MANOR

1405 Queen Anne Avenue North, Seattle, WA 98109
Virginia Lucero, Resident Owner

206-281-7037
FAX 206-284-2350

BLUE WILLOW BED & BREAKFAST

213 Comstock, Seattle, WA 98119   *206-284-4240*

KUDOS/COMMENTS   "Quaint, charming."

CAPITOL HILL INN

1713 Belmont Avenue, Seattle, WA 98122   *206-323-1955*

Katie & Joanne Godmintz, Innkeepers   *FAX 206-322-3809*

CHAMBERED NAUTILUS BED & BREAKFAST INN

5005 22nd Avenue NE, Seattle, WA 98105   *206-522-2536*

Joyce Schulte & Steve Poole, Innkeepers   *800-545-8459*

French spoken   *FAX 206-528-0898*

EMAIL *chamberednautilus@msn.com*

WEBSITE *www.chamberednautilus.com*

LOCATION	Ten minutes north of downtown Seattle and three blocks from the University of Washington campus. From I-5 northbound, take the 50th Street exit and turn right on 50th. Follow 50th until it almost ends, at 20th Avenue NE. Turn left onto 20th NE at the flashing red stoplight, go to 54th Street, and turn right. At the bottom of the hill, turn right onto 22nd Avenue NE. The inn is 200-300 yards down on the right.
OPEN	All year
DESCRIPTION	A 1915 three-story Georgian colonial inn with English and American antiques, lots of golden oak furniture, hardwood floors, and casual yet elegant decor.
NO. OF ROOMS	Six rooms with private bathrooms. Joyce and Steve suggest the Crow's Nest in winter and the Scallop Chamber in summer.
RATES	May through October, rates are $84-119 for a single or double and $119 for a suite. November through April, rates are $74-104 for a single or double and $50-109 for a suite. There is a two-night minimum stay on weekends, three nights during holidays. Cancellations require one weeks' notice.
CREDIT CARDS	American Express, MasterCard, Visa

BREAKFAST	Full breakfast is served in the dining room or on the sun porch and includes fresh fruit, juice, homemade granola, and entrées such as Northwest breakfast pie (a salmon and dill quiche) with rosemary buttermilk muffins or stuffed French toast with homemade orange syrup, plus plenty of fresh-roasted Seattle coffee and a selection of gourmet teas.
AMENITIES	All guest rooms have desks, private phones, computer access, well-stocked bookshelves, down comforters, robes, bottled water, and a resident teddy bear; four rooms with porches and one with a fireplace; guest refrigerator; tea, cookies, and fruit always available in the living room; large living room with fireplace, well-stocked bookshelves, and a work table; enclosed sun porch with a couch and a table for game-playing or working; garden.
RESTRICTIONS	No smoking, no pets, children over eight are welcome.
REVIEWED	*Fodor's Seattle & Vancouver, The Complete Guide; Romantic Days and Nights in Seattle; Seattle Best Places; Northwest Best Places; The ACCESS Guide to Seattle; America's Favorite Inns, B&Bs and Small Hotel; Frommer's 1998 Guide to Seattle and Vancouver; Fodor's Bed & Breakfasts, Country Inns, and Other Weekend Pleasures*
MEMBER	Professional Association of Innkeepers International, Washington State Bed & Breakfast Guild, Bed & Breakfast Association of Seattle
RATED	Mobil 2 Stars
KUDOS/COMMENTS	"1915 Georgian Colonial, large comfortable rooms, excellent breakfasts, well-informed friendly innkeepers."

CHELSEA STATION ON THE PARK

4915 Linden Avenue North, Seattle, WA 98103
Carolanne & Eric Watness, Resident Owners
WEBSITE *www.bandbseattle.com*

206-547-6077
800-400-6077
FAX 206-632-5107

LOCATION	Just minutes north of downtown Seattle and 1.3 miles west of I-5 off exit 169.
OPEN	All year
DESCRIPTION	A 1929 two-story Federal colonial decorated in mission style with antiques throughout.
NO. OF ROOMS	Six rooms with private bathrooms. Try the Rose Suite.
RATES	June through September, rates are $95 for a single or double and $110-135 for suites. December through March, rates are $75 for a room and $90-105 for a suite. Holiday and weekend rates are at the

high-season price range year-round. There is a two-night minimum stay on weekends (flexible three days during holidays), and cancellation requires seven days' notice (14 days during holidays) less a $10 handling fee.

CREDIT CARDS	American Express, Diners Club, Discover, MasterCard, Visa
BREAKFAST	Full breakfast, served in the dining room, includes a hot entrée such as fresh orange French toast, a vegetable frittata, ginger pancakes with fresh lemon sauce, Brie and apple stuffed French toast, or baked eggs, sautéed potatoes, breakfast meats, fresh fruit and nut salads, warm scones, jam, and beverages. Dietary restrictions and preferences are always accommodated.
AMENITIES	Selection of teas, coffees, hot cocoa, and hot spiced cider available anytime; bottomless cookie jar; neighborhood strolls to the Seattle Rose Garden, Green Lake, Woodland Park and Zoo; jigsaw puzzle always in progress; peek-a-boo views of the Cascades from second-floor suites.
RESTRICTIONS	No smoking inside the inn, no pets, children over 12 are welcome. Alex is the resident pooch.
REVIEWED	*Northwest Best Places; Seattle Best Places*
MEMBER	Bed & Breakfast Association of Seattle, Professional Association of Innkeepers International, Washington State Bed & Breakfast Guild
KUDOS/COMMENTS	"Warm hospitality, very well-done rooms, clean."

THE COLLEGE INN

4000 University Way NE, Seattle, WA 98105   *206-633-4441*
Tom Wall, Resident Innkeeper   *FAX: 206-547-1335*
Some German and French spoken
EMAIL *c-inn@speakeasy.org*   WEBSITE *www.speakeasy.org/collegeinn*

LOCATION	Ten minutes north of downtown directly across the street from the University of Washington campus.
OPEN	All year
DESCRIPTION	A 1904 four-story Tudor guesthouse with European-style decor, listed on the National and State Historic Registers. The building also houses a restaurant and English-style pub.
NO. OF ROOMS	Twenty-six rooms share four bathrooms.
RATES	Year-round rates are $45-75 for a single or double and $75 for a suite. Prices are subject to change. There is no minimum stay and cancellation requires 24 hours' notice.
CREDIT CARDS	MasterCard, Visa

BREAKFAST	Continental breakfast is served in the dining room and includes breads, muffins, fruits, pastries, cereals, and beverages.
RESTRICTIONS	No smoking, no wedding parties. No handicapped access. Pasquall and Salvatore are the resident cats.
REVIEWED	*Northwest Best Places; Seattle Best Places; Northwest Budget Traveler; Seattle Access; Let's Go Alaska and the Pacific Northwest; Best Places to Stay in America's Cities; Washington Handbook; The Berkeley Guide to the Pacific Northwest and Alaska*

DIBBLE HOUSE BED & BREAKFAST

7301 Dibble Avenue NW, Seattle, WA 98117   206-783-0320

DUCK-IN

4118 100th Avenue SE, Mercer Island, WA 98040   *206-232-2554*
Ruth Mullen, Innkeeper   *FAX 206-232-2554*
EMAIL *duck-in@web.net*
WEBSITE *www.nwlink.com/~holihedg/ssbba.html/di.html*

LOCATION	Heading east on I-90 from Seattle, cross the floating bridge to Mercer Island. Take the last exit on Mercer Island (exit 8) and turn right at the light. Follow straight through the intersection along East Mercer Way for 0.25 mile. Turn left at 100th Avenue SE and turn into the third driveway.
OPEN	All year
DESCRIPTION	A 1938 one-story cottage with country decor, on the waterfront of Lake Washington.
NO. OF ROOMS	One room with a private bathroom.
RATES	Year-round rate is $125 for a single or double. There is a two-night minimum stay and cancellation requires 48 hours' notice.
CREDIT CARDS	No
BREAKFAST	Continental breakfast is served in the dining room and includes juices, fresh fruit, cereal, homemade muffins and breads, and coffee, tea, or hot chocolate.
RESTRICTIONS	No smoking, no pets
MEMBER	Bed & Breakfast Association of Suburban Seattle

GASLIGHT INN AND HOWELL STREET SUITES

1727 15th Avenue, Seattle, WA 98122　　　　　206-325-3654
Trevor Logan & Steve Bennett, Resident Owners

KUDOS/COMMENTS　"Wonderful old mansion, off-the-charts gorgeous, beautifully furnished with antiques, excellent innkeepers." (1996)

GREEN GABLES GUESTHOUSE

1503 Second Avenue West, Seattle, WA 98119　　206-282-6863
David & Lila Chapman, Resident Owners　　　　800-400-1503
　　　　　　　　　　　　　　　　　　　　　　　FAX 206-286-8525

KUDOS/COMMENTS　"Very nice. Great integrity."

HILL HOUSE BED & BREAKFAST

1113 East John Street, Seattle, WA 98102　　206-720-7161
Herman & Alea Foster, Innkeepers　　　　　800-720-7161
EMAIL *hillhouse@foxinternet.net*　　　　　FAX 206-323-0772
WEBSITE *www.seattlebnb.com*

LOCATION	Located 0.75 mile east of downtown Seattle (a 15-minute walk) in historic Capitol Hill. Take I-5 exit 166 east.
OPEN	All year
DESCRIPTION	A 1903 two-story A-frame Victorian inn furnished with antiques, oriental rugs, lace curtains, and embroidered duvet covers.
NO. OF ROOMS	Three rooms with private bathrooms and two rooms with one shared bathroom.
RATES	April through October and during winter holidays, rates are $105-135 for a single or double with a private bathroom, $85-100 for a single or double with a shared bathroom, and $135-145 for a suite. November through March, rates are $100-120 for a single or double with a private bathroom, $80-90 for a single or double with a shared bathroom, and $125-130 for a suite. There is a two-night minimum stay during high season and three nights during holiday weekends. Cancellation requires seven days' notice with a $35 flat fee plus one night's charge if the room is not rebooked.
CREDIT CARDS	American Express, Diners Club, Discover, MasterCard, Visa

BREAKFAST	Full gourmet breakfast is prepared to order and served on china and crystal in the dining room or on the back deck. Herman is a professional chef, having previously owned his own restaurant. Typical entrées include smoked salmon omelets, oatmeal pancakes, and eggs Benedict. The main course is always preceded by a fruit course, such as baked pears, oranges in a cinnamon-zinfandel sauce, or a baked crisp with mango, apple, and raspberry. Coffee, juice, and homemade jams accompany the entrées.
AMENITIES	Sit-down dinners for 6-18 people can be prearranged; each room with down comforter and pressed cotton sheets, fresh flowers, handmade soaps, and Hill House robes; most rooms with TVs and private phone lines with answering machines; backyard deck shaded by a weeping willow; off-street parking; bus transportation within a block; less than a mile from downtown attractions, the Convention Center, and Pike Place Market; innkeepers are readily available to help with directions, arranging transportation, or suggesting fun and interesting activities.
RESTRICTIONS	No smoking, no pets, no children
REVIEWED	*Fodor's; The Best Places to Kiss in the Northwest; America's Wonderful Little Hotels & Inns; Seattle Access*
MEMBER	Seattle Bed & Breakfast Association
RATED	AAA 3 Diamonds, Mobil 4 Stars

LA PALOMA BED & BREAKFAST

2113 13th Avenue South, Seattle, WA 98144   *206-323-1283*

LAKE UNION BED & BREAKFAST

2217 North 36th Street, Seattle, WA 98103   *206-547-9965*

LANDES HOUSE BED & BREAKFAST

712 11th Avenue East, Seattle, WA 98102   *206-329-8781*

Mildred's Bed & Breakfast, Seattle

MILDRED'S BED & BREAKFAST

1202 15th Avenue East, Seattle, WA 98112   206-325-6072
Melody & Mildred Sarver, Resident Owners   FAX 206-860-5907
EMAIL *mildredsbb@foxinternet*   WEBSITE *www.mildredsbnb.com*

LOCATION	Take I-5 north from Sea-Tac airport to Seattle. Take exit 166 (Olive Way) to the top of the hill. Turn left onto 15th Avenue East and go one mile. The B&B is across the street from Volunteer Park on Capitol Hill.
OPEN	All year
DESCRIPTION	An 1890 three-story, double-turreted Victorian inn with natural wood entryway and staircase, lace curtains, red carpets, and traditional Victorian decor.
NO. OF ROOMS	Four rooms with private bathrooms.
RATES	April through October, rates are $95-130 for a single or double. November through March, rates are $90-125 for a single or double. There is no minimum stay and cancellation requires seven days' notice.
CREDIT CARDS	American Express, MasterCard, Visa

BREAKFAST	Full gourmet breakfast is served in the dining room and includes fresh fruit, homemade muffins, scones, a main course, and beverages. Coffee and juice are delivered to guestrooms half an hour before breakfast.
AMENITIES	Shampoos and conditioners, hair dryers, TV/VCRs, and writing desks in rooms; alcove with small fridge, sink, coffee, tea, and brownies or cookies; iron and drop-down ironing board; telephone; reading materials.
RESTRICTIONS	No smoking, no pets, children are welcome. Louie is the resident cockatiel.
REVIEWED	*Lonely Planet; Bed & Breakfast USA; West Coast Bed & Breakfasts; Washington Handbook*
MEMBER	Seattle Bed & Breakfast Association, Hotel & Motel Association

MV CHALLENGER BED & BREAKFAST

1001 Fairview Avenue North, Seattle, WA 98109   *206-340-1201*
Jerry & Buff Brown, Resident Owners   *FAX 206-621-9208*

LOCATION	Ten city blocks north of downtown Seattle, docked on Lake Union. Take exit 167 off I-5, staying right off the ramp, which will force two right turns. The parking lot is three blocks up on the left side of the road.
OPEN	All year
DESCRIPTION	A 1944 tugboat with three decks and nautical decor, including portholes and polished brass.
NO. OF ROOMS	Five rooms with private bathrooms and three rooms share one bathroom. The best room is the Admiral's Cabin.
RATES	Year-round rates are $55-105 for a single or double on the main deck and $130-170 for a room on the upper deck.
CREDIT CARDS	American Express, Diners Club, Discover, MasterCard, Visa
BREAKFAST	Full all-you-can-eat breakfast is served in the dining room and includes seafood omelets, pancakes, potatoes, sausage, bacon, pound cakes, fresh fruit, cereal, yogurt, fresh-squeezed orange juice, and coffee.
AMENITIES	Validated parking, every cabin is unique, dining area surrounded by windows, VCRs in all cabins with private baths, TVs in all cabins except two, video library with 300 films, telescope in Captain's Cabin, coffee and tea 24 hours a day.
RESTRICTIONS	No smoking, no pets, children over seven are welcome "provided they can swim."

REVIEWED   Northwest Best Places; Seattle Best Places; Fodor's Seattle and
            Portland; Frommer's Seattle and Portland; Alaskan and American
            Airlines, 28 Great American Cities B&B Guide

MEMBER   American Bed & Breakfast Association

ParGardens Bed & Breakfast

14716 26th Avenue NE, Seattle WA 98155   *206-367-1437*
Patti Par Norwood, Innkeeper   *888-742-2632*
American sign language "spoken"   *FAX 206-367-0088*
EMAIL *parbandb@halcyon.com*

LOCATION	Just six miles north of downtown Seattle, one mile east of I-5, near the north end of Lake Washington (exit 175 off I-5, 145th NE).
OPEN	All year
DESCRIPTION	A 1950s-era two-story host home, extensively remodeled and stylishly landscaped gardens, with contemporary, comfortable decor. "No clutter, no fancy knicknacks or antiques, very family friendly."
NO. OF ROOMS	One room with a private bathroom and two rooms share one bathroom. The Suite is the best room.
RATES	Year-round rates are $70-75 for a single or double with a private bathroom and $60-65 for a single or double with a shared bathroom.
CREDIT CARDS	American Express, MasterCard, Visa
BREAKFAST	Full breakfast is served "when they want it (anytime between six and ten in the morning) and where they want it (in the guestrooms or in the dining room)." Guests are given an extensive menu at check in. They can choose what they want for breakfast, including everything from bacon and eggs or waffles to organic produce and whole grains. "We cater to dietary preference."
AMENITIES	Main-floor lobby has fireplace and VCR with video library; second-floor lobby (the loft) has phone, coffee and tea service, and a paperback library; the hostess was a Seattle area radio personality for 17 years, so she has an extensive knowledge of local attractions.
RESTRICTIONS	No smoking, children are welcome, and pets are OK (with an additional cleaning fee). "We are extremely allergy-conscious. We have a cat and a small dog, but neither are allowed in the public part of the house." The property is also a mini-farm with chickens, rabbits, and doves (guests might hear some cooing and crowing out back).

PENSIONE NICHOLS

1923 First Avenue, Seattle, WA 98101   206-441-7125

PRINCE OF WALES BED & BREAKFAST

133 13th Avenue East, Seattle, WA 98102   206-325-9692
Carol Norton, Resident Owner   800-327-9692
Some Spanish and Italian spoken   FAX 206-322-6402

LOCATION	On the corner of 13th Avenue East and East John Street. Take the Madison exit off I-5 and drive up the hill about 0.5 mile to 12th Avenue, then go east seven blocks to John, take a right, and go one block to the corner of 13th Avenue East.
OPEN	All year
DESCRIPTION	A 1903 three-story Victorian host home with Victorian interior decor and eclectic collections.
NO. OF ROOMS	Four rooms with private bathrooms.
RATES	Please call for current rates and cancellation information.
CREDIT CARDS	American Express, Discover, MasterCard, Visa
BREAKFAST	Full "low-fat, heart-healthy" breakfast includes fresh fruit, cereals, a hot dish, baked goods, and beverages. Special diets are accommodated.
AMENITIES	Microwave and refrigerator available at all times in guest area, daily delivery of *The New York Times*, travel information, maps, timetables, and guest telephone.
RESTRICTIONS	Smoking permitted outdoors only, no pets, children over three are welcome.
REVIEWED	*The Berkeley Guide: The Budget Traveler's Handbook; Pacific Northwest and Alaska on the Loose; Seattle Access*
MEMBER	Bed & Breakfast Association of Seattle, Professional Association of Innkeepers International, Washington State Hotel and Motel Association

QUEEN ANNE HILL BED & BREAKFAST

1835 7th Avenue West, Seattle, WA 98119   206-284-9779
Mary & Chuck McGrew, Innkeepers
EMAIL *QABedBrk@aol.com*

LOCATION	From I-5, take exit 167 and go left on Fairview Avenue. Take a right onto Denny Way and another right onto 1st Avenue North. Take a left onto Roy Street and a right onto Queen Anne Avenue. Take a left onto Galer Street, a right onto 7th Avenue West, and go three blocks.
OPEN	All year
DESCRIPTION	A 1906 three-story Seattle saltbox Victorian host home on a quiet residential street with beautiful views of the Olympic Mountains and Puget Sound. The house is surrounded by a large garden and decorated with antiques, artwork, books, and unique collectibles.
NO. OF ROOMS	Three rooms with private bathrooms and two rooms share two bathrooms.
RATES	April through September, rates are $99-119 for a single or double with a private bathroom and $59-69 for a single or double with a shared bathroom. October through March, rates are $79-89 for a single or double with a private bathroom and $55-59 for a single or double with a shared bathroom. There is no minimum stay and cancellation requires 24 hours' notice.
CREDIT CARDS	MasterCard, Visa
BREAKFAST	Full breakfast is served in the dining room and includes fresh bakery items, cereals, fruit, hot egg dishes, toast, and coffee.
RESTRICTIONS	No smoking, no pets, children over four are welcome.
MEMBER	Seattle Bed & Breakfast Association

ROBERTA'S BED & BREAKFAST

1147 16th Avenue East, Seattle, WA 98112   206-329-3326
Roberta Barry, Resident Owner   FAX 206-324-2149
WEBSITE *www.robertas.com*

LOCATION	One mile northeast of downtown Seattle and one block east of Volunteer Park atop Capitol Hill.
OPEN	All year
DESCRIPTION	A 1903 three-story "classic box-style" inn decorated with antiques and "no lace or doilies."

NO. OF ROOMS	Five rooms with private bathrooms. Roberta recommends the Hideaway, with a skylight above the bed.
RATES	Please call for current rates and cancellation information.
CREDIT CARDS	MasterCard, Visa
BREAKFAST	Full breakfast is served in the dining room.
AMENITIES	Early morning coffee or tea delivered to bedrooms "to wake guests gently," robes, many books, wonderful neighborhood for "walking, strolling, gamboling about," daily newspapers and *The New York Times* every morning.
RESTRICTIONS	No smoking, no pets
REVIEWED	*Northwest Best Places; Seattle Best Places; Fodor's Pacific North Coast; America's Wonderful Little Hotels & Inns; Best Places to Stay in the Pacific Northwest; Ultimate Washington; Seattle Access*
KUDOS/COMMENTS	"Warm hospitality, beautifully appointed gardens and rooms, wonderful breakfast and a terrific location on Capitol Hill." "Beautiful home in a good Seattle neighborhood. Roberta is very friendly and accommodating."

SALISBURY HOUSE BED & BREAKFAST

750 16th Avenue East, Seattle, WA 98112   206-328-8682
Cathryn & Mary Wiese, Resident Owners   FAX 206-720-1019
Limited Spanish spoken
EMAIL *sleep@salisburyhouse.com*   WEBSITE *www.salisburyhouse.com*

LOCATION	From the airport, exit I-5 north at 164A and turn right on Madison Street, go 0.5 mile to 15th Avenue and turn left, then go another 0.5 mile to Aloha and take a right to the corner of 16th Avenue East.
OPEN	All year
DESCRIPTION	A 1904 three-story Victorian/prairie-style inn with wide eaves and porches and an eclectic interior decor including English and American antiques, maple floors, and oriental carpets.
NO. OF ROOMS	Five rooms with private bathrooms. Cathryn recommends the suite.
RATES	May through October, rates are $89-140 for a double and $140 for the suite. November through April, rates are $78-120 for a double and $120 for the suite. Single rates are $10 less. There is a two-night minimum stay on weekends and during the summer, longer for some holidays. Cancellations require seven days' notice.
CREDIT CARDS	American Express, MasterCard, Visa

Salisbury House Bed & Breakfast, Seattle

BREAKFAST	Full breakfast, served in the dining room, features a varied menu of fruit, fresh-baked muffins, scones, brioche, croissants, coffeecakes, eggs (baked, frittatas, quiches, omelets), oatmeal, pancakes, French toast, waffles, and great coffee. No meats.
AMENITIES	Fresh flowers, down comforters, fireplaces, 24-hour tea and coffee, guest refrigerator, hair dryers, clock radios, well-stocked library, wraparound porch, lush gardens and large, sunny rooms.
RESTRICTIONS	No smoking, no pets, children over 12 are welcome. Jane and Emily are the resident cats, twins named after Jane Austin and Emily Brontë.
REVIEWED	*Northwest Best Places; Seattle Best Places; Best Places to Kiss in the Northwest; Frommer's Northwest; Pacific Northwest's Best Bed & Breakfasts; The Non-Smokers Guide to Bed & Breakfasts; Hidden Pacific Northwest; Rough Guide*
MEMBER	Washington Bed & Breakfast Guild
RATED	Mobil 3 Stars
AWARDS	1994, Nominee for Mayor's Small Business Award

SHAFER-BAILEY MANSION

907 14th Avenue East, Seattle, WA 98112   *206-322-4654*

SOUND VIEW BED & BREAKFAST

17600 Sylvester Road SW, Seattle, WA 98166
Gerry & Dick Flaten, Resident Owners
EMAIL soundview@sprynet.com
WEBSITE www.soundviewbandb.com

206-244-5209
888-244-5209
FAX 206-243-8687

LOCATION	Twelve miles south of downtown Seattle. Take the Burien exit from I-5 near Southcenter Mall, go west on Highway 518 to exit 509, and go south one block. Turn right on 160th, go four blocks, take a left onto Sylvester Road, and drive 2.25 miles.
OPEN	All year
DESCRIPTION	A 1982 one-story Northwest contemporary guesthouse with a deck overlooking Puget Sound and the Olympic Mountains.
NO. OF ROOMS	One room with a private bathroom.
RATES	The guesthouse rents for $125. There is a two-night minimum stay and cancellation requires seven days' notice.
CREDIT CARDS	American Express, MasterCard, Visa
BREAKFAST	Full breakfast is served in the guestroom and includes fresh fruit, toast, homemade jam, coffeecake, cheese, egg puff dish, sausage or bacon, juice, coffee, tea, and milk. Vegetarian and other special diets are accommodated.
AMENITIES	King-size bed; deck with hot tub; TV/VCR and CD player; video and CD library; private phone line; fax available; robes, hair dryer; fresh flowers.
RESTRICTIONS	No smoking, no pets
MEMBER	Washington Bed & Breakfast Guild, Bed & Breakfast Association of Suburban Seattle

THREE TREE POINT BED & BREAKFAST

17026 33rd SW, Seattle, WA 98166
EMAIL Whisler@3TreePointBnB.com

206-669-7646
888-369-7696
FAX 206-242-7844

VILLA HEIDELBERG

4845 45th Avenue SW, Seattle, WA 98116
Barb & John Thompson, Resident Owners
Spanish spoken

206-938-3658
800-671-2942
FAX 206-935-7077

LOCATION	From I-5, take exit 163 to the West Seattle Bridge and go three miles to SW Oregon Street (staying in the lane marked Fauntleroy Way), turn right on SW Oregon Street and go 0.5 mile to 45th Avenue SW, turn left and go three blocks to the corner of 45th and Erskine Way.
OPEN	All year
DESCRIPTION	A 1909 three-story Craftsman host home with mission and Craftsman interior decor and family antiques.
NO. OF ROOMS	One room with a private bathroom and four rooms share two bathrooms. The Munchen is the best room.
RATES	Year-round rates are $100-110 for a single or double with a private bathroom and $60-90 for a single or double with a shared bathroom. There is a two-night minimum stay from May through September and cancellation requires seven days' notice for refund of deposit.
CREDIT CARDS	American Express, MasterCard, Visa
BREAKFAST	Full breakfast, served in the dining room, includes an entrée such as Dutch babies, croissant French toast, egg casserole, or pecan waffles, plus fresh-squeezed orange juice, fresh fruit, and beverages. Special dietary needs are accommodated.
AMENITIES	Robes, king-size beds, fireplace in Heidelberg Room, fresh flowers, gardens with fish pond, wicker furniture on wraparound porch, rooftop deck with view of Puget Sound and Olympic Mountains.
RESTRICTIONS	No smoking, no pets, children over 12 are welcome. Frisky is the resident Russian blue cat. "Frisky has taken it upon herself to be the 'greeter,' trotting to the door and leading guests upstairs."
REVIEWED	*Seattle Best Places; Fodor's Bed & Breakfasts, Country Inns and Other Weekend Pleasures; Seattle Access*
MEMBER	Bed & Breakfast Association of Seattle, Washington Bed & Breakfast Guild

VINCENT'S GUEST HOUSE

527 Malden Avenue East, Seattle, WA 98112

206-323-7849

WILDWOOD BED & BREAKFAST

4518 SW Wildwood Place, Seattle, WA 98136   206-819-9075
Carol & Morgan Warehime, Resident Owners
WEBSITE www.wildwoodseattle.com

SEAVIEW

Some of the peninsula's prettiest stretches (and a couple of its finest restaurants and lodgings) are tucked into this small, beachfront, bedroom community. Almost every westward road leads to the beach, where you can park your car to stroll the quaint neighborhoods and traverse the rolling dunes. The Charles Mulvey Gallery displays quintessential peninsula watercolors of ocean, beach, and bay. Campiche Studios features watercolors, sculptures, and photography.

THE SHELBURNE COUNTRY INN

4415 Pacific Highway 103, Seaview, WA 98644   360-642-2442
Laurie Anderson & David Campiche, Innkeepers   FAX 360-642-8904
German, French, Portuguese, and Spanish spoken.
EMAIL shelinn@aone.com   *WEBSITE www.theshelburneinn.com*

LOCATION	From Seattle, take I-5 south to Olympia and the Highway 12 exit. Folllow the signs west to Montesano, then to Raymond and South Bend, then to the Long Beach Peninsula. From Portland, take Highway 30 to Astoria or Highway 26 to Seaside, then go north on Highway 101 across the Astoria Bridge and left to Ilwaco, and north again two miles to Seaview.
OPEN	All year
DESCRIPTION	An 1896 three-story Victorian/Craftsman country inn with Edwardian and Victorian interior, including stained-glass window panels imported from England. "The Shelburne Inn is the oldest continuously operating hotel in Washington."
NO. OF ROOMS	Fifteen rooms with private bathrooms. Try room 9 or 17.
RATES	Year-round rates are $109-149 for a single or double and $179 for a suite. Dining packages are available for midweek lodgers (Sunday through Thursday) from October through June. There is a minimum stay most, but not all, weekends and cancellation requires five days' notice.
CREDIT CARDS	American Express, MasterCard, Visa

BREAKFAST	Full breakfast features David's own Italian sausage omelet, scrambled eggs with smoked salmon, hangtown fry with fresh local oysters, razor clam fritters, blueberry pancakes, and Belgian waffles. Lunch and dinner are also available.
AMENITIES	Fresh flowers, fresh-baked cookies upon arrival, coffee and tea service in lobby all day, free copy of *The Innkeeper's Register*, handicapped access to one room.
RESTRICTIONS	No smoking, no pets, quiet and well-supervised children are welcome.
REVIEWED	*Weekends for Two in the Pacific Northwest; Recommended Country Inns; Special Places; The Official Guide to American Historic Inns; Northwest Best Places; Country Inns and Backroads; Fodor's; Frommer's*
MEMBER	Independent Innkeepers Association, Unique Northwest Country Inns
AWARDS	One of Uncle Ben's Ten Best Inns of 1990
KUDOS/COMMENTS	"Remodeled historical inn with fine rooms and great restaurant." "Very welcoming. Breakfast was wonderful. The owners are patient and kind. Inspired us to open our own country inn."

SEDRO-WOOLLEY

From Sedro-Woolley, you have easy access to Bellingham, Anacortes, and Mount Baker National Forest.

SOUTH BAY BED & BREAKFAST

4095 South Bay Drive Lake Whatcom　　　　　　　360-595-2086
Sedro-Woolley, WA 98284　　　　　　　　　　FAX 360-595-1043
Dan & Sally Moore, Innkeepers
Spanish spoken
EMAIL *southbay@gte.net*

WEBSITE *www.southbaybb.com*

LOCATION	Take exit 240 (Alger) off I-5 north and turn right onto Cain Lake Road. From I-5 south, take exit 240 (Alger) and go left over the freeway on Cain Lake Road. Stay on Cain Lake Road, cross old Highway 99, and continue five miles to the "Y" in the road. Stay right, toward the lake, and turn right onto South Bay Drive. Continue for three miles and take a sharp right into the driveway.
OPEN	All year

South Bay Bed & Breakfast, Sedro-Woolley

DESCRIPTION	A 1996 three-story Craftsman lakeside retreat, decorated with understated elegance.
NO. OF ROOMS	Five rooms with private bathrooms.
RATES	Year-round rates are $150 for a single or double and $1500 for the entire inn. There is a minimum stay when the entire inn is rented. Ask about a cancellation policy.
CREDIT CARDS	MasterCard, Visa
BREAKFAST	Full breakfast is served in the dining room, on the patio, or on the wraparound porch. Breakfast is freshly prepared in the healthiest manner and beautifully presented; it includes homemade granola or baked oatmeal, fresh fruit, a main entrée with unusual breakfast meats, some type of potato, popovers or other homemade breads, plus tea, juice, and fresh-ground, French-press coffee.
AMENITIES	Unique flowers in rooms and baths; candles, robes, toiletries; CD players; evening herbal tea trays; cheese and fruit trays; guest kitchen stocked with juice, soft drinks, coffee, tea, snacks, and cookies; microwave, cooktop, and refrigerator; kayak, canoe, trails, mountain biking; meeting facilities, intimate weekend weddings for up to 50 inside, 100 outside; whirlpool baths for two; gas fireplaces; private patios; sun room; wraparound porch; secluded location; beach access.
RESTRICTIONS	No smoking, no pets, children over 14 are welcome. "Hawks, eagles, deer, chipmunks, rabbits, and coyotes traverse our property."
REVIEWED	*Fodor's; The Best Places to Kiss in the Northwest*
MEMBER	Professional Association of Innkeepers International, Washington

Bed & Breakfast Guild, Bed & Breakfast Guild of Whatcom County, Tulip Valley Bed & Breakfast Association

RATED   AAA 3 Diamonds

AWARDS   1997, Award for Excellence in Commercial Remodeling, Washington State Building Industry Association

SEQUIM

Sequim sits smack in the middle of the rain shadow cast by the Olympic Mountains: The sun shines 306 days a year, and annual rainfall is only 16 inches. Dungeness Spit, six miles northwest of Sequim, is a national wildlife refuge for birds and one of the longest natural sand spits in the world. The driftwood is extraordinary, the winds are often good for kite flying, and a long walk down the narrow 5.5-mile beach takes you to a remote lighthouse. On Sequim Bay, near Blyn, the S'Klallam Indians operate the unique Northwest Native Expressions art gallery. Across the highway stands the Seven Cedars, a truly mammoth gambling casino. Olympic Game Farm breeds endangered species and raises a few animals for Hollywood roles. An hour-long guided walking tour is available mid-May to Labor Day, with a driving tour available year-round.

BRIGADOON BED & BREAKFAST

62 Balmoral Court, Sequim, WA 98382   360-683-2255
Larry & Marilyn Cross, Innkeepers   800-397-2256
EMAIL *brigadoon2@webtv.net*   FAX 360-681-5285
WEBSITE *www.northolympic.com/brigadoon*

LOCATION	Approximately 3.8 miles from Highway 101 toward the water off Sequim Dungeness Way.
OPEN	All year
DESCRIPTION	A 1920 two-story Craftsman host home decorated with lace curtains, English antiques, and many collectibles.
NO. OF ROOMS	Three rooms with private bathrooms. Try the Green Room.
RATES	Year-round rates are $80-95 for a single or double and $260 for the entire B&B. There is no minimum stay and cancellation requires 72 hours' notice.
CREDIT CARDS	No
BREAKFAST	Full hearty breakfast is served in the dining room and includes a starter course of oatmeal, broiled grapefruit, or fresh berries and cream in season, followed by an egg dish, sausage, fruit compote, and dessert. Breakfast "to go" is also available for guests rushing to meet an early ferry.

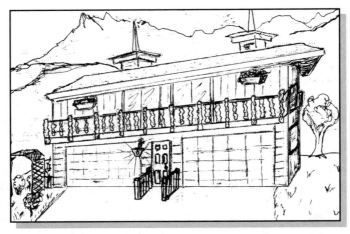

Dungeness Panorama, Sequim

AMENITIES	Hot tub in enclosed courtyard, fresh flowers in all rooms, evening tea or coffee, cookies and brownies at most times.
RESTRICTIONS	No smoking, no pets, children over 12 are welcome. Donald and Daisey are the resident mini-ducks; they roam the garden by day and return to their duck house at night. There are also bald eagles, hawks, falcons, yellow finches, and pine siskins flying around.
MEMBER	Olympic Peninsula Bed & Breakfast Association, Dungeness Guild Lodging Association
RATED	AAA 2 Diamonds

DUNGENESS PANORAMA

---

630 Marine Drive, Sequim, WA 98382　　　　　*360-683-4503*
Paulette & Roger Ferrari, Innkeepers　　　　*FAX 360-683-4503*
EMAIL pmpanorama@webtv.net
WEBSITE www.northolympic.com/panorama

GLENNA'S GUTHRIE COTTAGE BED & BREAKFAST

10083 Old Olympic Highway, Sequim, WA 98382   360-681-4349
Jack & Glenna O'Neil, Innkeepers   800-930-4349
EMAIL glennas@olypen.com   FAX 360-681-4349

GRANNY SANDY'S ORCHARD BED & BREAKFAST

405 West Spruce, Sequim, WA 98382   360-683-5748
Sandy Kucera & Paul Moore, Resident Owners   FAX 360-683-4365
EMAIL moorross@olypen.com   WEBSITE www.olypen.com/moorross

LOCATION	Two blocks north of Highway 101 on the southwest corner of 4th Street in downtown Sequim.
OPEN	All year
DESCRIPTION	A 1930 two-story traditional frame host home with "late garage sale and early goodwill" interior decor.
NO. OF ROOMS	Two rooms share one bathroom.
RATES	June through September, rate is $70 for a single or double. Regular season rate is $60. Cancellation requires two weeks' notice.
CREDIT CARDS	MasterCard, Visa
BREAKFAST	Full breakfast, served in the dining room, includes freshly prepared eggs, sausages, breakfast breads made from scratch, and beverages. Picnic breakfasts are also available for those leaving early.
AMENITIES	Plenty of blankets, pillows, music, and good books; deck; gardens; off-street paved parking; greenhouse; fruit trees; iris garden open April through July.
REVIEWED	*Northwest Cheap Sleeps; Travelers Affordable Accommodations; Breakfast'n Bed; Where to Stay and Play on the Pacific Coast; The Non-Smokers Guide to Bed & Breakfasts*

GREYWOLF INN

395 Keeler Road, Sequim, WA 98382
Peggy & Bill Melang, Innkeepers
EMAIL info@greywolfinn.com
WEBSITE www.greywolfinn.com

360-683-5889
800-914-WOLF
FAX 360-683-1487

LOCATION	A two-hour scenic drive from Seattle, one mile east of Sequim and 0.5 mile north of Highway 101 on Keeler Road. Watch for the signs.
OPEN	All year
DESCRIPTION	A secluded 1976 two-story Northwest country inn with traditional decor and selected antiques, on five wooded acres with views of the Dungeness Valley, Mount Baker, and Sequim Bay.
NO. OF ROOMS	Five rooms with private bathrooms. Try the Marguerite Room.
RATES	High-season rates are $65-130 for a single or double and $185 for a suite. Regular rates are $65-105 for a single or double and $150 for a suite. There is a minimum stay during weekends in July and August, and cancellation requires 72 hours' notice for a full refund.
CREDIT CARDS	American Express, Discover, MasterCard, Visa
BREAKFAST	Full "Olympian" breakfast is served in the dining room and features tastes of the Northwest with specialties such as eggs melange; savory sausage, spinach, or wild rice quiche; or French toast Grand Marnier, served with fresh fruit, assorted hot rolls, muffins, and beverages, followed by a light dessert. Picnic lunches are packed by request (for a fee).
AMENITIES	Gathering room with fireplace, books, board games, beverages, and great music; guest rooms with international themes; rooms have designer robes, down pillows, silky-smooth sheets, hair dryers, lots of books, and TV; the Marguerite Room has a phone and fireplace; Japanese star-lit bathhouse with whirlpool spa; broad decks; gazebos; stream with little bridges; walking path and courtyard with umbrella-topped tables.
RESTRICTIONS	No pets, children over 12 are welcome. Smoking is limited to the covered porch and outdoors. Fred is the resident yellow Lab and Tar Baby is the black Lab. They will happily escort guests on a tour of the grounds, demonstrate their skills as mole catchers, join guests in a game of "catch," or pose for a picture.
REVIEWED	*Inspected, Rated and Approved B&Bs and Country Inns; Northwest Best Places; Fodor's Pacific North Coast; Recommended Country Inns; America's Favorite Little Inns and Hotels; Sweetheart's Getaway Guide; Washington State Travelers:*

Affordable Accommodations; Great Affordable Bed & Breakfast Getaways

MEMBER   Professional Association of Innkeepers International, Olympic
                    Peninsula Bed and Breakfast Association

RATED   AAA 3 Diamonds, ABBA 3 Crowns, Mobil 3 Stars

GROVELAND COTTAGE BED & BREAKFAST

4861 Sequim Dungeness Way, Sequim, WA 98382   360-683-3565
WEBSITE *www.northolympic.com/groveland*   800-879-8859
                                                       FAX 360-683-5181

MARGIE'S INN ON THE BAY

120 Forrest Road, Sequim, WA 98382   360-683-7011
Margie & Don Vorhies, Resident Owners   800-730-7011
EMAIL *margies@olypen.com*   FAX 360-683-7011
WEBSITE *www.northolympic.com/margies*

LOCATION   Heading west on Highway 101, go north on West Sequim Bay
                    Road. Go two miles to Forrest Road and turn right. Heading east
                    on 101, turn left to West Sequim Bay Road, go to Forrest Road and
                    take a left.

OPEN   All year

DESCRIPTION   A 1975 two-story contemporary ranch-style inn with contemporary
                    decor and four rooms with water views.

NO. OF ROOMS   Five rooms with private bathrooms. The Marina Suite is the best.

RATES   May 15 through October 15, rates are $75-142 for a single or
                    double and $523 for the entire B&B. Mid-October through mid-
                    May, rates are $75-132 for a single or double and $501 for the
                    entire B&B. There is a two-night minimum stay during holidays
                    and cancellation requires 72 hours' notice.

CREDIT CARDS   American Express, Discover, MasterCard, Visa

BREAKFAST   Full breakfast, served in the dining room, includes a meat and egg
                    dish or waffles, etc, homemade bread, fresh fruit, and beverages.
                    "Breakfast depends on the group; we want everyone to be happy."
                    Breakfast to go is also available for early rising adventurers.

AMENITIES	A large entertainment room with TV/VCR and over 200 movies, refrigerator, telephone in the hall for guests, air conditioning, hair dryers in all bathrooms, TVs in all bedrooms, hot tub with water view, beaches overlooking the water, menus from local restaurants, some snacks in TV room, frequent wildlife in the yard, one room with handicapped access, near John Wayne Marina.
RESTRICTIONS	No smoking, children over 12 are welcome. Junior and Tasha are the resident Persian cats and Kookie is the chatty African gray parrot. "She keeps our guests laughing when she talks," says Margie. Currently her favorite saying is "Back off I'm an Eagle." Last but not least, Nikita is the resident pooch.
REVIEWED	*The Non-Smoker's Guide to Bed & Breakfasts; From Sea to Shining Sea; West Coast Town & Country Bed & Breakfasts*
MEMBER	Olympic Peninsula Bed & Breakfast Association, Dungeness Valley Lodging Association
RATED	AAA 2 Diamonds, Mobil 2 Stars

RANCHO LAMRO

1734 Woodcock Road, Sequim, WA 98382   *360-683-8133*

SHELTON

The logging community of Shelton sells thousands upon thousands of Christmas trees nationwide each year. In the nearby bays and inlets, the oyster and clam populations are making a comeback, and vacation homes line the miles of scenic shoreline. Traveling on Highway 101, which hugs the west side of Hood Canal, stop at any roadside stand or store for fresh crabs and oysters. Sample Hoodsport Winery's selection at their cottage tasting room. This stretch of highway serves as the jumping-off spot for many recreational areas in the Olympic National Forest, including Lake Cushman and its state park. Every summer weekend, the Olympic Music Festival is home to internationally acclaimed Seattle-based Philadelphia String Quartet and world-class guest artists—music lovers sit on hay bales in an 80-year-old Dutch colonial barn or stretch out on the gentle hillside.

TWIN RIVER RANCH BED & BREAKFAST

5730 East State Route 3, Shelton, WA 98584   *360-426-1023*
Phlorence Rohde, Innkeeper

LOCATION	On Route 3, 5.7 miles north of Shelton.
OPEN	All year
DESCRIPTION	A 1918 two-story manor house with dark timber beams, maple floors, oriental carpets, and antiques, situated on a 140-acre hay ranch fronting a saltwater bay with a stream meandering past the house.
NO. OF ROOMS	Two rooms with two shared bathrooms.
RATES	Year-round rate is $63 for a single or double. There is no minimum stay and cancellation requires 14 days' notice or a $20 deposit is forfeited.
CREDIT CARDS	MasterCard, Visa
BREAKFAST	Full ranch breakfast, served in the formal dining room with silver and crystal settings. Breakfast includes a variety of entrées such as Mount St. Helens pancakes, Belgian waffles, and crab quiche; plus fresh fruit, hot rolls, and breads.
AMENITIES	Robes and slippers in each room, maps, directions for hiking and viewing areas, antiques, trails to saltwater marsh for bird-watching, iron bedsteads, ranching activities to observe, old farm buildings to explore, cozy old stone fireplace.
RESTRICTIONS	Smoking permitted downstairs only, no pets, no children. Spider Legs is the resident cat.
REVIEWED	*Northwest Budget Traveler*

SILVER LAKE

BG's BED & BREAKFAST

405 Hall Road, Silver Lake, WA 98645
Ginger Lasater, Resident Owner

253-274-8573

SILVERDALE

Old Towne Silverdale features a waterfront park, nice for walks along the beach. Just to the west lies the 7,000-foot Bangor Naval Base, home to the Pacific fleet's Trident nuclear submarines. Nearby in Keyport, check out the Naval Undersea Museum.

HEAVEN'S EDGE BED & BREAKFAST

7410 NW Ioka Drive, Silverdale, WA 98383   360-613-1111
Mary Lee Duley, Resident Owner   800-413-5680
EMAIL *heaven@tscnet.com*   FAX 360-692-4444
WEBSITE *www.kitsap.net/business/bnb/heaven or*
     www.heavensedge.com

LOCATION	From Seattle, take the Bainbridge Island ferry. On Bainbridge, follow Highway 305 to Highway 3 south to Bremerton. Go past the Bangor Sub Base and take the Trigger exit. Turn right, drive 0.5 mile to Old Frontier Road, and turn left. Go 1.8 miles to Anderson Hill Road and turn right. Drive 1.7 miles to Willamette Meridian and turn right again. Drive 0.5 mile to Ioka Drive and turn left. Go 0.5 mile to where Ioka Drive makes a hard right, and continue 0.2 mile to inn.
OPEN	All year
DESCRIPTION	Waterfront inn with views of Hood Canal and the Olympic Mountains.
NO. OF ROOMS	One room with a private bathroom.
RATES	Year-round rates are $115-130 for a single or double. June through September, there is two-night minimum stay on weekends. Cancellation requires seven days' notice.
CREDIT CARDS	MasterCard, Visa
BREAKFAST	Full breakfast is served in either the suite, the Game Room, or on the deck (your choice) and includes local specialties and seasonal fruit.
AMENITIES	Sparkling cider and cheese; fresh fruit; flowers; meeting facilities for up to 10.
RESTRICTIONS	No smoking, no pets
REVIEWED	*Innviews*
MEMBER	Washington Bed & Breakfast Guild, Professional Association of Innkeepers International, Kitsap Lodging Association, Kitsap Peninsula Bed & Breakfast Association

SNOHOMISH

This small community, formerly an active lumber town, now bills itself as the "Antique Capital of the Northwest." It certainly has plenty of antique shops filling the downtown historic district; the Star Center Mall is the largest, with 175 antique dealers from all over the area. When you're through taking in the old, get a new perspective on Snohomish from the air. Charter a scenic flight at Harvey Field, go up-up-and-away with Airial Hot Air Balloon, or skydive with the folks at Snohomish Parachute Center. Local festivals and celebrations include Kla Ha Ya Days in mid-July, the historic home tour in September, the Christmas Parlour Tour, and the Easter Parade.

COUNTRYMAN BED & BREAKFAST

119 Cedar, Snohomish, WA 98290
Larry & Sandy Countryman, Innkeepers
EMAIL *countrym@premier/.net*

360-568-9622
800-700-9622
FAX 360-568-3422

LOCATION	Between First and Second Streets on Cedar, next to the public library.
OPEN	All year
DESCRIPTION	A landmark 1896 two-and-a-half-story Queen Anne host home with antique decor, listed on the National Historic Register.
NO. OF ROOMS	Three rooms with private bathrooms.

Countryman Bed & Breakfast, Snohomish

RATES	Year-round rates are $75 (continental breakfast) or $85 (full breakfast) for a single or double. There is no minimum stay and cancellation requires one weeks' notice.
CREDIT CARDS	Discover, MasterCard, Visa
BREAKFAST	Full breakfast is served in the dining room or guestrooms and includes coffee/tea, hot chocolate, orange juice, fruit plate with toast, sweet rolls, muffins, and a choice of entrée.
AMENITIES	Jetted Jacuzzi in the garden room, tour of historic Snohomish, within three blocks of more than 400 antique dealers.
RESTRICTIONS	No smoking
REVIEWED	*Lanier's Complete Guide to Bed & Breakfasts; Best Choices in Western Washington; Washington State Travelers: Affordable Accommodations*

THE JAVA INN—SNOHOMISH COFFEE ROASTERS

1120 First Street, Snohomish, WA 98290   360-568-8254
WEBSITE *www.javainn.com*   877-877-5282

LOCATION	Eight miles east of Everett and 25 miles north of Seattle, in the heart of the Snohomish Historic District on First Street across from the Snohomish River.
OPEN	All year
DESCRIPTION	Originally the Northern Hotel in the 1880s, this two-story building has been totally renovated and features custom lodgepole interiors. It now houses Snohomish Coffee Roasters on the main level and the four-room Java Inn on the second level.
NO. OF ROOMS	Two rooms with private bathrooms and two rooms share one bathroom.
RATES	Year-round rates are $75 for a room with a private bathroom and $60 for a room with a shared bathroom.
CREDIT CARDS	American Express, Diners Club, Discover, MasterCard, Visa
BREAKFAST	Breakfast includes your choice of a fresh-roasted coffee and a dessert for up to two guests per room.
AMENITIES	Down comforters, cable TV, digital telephones with modem ports, air conditioning, linens, river views, meeting/conference facilities.
RESTRICTIONS	No smoking, no pets, children over five are welcome.

Redmond House Bed & Breakfast, Snohomish

REDMOND HOUSE BED & BREAKFAST

317 Glen Avenue, Snohomish, WA 98290   *360-568-2042*
Ken & Mary Riley, Innkeepers

LOCATION	From I-5, take the Wenatchee-Stevens Pass exit to Highway 2. Cross the trestle and stay to the right. The first exit will take you into town on Avenue D. Turn east (left) onto 4th and turn right onto Glen.
OPEN	All year
DESCRIPTION	An 1890 two-story Queen Anne Victorian, exquisitely restored with an elegant, nonfussy period interior, antiques, quilts, and feather beds.
NO. OF ROOMS	Two rooms with private bathrooms and two rooms with one shared bathroom. Try the Pilchuck Room.
RATES	May through September, rates are $100-125 for a single or double with a private bathroom and $90-100 for a single or double with a shared bathroom. October through April, rates are $95-110 for a single or double with a private bathroom and $85-90 for a single or double with a shared bathroom. There is no minimum stay and cancellation requires seven days' notice.
CREDIT CARDS	MasterCard, Visa

BREAKFAST	Full breakfast, served on china with crystal and silver in the dining room or on the veranda, includes a cereal course, baked item, fruit course, and a main entrée, plus coffee, tea, and juice.
AMENITIES	Robes, hot tub in solarium, dance floor with music, game and TV room, wraparound veranda and old-fashioned porch swing, romantic breakfast on veranda as weather permits, feather beds, hot beverage and snack on sideboard in the afternoon and evening, meeting room for up to 20.
RESTRICTIONS	No smoking inside, no pets. Lady Jane is the resident cat.
REVIEWED	*Washington State Bed & Breakfast Guild*
KUDOS/COMMENTS	"Comfortable, Victorian-style B&B, roomy." "Lovely Victorian home on quiet, dead-end street, charming hosts."

SUSAN'S SURREY HOUSE— A COUNTRY BED & BREAKFAST

425 9th Street, Snohomish, WA 98290   360-568-7081
Gary & Susan McDonald, Resident Owners
WEBSITE *www.surreyhouse.com*

LOCATION	From Sea-Tac Airport, take Highway 405 to I-5 north, then take Highway 2 east, exiting on Bickford Avenue (the first Snohomish exit). Follow Bickford (which will become Avenue D) to Second Street and take a left. Then turn left on Maple and left again on Pine to 9th Street.
OPEN	All year
DESCRIPTION	An 1884 two-story country inn, renovated in 1996, with country primitive antiques.
NO. OF ROOMS	Two rooms with private bathrooms.
RATES	Year-round rate is $95 for a double. There is no minimum stay and cancellation requires seven days' notice.
CREDIT CARDS	MasterCard, Visa
BREAKFAST	Country breakfast, served in the dining room or on the terrace, always includes a hot entrée, with fresh fruit and homemade breads, plus beverages.
AMENITIES	Robes, afternoon tea or other beverage, hair dryer, soaps and shampoos, heated pool, spa, reading material, formal gardens, luxurious linens and towels, romantic atmosphere.
RESTRICTIONS	No smoking, no pets, limited accommodations for children.
MEMBER	Washington Bed & Breakfast Guild

SNOQUALMIE

This lovely country, where the dairyland folds into the mountains, is best known for its falls and its scenery, once the setting for the TV series Twin Peaks. The series is long since over, but Peakers can still purchase a T-shirt almost anywhere (even at the bank). The 268-foot Snoqualmie Falls just up the road is a thundering spectacle. There is an observation deck, or you can pack a lunch and hike down the one-mile trail to the base of the falls. Puget Sound Railway runs a scenic tour up to the Snoqualmie Falls gorge most Saturdays and Sundays from April through October. There's also a good railroad museum. The Snoqualmie Winery, under the ownership of Stimson Lane is a splendid stop on the way through the Cascades, with tours, tastings, and a marvelous view. There are four ski areas close at hand: Alpental, Snoqualmie, Ski Acres, and Hyak.

THE OLD HONEY FARM COUNTRY INN

8910 38th Avenue Southeast, Snoqualmie, WA 98065   *800-826-9077*

SOAP LAKE

Early settlers named the lake for its unusually high alkali content, which gives the water a soapy feel. Check out Dry Falls, off Route 17 north of town, where the torrential prehistoric Columbia River once crashed over falls three miles wide and 400 feet high; an interpretive center explains the local geology, which has been compared to the surface features of Mars. From this lookout, you can also see Sun Lakes, puddles left behind by the ancient Columbia. It's RV territory, but the waters are prime spots for swimming and fishing.

THE INN AT SOAP LAKE

226 Main Avenue East, Soap Lake, WA 98851   *509-246-1132*
Cory & Nancy Wold, Resident Owners   *800-557-8514*
                                       FAX 509-246-1132 (call first)

LOCATION	West of Highway 17 on Main.
OPEN	All year
DESCRIPTION	A 1905 two-story European country inn with health-resort facilities.
NO. OF ROOMS	Twenty rooms with private bathrooms. Nancy recommends rooms 101 and 129.

RATES	May 1 through September 30, rates are $65-90 for a single or double and $80-110 for a guesthouse. October 1 through April 30, rates are $55-85 for a single or double and $75-100 for a guest-house. There is no minimum stay and cancellation requires 48 hours' notice.
CREDIT CARDS	American Express, Discover, MasterCard, Visa
BREAKFAST	Continental plus is served in the dining room and includes bagels, English muffins, breads, hard-boiled eggs, cold cereal, milk, juice, coffee, tea, butter, and jams.
AMENITIES	Hot mineral baths in rooms, mud baths, meeting facilities, air conditioning, fireplaces, kitchenettes, cable TV, phones in rooms, picnic area.
RESTRICTIONS	No pets
REVIEWED	*Hot Springs and Hot Pools of the Northwest*
RATED	AAA 3 Diamonds
AWARDS	Business of the Year, Soap Lake Chamber of Commerce

SOUTH BEND

On scenic Highway 101, where the Willapa River drains into the bay of the same name. Toward the southern end of Willapa Bay, and accessible only by boat, is Long Island, a 274-acre old-growth cedar grove; some of the trees here are over 200 feet tall, with trunks 11 feet in diameter. The island is part of the Willapa National Wildlife Refuge.

MARING'S COURTHOUSE HILL BED & BREAKFAST

602 West 2nd Street, South Bend, WA 98586　　　　360-875-6519
Ed & Frances Maring, Innkeepers　　　　　　　　800-875-6519
EMAIL *maringbb@willapabay.org*
WEBSITE *www.willapabay.org/~maringbb*

LOCATION	Turn off Highway 101 at Memorial Drive (Seafirst Bank), proceed up the hill two blocks, turn left on Cowlitz to Cedar, and follow the signs to 2nd Street. Turn left on 2nd Street.
OPEN	All year
DESCRIPTION	A historic 1891 two-story early Victorian church furnished with antiques, traditional furniture, and period decor, with views of the river and hills beyond.

Maring's Courthouse Hill Bed & Breakfast, South Bend

NO. OF ROOMS	Two rooms with private bathrooms. Try Mary's Room.
RATES	Year-round rates are $55-170. There is no minimum stay and cancellation requires 72 hours' notice.
CREDIT CARDS	Discover, MasterCard, Visa
BREAKFAST	Full breakfast is served in the dining room and includes a hot entrée such as quiche, blueberry pancakes, or stuffed French toast, plus sausage, bacon, biscuits, jams, sliced melon or tomatoes, homemade muffins, fresh fruit bowl, and beverages. Special diets are accommodated.
AMENITIES	Flowers, robes, cable TV, cold water in decanters, magazines, menus from local restaurants, large yard with shaded deck, maps of surrounding areas, walking tour guide, general information about the area.
RESTRICTIONS	No smoking, children with well-behaved parents are welcome.
REVIEWED	*Washington State Travelers: Affordable Accommodations*
MEMBER	Willapa Harbor Bed & Breakfast Association, Washington State Hotel & Motel Association

SPOKANE

This friendly city is full of old buildings of note, marvelous parks, and splendid vistas, and the compact downtown is most pleasant for strolling. The Gold Rush of the 1880s brought it wealth, and railroads brought it people. Riverfront Park is the pleasant green heart of the old city. Developed from old railroad yards for Expo '74, the park is now an airy place full of meandering paved paths, with entertainments ranging from ice-skating to an IMAX theater. The 1909 carousel is a local landmark, hand-carved by master builder Charles Looff. Two natural areas just a couple of miles outside Spokane's city limits offer excellent places to hike and see birds and wildlife: the Little Spokane Natural Area and the Spokane Fish Hatchery. Just 25 miles south of Spokane you'll find the 15,000-acre Turnbull National Wildlife Refuge, especially interesting during fall and spring bird migration.

ANGELICA'S MANSION BED & BREAKFAST

West 1321 Ninth Avenue, Spokane, WA 99204　　　509-624-5598
Lynda & Dan Tortarolo, Resident Owners

COBBLESTONE INN & BAKERY

620 South Washington, Spokane, WA 99204　　　509-624-9735
Matt & Robin Duval, Resident Owners

THE FOTHERINGHAM HOUSE

2128 West Second Avenue, Spokane, WA 99204　　　509-838-1891
Jackie & Graham Johnson, Resident Owners　　　FAX 509-838-1807
EMAIL innkeeper@fotheringham.net　　　*WEBSITE www.fotheringham.net*

LOCATION	One mile west of downtown Spokane in historic Browne's Addition. From I-90, take exit 280 and turn north to 2nd Avenue, turn left, and stay in the right lane.
OPEN	All year
DESCRIPTION	A fully restored 1891 three-story Queen Anne inn with Victorian furnishings, wraparound porch, and perennial gardens. Listed on the National Historic Register, the inn was the home of Spokane's first mayor.
NO. OF ROOMS	One room with private bathroom and three rooms share two bathrooms. The Mayor's Room is the best.

The Fotheringham House, Spokane

RATES	Year-round rates are $85-105 for a single or double with a private bathroom or shared bathroom. There is no minimum stay and cancellation requires seven days' notice.
CREDIT CARDS	American Express, Discover, MasterCard, Visa
BREAKFAST	Full breakfast, served in the dining room, features berry frappé; fruit; malted hazelnut waffles, huckleberry pancakes, or baked peach French toast; and a side dish of meat. Dietary restrictions are accommodated.
AMENITIES	Evening tea and homemade hazelnut truffles, early morning coffee or tea, self-guided walking tour of historic neighborhood, rose and perennial gardens with fountain and seating, robes, down comforters, quilts, extra pillows, bedside reading, sinks in all rooms.
RESTRICTIONS	No smoking except on veranda, children over 12 are welcome.
REVIEWED	*Northwest Best Places; Ultimate Washington; Hidden Pacific Northwest; America's Wonderful Little Hotels and Inns; On the Road Around the Pacific Northwest*
MEMBER	Washington Bed & Breakfast Guild, Professional Association of Innkeepers International, Spokane Bed & Breakfast Association
RATED	AAA 3 Diamonds, Mobil 3 Stars, Northwest Best Places 2 Stars
AWARDS	1994 and 1997, Eastern Washington Historical Society Historic Preservation Award; 1995 and 1997, Inland Northwest Home Award for Historic Restoration, *The Spokesman Review*; 1998, Washington Trust for Historic Preservation State Award of Merit for Rehabilitation
KUDOS/COMMENTS	"A well-run B&B with an extraordinary host and hostess, super location, a wonderful restoral of a historic home." (1996)

Marianna Stoltz House Bed & Breakfast, Spokane

MARIANNA STOLTZ HOUSE BED & BREAKFAST

East 427 Indiana Avenue, Spokane, WA 99207　　　509-483-4316
Jim & Phyllis Maguire, Resident Owners　　　　　800-978-6587
　　　　　　　　　　　　　　　　　　　　　　FAX 509-483-6773

OSLO'S BED & BREAKFAST

1821 East 39th Avenue, Spokane, WA 99203　　　509-838-3175

RIVERSIDE BED & BREAKFAST

2104 West Clarke Avenue, Spokane, WA 99201　　　509-459-9396

A SPOKANE BED & BREAKFAST

627 East 25th Avenue, Spokane, WA 99203　　　509-624-3776

WAVERLY PLACE BED & BREAKFAST

709 W Waverly Place, Spokane WA 99205　　　　509-328-1856
Marge & Tammy Arndt, Innkeepers　　　　　　FAX 509-326-7059
EMAIL waverly@ior.com

LOCATION	From I-90, take exit 281 north two miles, turn left on North Foothills Drive, and turn right at the second stoplight (Washington). Go two blocks to Waverly Place. The B&B is on the left.
OPEN	All year
DESCRIPTION	A 1900 three-story Victorian Queen Anne inn with period decor.
NO. OF ROOMS	Two rooms with private bathrooms and two rooms with two shared bathrooms. Marge and Tammy recommend the Waverly Suite.
RATES	Year-round rates are $84-105 for a single or double with a private bathroom and $70-75 for a single or double with a shared bathroom. Suites are $95-105, and the entire B&B rents for $345. There is a minimum stay during some holidays and cancellation requires one weeks' notice.

Waverly Place Bed & Breakfast, Spokane

CREDIT CARDS	American Express, Discover, MasterCard, Visa
BREAKFAST	Full breakfast is served in the dining room and includes fresh fruit, Swedish pancakes with huckleberry sauce, sausage, juice, coffee, and tea.
AMENITIES	Swimming pool in summer, homemade fresh cookies every afternoon, robes, air conditioning, small meeting and events facility, Jacuzzi tub (in one of the shared bathrooms), fresh flowers in rooms.
RESTRICTIONS	No smoking, no pets, and please, no high-heeled shoes in the house.
REVIEWED	*Northwest Best Places; Fodor's B&B Country Inns; Best Places to Stay in the Pacific Northwest; The Chocolate Lover's Guide to the Pacific Northwest; Northwest Budget Traveler*
MEMBER	Spokane Bed & Breakfast Association, Washington State Bed & Breakfast Guild, Washington Hotel and Motel Association
RATED	Northwest Best Places 2 Stars, AAA 3 Diamonds
AWARDS	1997, Historic Preservation Award, Eastern Washington State Historical Society; 1997, Award of Merit for Preservation Design, Washington Trust for Historic Places

STANWOOD

Stanwood is a sleepy little farm center with a Scandinavian heritage, a Midwestern air, and a good reason for a little sightseeing: Years ago, local daughter Martha Anderson started working at rosemaling (traditional Norwegian flower painting) and teaching it to her fellow Stanwoodians. Now they've embellished many everyday businesses with charming signs decorated in this genre—not for tourist show, as in Leavenworth, but out of an authentic impulse to express their heritage and to make Main Street pretty.

SUNDAY LAKE BED & BREAKFAST

2100 Sunday Lake Road, Stanwood 98292   360-629-4356

SUNNYSIDE

In the heart of Washington's wine country, Sunnyside offers easy access to over 20 wineries. Local fests include the Sunshine Days in September, the Lighted Farm Implement Parade during Christmas, and the Barrel Tasting Grape Stomp in April. Also check out the Yakima Indian Cultural Center and the many historical murals located throughout the town of Toppenish.

SUNNYSIDE INN BED & BREAKFAST

804 East Edison Avenue, Sunnyside, WA 98944　　　509-839-5557
Donavon & Karen Vlieger, Resident Owners　　　800-221-4195
EMAIL suninn@bentonrea.com　　　FAX 509-839-3520
WEBSITE www.bbhost.com/sunnysideinn

LOCATION	From I-82, take exit 69 and go north one block to Yakima Valley Highway. Go left (west) approximately one mile to Edison Avenue and turn left.
OPEN	All year
DESCRIPTION	A 1919 three-story neoclassical country inn located off downtown in a small farming community in the heart of Washington wine country.
NO. OF ROOMS	Twelve rooms with private bathrooms. The owners recommend the Jean Room.

Sunnyside Inn Bed & Breakfast, Sunyside

RATES	Year-round rates are $59-89 for a single or double and $899 for the entire B&B. There is no minimum stay and cancellation requires 14 days' notice.
CREDIT CARDS	American Express, Discover, MasterCard, Visa
BREAKFAST	Full breakfast, served in the dining room, includes juice; pastries, fresh fruit; pancakes, waffles, or French toast; ham, bacon, or sausage; coffee, tea, and hot chocolate.
AMENITIES	Double Jacuzzis in the rooms, fountain Pepsi machine, cookies, ice cream, popcorn, candy, hot and iced tea, air conditioning.
RESTRICTIONS	No smoking. Children are welcome.
REVIEWED	*Northwest Best Places; A Treasury of Bed & Breakfasts; Northwest Budget Traveler*
MEMBER	American Bed & Breakfast Association
RATED	AAA 2 Diamonds

VON HELLSTRUM INN BED & BREAKFAST

51 Braden Road, Sunnyside, WA 98944   509-839-2505

TACOMA

Flanked by Commencement Bay and the Tacoma Narrows and backed by Mount Rainier, Tacoma is no longer just a blue-collar mill town, but a growing urban center with a thriving cultural core. The city has fervently embraced the idea of preservation. The restored 1,100-seat Pantages Theater, featuring dance, music, and stage presentations, is the focal point of downtown cultural life. And the nearby Rialto Theatre has been restored for smaller performance groups. The Tacoma Art Museum has paintings by Renoir, Degas, and Pissarro, as well as a collection of contemporary American prints. The Washington State Historical Museum offers a state-of-the-art museum experience, providing history and innovation under the same roof. Don't miss Point Defiance Park—500 acres of untouched forest jutting out into Puget Sound—one of the most dramatically sited and creatively planned city parks in the country.

AUSTRIAN BED & BREAKFAST AND SUITES

723 North Cushman, Tacoma, WA 98403   253-383-2216
Eveline Smith, Innkeeper   FAX 253-495-4293/7097
German spoken
EMAIL *evelinesb&b@narrows.com*   WEBSITE *www.narrows.com/eb&b*

LOCATION	From I-5, take exit 133 to Highway 705, go one mile to the Schuster Parkway exit and one mile on Schuster Parkway to the Stadiumway exit. Turn right onto Stadiumway, drive 0.5 mile uphill, and turn left onto 1st Avenue, which turns into Division Avenue. Go six blocks, turn right onto North Cushman, and drive three blocks to North 8th. The B&B's entrance is on North 8th Street.
OPEN	All year
DESCRIPTION	An 1892 three-story Victorian inn filled with authentic Austrian antiques, two armoires from about 1750, and lots of antique pine furniture. Located on a quiet residential street.
NO. OF ROOMS	Four rooms with private bathrooms and one room with one shared bathroom. Eveline suggests the Mozart Suite.
RATES	High-season rates are $55-65 for a single or double with a private bathroom and $65-85 for a single or double with a shared bathroom. Regular rates are $45-55 for a single or double with a private bathroom and $55-75 for a single or double with a shared bathroom. There is no minimum stay and cancellation requires seven days' notice.
CREDIT CARDS	MasterCard, Visa
BREAKFAST	Full breakfast is served in the dining room and includes juice or fruit, an entrée plus two side dishes, breads, scones or muffins, and a small dessert.
AMENITIES	Occasional transportation; maps to hiking trails, activities, points of interest.
RESTRICTIONS	No smoking, no pets, children are welcome.
MEMBER	Bed & Breakfast Association of Tacoma and Mount Rainier

BAY VISTA BED & BREAKFAST

4617 Darien Drive, Tacoma, WA 98407
Fran Borhek, Resident Owner

253-759-8084

BLOUNT'S GUEST HOME

2702 North Bristol, Tacoma, WA 98407
Mrs. Blount, Resident Owner

253-759-4534

CHINABERRY HILL, A VICTORIAN BED & BREAKFAST

302 Tacoma Avenue N, Tacoma, WA 98403   253-272-1282
Cecil & Yarrow Wayman, Resident Owners   FAX 253-272-1335

COMMENCEMENT BAY BED & BREAKFAST

3312 North Union Avenue, Tacoma, WA 98407   253-752-8175
Sharon & Bill Kaufmann, Resident Owners   FAX 253-759-4025
Some Spanish spoken
EMAIL *greatviews@aol.com*   WEBBSITE *www.bestinns.net/usa/wa/cb.html*

LOCATION	Take exit 132 off I-5 onto Highway 16, turn right onto Union Avenue (the second exit), go two miles to North 26th Street and turn left. Turn right at the first stoplight (Proctor Avenue), go eight blocks to North 34th Street and turn right, then drive to Union Avenue and turn right again. The inn is the second house on the right.
OPEN	All year
DESCRIPTION	A 1937 three-story colonial host home with an interior of traditional elegance overlooking the scenic north end of Tacoma.
NO. OF ROOMS	Three rooms with private bathrooms. Myrtle's Room is the owners' favorite.
RATES	April through October, rates are $90-120 for a single or double. November through March, rates are $85-110. There is a two-night minimum stay during weekends from April through October. Cancellations require seven days' notice; guests will be charged only if the room is not rebooked.
CREDIT CARDS	American Express, Discover, MasterCard, Visa
BREAKFAST	Full breakfast, served in the dining room, includes "Sharon's specialties" such as poached pears with local raspberry sauce, peach-melba Dutch babies, gourmet cinnamon French toast, or seasoned eggs Benedict, plus seasonal local fruits, juices, fresh-baked pastries or whole-wheat croissants, and gourmet coffees and teas (which change daily). An early morning business traveler's continental plus is available on weekdays.
AMENITIES	Secluded outdoor hot tub in garden; fireside reading area with a view of the bay; plush robes; fresh flower arrangements in rooms for special occasions; on-site massages; telephones in rooms; all rooms have cable TV/VCRs and modem ports; office area for

Commencement Bay Bed & Breakfast, Tacoma

business travelers; mountain bikes; game room with puzzles, darts, large TV, video and book library, exercise equipment, microwave, and well-stocked bar with sodas and snacks.

RESTRICTIONS   No smoking, no pets, children over 12 are welcome "with well-trained parents especially." Lady Di is the resident cocker spaniel.

REVIEWED   *Northwest Best Places; Sweetheart's Getaway Guide; The Best Places to Kiss in the Northwest*

MEMBER   Professional Association of Innkeepers, Washington Bed & Breakfast Guild, National Bed & Breakfast Association

RATED   AAA 3 Diamonds, Mobil 3 Stars

AWARDS   1998 Second Place in Top Escape in Western Washington, selected by KING-TV's Evening Magazine; 1997 Washington Family Business of the Year

---

THE DE VOE MANSION BED & BREAKFAST

208 East 133rd Street, Tacoma, WA 98445   253-539-3991
Dave & Cheryl Teifke, Resident Owners   888-539-3991
EMAIL *devoe@wolfenet.com*   FAX 253-539-8539
WEBSITE *www.wolfenet.com/~devoe*

LOCATION   From I-5, take exit 127 to Highway 512 east. Take the second exit (Parkland, Mount Rainier) and turn right onto Pacific Avenue. Go two miles and turn left on 133rd Street.

OPEN   All year

DESCRIPTION	A 1911 three-story colonial mansion decorated with period antiques, on 1.5 acres of beautiful grounds, and listed on the National and State Historic Registers.
NO. OF ROOMS	Four rooms with private bathrooms. Cheryl suggests the Emma Room.
RATES	Year-round rates are $85-110 for a single or double. There is a minimum stay during some holiday weekends and university events, and cancellation requires seven days' notice.
CREDIT CARDS	MasterCard, Visa
BREAKFAST	Full breakfast is served in the dining room and begins with fresh-ground gourmet coffee, followed by an assortment of fresh fruits, homemade breads and muffins, and a seasonal entrée and side dish featuring fresh herbs from the garden.
AMENITIES	Antique-filled guest rooms; queen-size beds with luxurious linens and down comforters and pillows; in-room guest phones; bottled water; terry robes; TV/VCRs; bathrooms with soaking tubs, bubble bath, hair dryers, curling irons, Egyptian cotton towels; common areas offer board games, library, bar with hot drinks; secluded garden hot tub.
RESTRICTIONS	No smoking, no pets, children over 12 are welcome. Reggie is the resident Maine coon cat who loves playing fetch.
REVIEWED	*The Best Places to Kiss in the Northwest; Sweetheart's Getaway Guide; Official Guide to American Historic Inns*
MEMBER	Washington Bed & Breakfast Guild, Professional Association of Innkeepers International, Bed & Breakfast Association of Tacoma and Mount Rainier
KUDOS/COMMENTS	"Cozy yet very elegant. Love the marble fireplace and soaking tubs. Friendly hosts."

GREEN CAPE COD BED & BREAKFAST

2711 North Warner, Tacoma, WA 98467   *253-752-1977*
Mary Beth King, Resident Owner

INGE'S PLACE

6809 Lake Grove Street West, Tacoma, WA 98499   *253-584-4514*

KEENAN HOUSE BED & BREAKFAST

2610 North Warner, Tacoma, WA 98407   253-752-0702
Lenore Keenan, Resident Owner

OAKES STREET BARN BED & BREAKFAST

5814 South Oakes Street, Tacoma, WA 98445   253-475-7047

THE OLALLA ORCHARD BED & BREAKFAST

12530 Orchard Avenue SE, Olalla, WA 98359   253-857-5915
Annette & Michael Manant, Resident Owners

LOCATION	From Tacoma, take Highway 16 north, turn right onto Olalla Road, and at the second stop sign turn right onto Olalla Valley Road. Drive 0.5 mile and make a left onto Orchard Avenue. The B&B is the sixth house on the left.
OPEN	All year
DESCRIPTION	A 1987 two-story Cape Cod with European antiques.
NO. OF ROOMS	One suite with a private bathroom.
RATES	The year-round rate for the suite is $95. There is no minimum stay requirement and cancellation requires three days' notice.
CREDIT CARDS	Discover, MasterCard, Visa
BREAKFAST	Full breakfast is served in the suite and includes large Belgian waffles, real whipped cream, freshly squeezed orange juice, homemade jam, and fresh-ground coffee.
AMENITIES	Fresh flowers, breakfast whenever you're ready, two-person whirlpool tub, 100 percent cotton towels (line dried in summer), bay windows, French doors, private porch, refrigerator in suite, full view of Mount Rainier.
RESTRICTIONS	None. Children and pets are welcome. "We'll set up a tent for the kids and provide flashlights if you like." Echo is the sheltie.

SALLY'S BEAR TREE COTTAGE

6019 West 64th Street, Tacoma, WA 98467

253-475-3144
FAX 253-475-3144

THORNEWOOD CASTLE INN & GARDEN

8601 North Thorne Lane SW, Lakewood, WA 98498
Richard & Deb Mirau, Innkeepers
Minimal German spoken
EMAIL *thornewood@mindspring.com*
WEBSITE *www.thornewoodcastle.com*

253-584-4393
FAX 253-584-4497

LOCATION	Take exit 123 off I-5 (Thorne Lane) and go west at the stop. Turn right on North Thorne Lane and take another right through the gate into Thornewood.
OPEN	All year
DESCRIPTION	A 1909 three-story brick Tudor mansion designed by architect Kelsey Cutter for Chester Thorne, and decorated with antique oil paintings and antique furnishings. Much of the materials came from Europe and are over 500 years old. Listed on the National and State Historic Registers.
NO. OF ROOMS	Six rooms with private bathrooms. Try the Grand View Room.
RATES	Year-round rates are $150-200 for a single or double. There is a minimum stay from July through September and on weekends. Cancellation requires seven days' notice.
CREDIT CARDS	American Express, MasterCard, Visa
BREAKFAST	Full breakfast is served in the dining room and includes fresh fruit, granola sundae, fresh-baked muffins, a hot entrée, tea, coffee, and juice.
AMENITIES	Robes, chocolates on bed, fully stocked guest kitchen, large library, half-acre sunken perennial English garden, lake (fishing and swimming), en suite coffee service, fax, gift baskets available, afternoon tea by reservation.
RESTRICTIONS	No smoking, no pets, children over 12 are welcome. Noel is the resident trick-performing cocker spaniel and Sophie is the cat.
REVIEWED	*The Best Places to Kiss in the Northwest; Sweethearts Getaway Guide*
MEMBER	Bed & Breakfast Association of Tacoma and Mount Rainier, Professional Association of Innkeepers International, Washington Bed & Breakfast Guild, Bed & Breakfast World Wide

VICTORIAN INN BED & BREAKFAST

3320 North Union Avenue, Tacoma, WA 98407   253-756-9044
WEBSITE *www.tribnet.com/adv/bb/vicinn*

THE VILLA BED & BREAKFAST

705 North 5th Street, Tacoma, WA 98403   253-572-1157
WEBSITE *www.villabb.com*   888-572-1157
          FAX 253-572-8105

KUDOS/COMMENTS   "Bright, sunny decor. Beautifully furnished. Very spacious rooms. Great business/retreat salon. Lovely gardens. Great hosts."

TEKOA

TOUCH O' COUNTRY BED & BREAKFAST

218 South Broadway, Tekoa, WA 99033   509-284-5183
Jerry & Mary Heitt, Resident Owners

TOLEDO

THE FARM

PO Box 639, Toledo, WA 98591   360-864-4200
WEBSITE *www.cport.com/bb*   FAX 360-864-4201

TONASKET

A number of lakes dot the landscape around Tonasket, which is situated 23 miles south of the Canadian border along the banks of the Okanogan River at the intersection of Highways 97 and 20. Check out the Omak Stampede during the second week in August.

HIDDEN HILLS

104 Hidden Hills Lane, Tonasket, WA 98855   509-486-1895
Ron & Martha Thomas, Innkeepers   800-468-1890

LOCATION	From Tonasket, go 10 miles south on Highway 97. Turn right on Pine Creek-Fish Lake Road. Go approximately seven miles to our gate. From Omak, go to the stoplight on Highway 97, then go 12 miles north, and take a left at Pine Creek-Fish Lake Road. Go approximately seven miles to Hidden Hills Lane.
OPEN	All year
DESCRIPTION	An upscale, reconstructed 1890s three-story hotel with turn-of-the-century atmosphere.
NO. OF ROOMS	Ten rooms with private bathrooms.
RATES	Year-round rates are $85-105 for a single or double.
CREDIT CARDS	MasterCard, Visa
BREAKFAST	Full breakfast is served in the dining room and includes a hearty country breakfast with fruit or juice, French toast, lean link sausage, milk, and coffee. Dinner also available.
AMENITIES	Auditorium, theater, and guest house corral.
RESTRICTIONS	No smoking, no pets, no children. Horses on property.
REVIEWED	*Washington State Travelers: Affordable Accommodations; Washington Off the Beaten Path*

TROUT LAKE

At the base of Mount Adams, Trout Lake is the gateway to a world of natural splendor largely overlooked by visitors, who seldom venture in from the Columbia Gorge. Besides climbing to the summit of the 12,276-foot mountain—greater in mass than any of the five other major volcanic peaks in the Northwest—hikers and skiers can explore miles of wilderness trails in the Mount Adams Wilderness Area and the Gifford Pinchot National Forest. Volcanic activity long ago left the area honeycombed with lava tubes and caves, including the Ice Caves near Trout Lake, with stalactites and stalagmites formed by dripping ice. To the southwest of Trout Lake is Big Lava Bed, a 12,500-acre lava field filled with cracks, crevasses, rock piles, and unusual formations.

THE FARM, A BED & BREAKFAST

490 Sunnyside Road, Trout Lake, WA 98650   *509-395-2499*
Dean & Rosie Hostetter, Innkeepers   *FAX 509 395-2127*
EMAIL *farmbnb@gorge.net*   WEBSITE *www.gorge.net/business/farmbnb*

LOCATION	From Portland, take I-84 east for approximately 64 miles to exit 64 (White Salmon). Cross over the Hood River Bridge to the Washington side and go west on Highway 14 for approximately two miles. Just before White Salmon River, turn north (right) onto Highway141 to Trout Lake. Continue north to just before milepost 21, turn east onto Warner Road, and go about 1.1 miles to the end. Turn north onto Sunnyside Road. The B&B is the second house on the right.
OPEN	All year
DESCRIPTION	An 1890 three-story saltbox-style farmhouse decorated with antiques and interesting art objects, on 6 acres with an old barn and perennial and vegetable gardens.
NO. OF ROOMS	Two rooms with two shared bathrooms. Try the 1890 Room.
RATES	High-season rates are $75-85 for a single or double. Regular rates are $65-75. There is no minimum stay and cancellation requires 48 hours' notice.
CREDIT CARDS	No
BREAKFAST	Full breakfast is served in the dining room or on the decks and includes fresh-ground coffee or teas, fresh seasonal fruit from the garden, hot scones, orange juice, wild huckleberry hot cakes with maple syrup, homemade sausage, and eggs. Breakfast is served with antique tableware and fresh flowers. Sack lunches are available on request.
AMENITIES	Complimentary afternoon beverage and cookies, fresh flowers in rooms, plush robes, interesting selection of reading material,

mountain bikes, two decks, horse boarding, fresh vegetables for guests to take home in the summer, restful and relaxing atmosphere.

RESTRICTIONS
No smoking, no pets, children over five are welcome. Levi is the resident golden Lab mix, Boots is the barn cat, and there are sheep on the property. "We get a lot of return visits from people who just want to see Levi."

REVIEWED
National Geographic Guide to America's Hidden Corners; Hot Showers, Soft Beds & Dayhikes in the Central Cascades; Fodor's

MEMBER
Washington State Bed & Breakfast Guild

TROUT LAKE COUNTRY INN

15 Guler Road, Trout Lake, WA 98650   509-395-2894
Gil & Milly Martin, Innkeepers

LOCATION
Half a mile west of town center at the end of Guler Road. Take a right turn just before the ranger station.

OPEN
All year

DESCRIPTION
A 1904 two-story western-style country inn with a false front and western and rustic decor, listed on the State Historic Register. The Creek House was the town's original ice house, and the main building is the oldest commercial building in Klickitat County.

NO. OF ROOMS
Three rooms with private bathrooms and two rooms with two shared bathrooms. The Martins suggest the Creek House.

RATES
High-season rates are $85 for a double with a private bathroom and $65 for a double with a shared bathroom. Low-season rates are $45-60. There is no minimum stay and cancellation requires 72 hours' notice.

CREDIT CARDS
MasterCard, Visa

BREAKFAST
Full breakfast is served in the dining room and includes huckleberry pancakes, omelets, or other egg dishes. Lunch and dinner are also available.

AMENITIES
Swimming hole, river and mountain views, dinner theater (at extra charge) featured in the summer.

RESTRICTIONS
No smoking, no pets, children over 12 are welcome. Milo and Whiskers are the resident cats. Bandit and Pirate are the local raccoons.

REVIEWED
Lonely Planet; America's Best Bed & Breakfasts

UNIONTOWN

On Highway 195, about 15 miles south of Pullman, Uniontown features several annual events: the Crab Feed in February, the Sausage Feed in March, and a bazaar in November. Hells Canyon is one hour away.

THE CHURCHYARD INN

206 St. Boniface Street, Uniontown, WA 99179   *509-229-3200*
Marv & Linda Entel, Resident Owners   *FAX 509-229-3213*
WEBSITE www.pullman-wa.com/housing/chrchbb.htm

LOCATION	From I-95, take the Uniontown Highway (seven miles south of Moscow, Idaho) and turn left at Uniontown Main Street, then turn right at Woodworth Street and drive two blocks. The inn is on the left.
OPEN	All year
DESCRIPTION	A 1905 three-story Flemish inn with Victorian interior and three balconies, originally a convent, listed on the National Registry of Historic Places.
NO. OF ROOMS	Seven rooms with private bathrooms.
RATES	Year-round rates are $55-90 for a single or double and $135 for a suite.
CREDIT CARDS	MasterCard, Visa
BREAKFAST	Full breakfast, served in the dining room, includes a hot entrée such as quiche with sausage; apple and cinnamon pancakes; scrambled eggs with ham or bacon; or ham and eggs with hashbrowns—all served with fruit, muffins, and beverages. Use of the dining room for catered dinners is available for a $10 charge.
AMENITIES	Evening beverages; one room with a two-person Jacuzzi; window air conditioning; one room with handicapped access; a seminar room; banquet room; facility for weddings, receptions, and other gatherings.
RESTRICTIONS	No smoking, no pets, children over 14 are welcome.
REVIEWED	*Heart of the Inland Northwest; The Official Guide to American Historic Inns*
MEMBER	Washington State Bed & Breakfast Guild

VASHON ISLAND

Faintly countercultural, this bucolic isle is a short ferry ride away from downtown Seattle (foot passengers only), West Seattle (take the Fauntleroy ferry), or Tacoma (from the Point Defiance ferry). It's a wonderful place to explore by bicycle, although the first long hill up from the north-end ferry dock is a killer. Few beaches are open to the public, but there are some public spots where you can take a stroll and enjoy the view. Vashon Island events include the Strawberry Festival the second weekend in July, artists' and artisans' studio tours in the spring and during Christmas holidays, and various concerts.

ALL SEASONS WATERFRONT

12817 SW Bachelor Road, Vashon Island, WA 98070   *206-463-3498*
David Thwing, Innkeeper
EMAIL dthwing@wolfenet.com

LOCATION	From West Seattle, take the Fauntleroy ferry to Vashon. Stay on Vashon Highway to the Talequah ferry landing on the south end of the island. Pass the ferry landing, go up the hill, and take the first road to the right. Go 0.2 mile and you're there.
OPEN	All year
DESCRIPTION	A 1935 ranch-style cottage with contemporary decor located on Puget Sound.
NO. OF ROOMS	Cottage with one bedroom and one private bath.
RATES	Year-round rate is $115 for the cottage. There is a two-night minimum stay.
CREDIT CARDS	No
BREAKFAST	Continental breakfast.
AMENITIES	Fireplace, deck with views of Puget Sound and Mount Rainier.
RESTRICTIONS	No smoking, no pets, no children
REVIEWED	*The Best Places to Kiss in the Northwest*

ANGELS OF THE SEA BED & BREAKFAST

26431 99th Avenue SW, Vashon Island, WA 98070   *206-463-6980*
Marnie Jones, Innkeeper   *800-798-9249*
EMAIL angelssea@aol.com   *FAX 206-463-2205*
WEBSITE www.angelsofthesea.com

LOCATION	From Vashon Highway, take SW 204th to Dockton Road. Staying to the right, go five miles to Dockton, around the left bend by the old store, and straight for another 0.5 mile. The B&B is on the right.
OPEN	All year
DESCRIPTION	A 1917 converted three-story Norwegian Lutheran country church furnished with antiques, handicrafts, and musical instruments, including an old organ.
NO. OF ROOMS	One room with a private bathroom and two rooms with one shared bathroom. Marnie suggests the Ocean Suite.
RATES	Year-round rates are $125 for a single or double with a private bathroom, $75-85 for a single or double with a shared bathroom, $125-150 for a suite, and $275 for the entire B&B. There is no minimum stay and cancellation requires two weeks' notice.
CREDIT CARDS	MasterCard, Visa
BREAKFAST	Full breakfast is served in the dining room or guestrooms and includes fresh orange juice, omelets, egg dishes, waffles and fruit, homemade muffins, gourmet coffee, tea, and cocoa. Dinner and box lunches are available by arrangement.
AMENITIES	Meeting facilities; membership privileges at Vashon Island Golf and Country Club (restaurant, pool, golf, tennis); hot beverages in rooms; cable TV/VCRs, lots of videos; kids' stuff: videos, puzzles, books.
RESTRICTIONS	No smoking, children are welcome. Lucky is the resident Lab, Henry is the black cat, and Black Beard is the black bunny. All animals reside next door in the innkeeper's home.

ARTIST'S STUDIO LOFT BED & BREAKFAST

16529 91st Avenue Southwest, Vashon Island, WA 98070   206-463-2583
Jacqueline Clayton, Resident Owner
EMAIL *medowart@asl-bnb.com*   WEBSITE *www.asl-bnb.com*

LOCATION	From the ferry dock, follow the main road about four miles to Gorsuch Road and take a left. Go 0.75 mile; the road will turn left and become 91st Avenue SW.
OPEN	All year
DESCRIPTION	A 1910 two-story French country house on 7 acres, with paths, flower gardens, and Northwest, country, and earthy southwest decor.
NO. OF ROOMS	Three rooms with private bathrooms.
RATES	Year-round rates are $85-130 for a single or double. There is a

minimum stay on holidays and weekends. Cancellation requires 10 days' notice, 30 days during holidays.

CREDIT CARDS	American Express, Discover, MasterCard, Visa
BREAKFAST	Continental plus is served in the kitchen and includes crumpets or toasted muffins, fruit cup, hot or cold cereal, and beverages.
AMENITIES	Hot tub nestled between lilac and spruce, soft robes, fireplace, skylights for stargazing, wishing well, strolling paths, ponds, flower gardens, arbors.
RESTRICTIONS	No smoking, no pets. Marmot is the resident cat.
REVIEWED	*The Best Places to Kiss in the Northwest; Ultimate Washington; Washington Fieldguide; Washington State Travelers: Affordable Accomodations*
MEMBER	Vashon Lodgings Group

BACK BAY INN

24007 Vashon Highway SW, Burton, WA 98013   *206-463-5355*
Stacey & Don Wolczko, Innkeepers

LOCATION	From the Fauntleroy ferry, eight miles south on Vashon Highway SW. From the Talequah ferry, four miles north on Vashon Highway SW.
OPEN	All year
DESCRIPTION	A 1992 two-story country inn with architecture and decor reminiscent of a late-Victorian-era inn.
NO. OF ROOMS	Four rooms with private bathrooms. Try the Inner Harbor Suite.

Back Bay Inn, Burton

RATES	Year-round rates are $103-118 for a single or double. There is a minimum stay during Thanksgiving and Christmas, and cancellation requires 10 days' notice.
CREDIT CARDS	Discover, MasterCard, Visa
BREAKFAST	Full breakfast is served in the dining room and includes fresh fruit, pastry, and a number of entrées to choose from, plus coffee, tea, and juice.
AMENITIES	Air conditioning, antique furnishings, harbor views, TV.
RESTRICTIONS	No smoking, well-mannered children are welcome.
REVIEWED	*Sweethearts' Getaway Guide; The Best Places to Kiss in the Northwest; Northwest Best Places*
MEMBER	Professional Association of Innkeepers International
RATED	AAA 2 Diamonds

BETTY MACDONALD FARM

12000 99th Avenue SW, Vashon Island, WA 98070   *206-567-4227*
Judith Manerud Lawrence, Resident Owner   *FAX 206-567-4227 (call first)*

LOCATION	Two blocks above the north ferry dock. Turn east on 116th Avenue SW, then right on 99th Avenue SW; proceed up a gravel road to the farm.
OPEN	All year
DESCRIPTION	A 1949 four-story, 7,500-square-foot gambrel barn with an all-cedar interior, oriental carpets, and rustic elegance, originally the home of author Betty MacDonald.
NO. OF ROOMS	Loft suite with a private bathroom and a cottage with a private bathroom.
RATES	Year-round rates are $100-135 for a double. Please call for reservation/cancellation policy.
CREDIT CARDS	American Express, Diners Club, MasterCard, Visa
BREAKFAST	Kitchens are supplied with farm-fresh eggs, waffle mix and waffle maker, English muffins, homemade jams, fresh fruits. Lunch supplies are also provided and are included in the price of the room. The loft and cottage have full kitchens with fridges, ovens, microwaves, dishes, linens, etc.
AMENITIES	Fresh flowers, library, antiques, terry robes, down comforters, china, linens, wood-burning stoves, private decks with view across Puget Sound to Mount Rainier, seasonal raspberries, Asian pears, mountain bikes, beach access, gardens, greenhouse.

RESTRICTIONS	No smoking inside. The resident English springer is Buddy. Spud, Buster, and Zeek are the cats. Watch for bald eagles in the 350-year-old tree, woodpeckers, and other feathered and furry creatures.
REVIEWED	*The Best Places to Kiss in the Northwest; Ultimate Washington; Hidden Pacific Northwest; Fodor's; Northwest Best Places*
MEMBER	Vashon Island Bed & Breakfast Association
RATED	AAA 4 Diamonds

CASTLE HILL BED & BREAKFAST

26734 94th Avenue Southwest, Vashon Island, WA 98070   206-463-5491
Ron Turner, Resident Owner

HARBOR INN BED & BREAKFAST

9118 SW Harbor Drive, Vashon, WA 98070   *206-463-6794*

OLD TJOMSLAND HOUSE BED & BREAKFAST

17011 Vashon Highway SW, Vashon Island, WA 98070   206-463-5275
Jan & Bill Morosoff, Resident Owners   FAX 206-463-5275 (call first)
French and German spoken "imperfectly by Bill"

LOCATION	The house is five miles from the north ferry dock and eight miles from the south ferry dock on Vashon Highway.
OPEN	All year
DESCRIPTION	An 1890 two-story American Craftsman host home with fieldstone and old-growth timber foundation, decorated with antiques and second-hand collectibles. There is also a one-bedroom cottage on the property.
NO. OF ROOMS	One room with a private bathroom and a two-room suite shares one bathroom. The Morosoffs recommend the separate cottage.
RATES	Year-round rates are $85-100 for a single or double with a private bathroom and $85-150 for a suite. The cottage rents for $100 for two people, and the entire B&B rents for $200-250 for four to six people. There is a two-night minimum stay from May through

	October, on all weekends, and on holidays. This is a flexible policy. Cancellation requires 10 days' notice.
CREDIT CARDS	Discover, MasterCard, Visa
BREAKFAST	Full breakfast is served in the dining room.
AMENITIES	Bicycles, souvenir coffee mugs with Tjomsland House logo, large book collection, grand piano, transportation for guests without cars to and from ferry docks or local airports.
RESTRICTIONS	No smoking, no alcohol. Pets OK as long as they have a carrying case in which they can sleep. Sassy and Barkley are the resident dogs and Barnaby, Big Red, and Princess are the cats. Sylvie and Kelly are the resident lovebirds.
REVIEWED	*The Official Guide to American Historic Inns; The Berkeley Guide; Uncle Ben's Bed & Breakfast Guide; Bic's Romantic Getaways; Complete American Bed & Breakfast Guide*
MEMBER	Washington Bed & Breakfast Guild, Professional Association of Innkeepers International, Vashon Island Lodging Association, Washington State Restaurant Association

PEABODY'S BED & BREAKFAST

23007 64th Avenue Southwest, Vashon Island, WA 98070   *206-463-3506*

VAN GELDER'S RETREAT

18522 Beall Road SW, Vashon Island, WA 98070   *206-463-3684*
Karma M. Van Gelder, Resident Owner   *FAX 206-463-1774*
EMAIL *kug@wolfenet.com*   WEBSITE *vangeldersretreat.com*

LOCATION	One mile from the town center's traffic light in Vashon. Go east on Bank Road for 0.5 mile, then south on Beall Road SW for 0.5 mile. The B&B is on the east side of Beall Road.
OPEN	All year
DESCRIPTION	Newly remodeled modern inn in a parklike setting.
NO. OF ROOMS	Three rooms with private bathrooms and one room with one shared bathroom. Karma recommends Unit B-2.
RATES	May 1 through September 30, rates are $75-100 for a single or double. October 1 through April 30, rates are $60-85. There is no minimum stay and cancellation requires two weeks' notice.

CREDIT CARDS	None
BREAKFAST	Continental plus is left in each room's refrigerator the night before and includes fresh fruit, berries, muffins, juice, milk, cereal, and coffee.
AMENITIES	Space for outdoor assemblies; outdoor pool surrounded by cedar deck; seven-person hot tub; outdoor shower; gas barbecue grills.
RESTRICTIONS	No smoking. Cats, deer, pheasants, and raccoons roam the property.

WALLA WALLA

Lewis and Clark passed through here in 1805, fur trappers began traveling up the Columbia River from Fort Astoria in 1811 and set up a fort in 1818, and in 1836 missionary Marcus Whitman built a medical mission west of the present town. Founded in 1856, Walla Walla is an Indian phrase for "small, rapid streams." Today, the community boasts the oldest symphony orchestra west of the Mississippi River. Don't leave town without onion breath; Walla Walla Sweets are splendid, truly sweet onions, great for sandwiches. The region is also home to some of the state's most celebrated wineries. Nearby Juniper Dunes Wilderness includes some of the biggest sand dunes and the largest natural groves of western juniper in the state.

GREEN GABLES INN

922 Bonsella, Walla Walla, WA 99362   509-525-5501
Jim & Margaret Buchan, Resident Owners   888-525-5501
EMAIL *greengables@wwics.com*   WEBSITE *www.greengablesinn.com*

LOCATION	From Highway 12, take the Clinton Street exit 0.33 mile south to Bonsella Street. Take a right and go one block.
OPEN	All year
DESCRIPTION	A 1909 four-story Craftsman mansion and carriage house cottage with an eclectic collection of antiques, artwork, and oriental rugs, located in the Whitman College campus area.
NO. OF ROOMS	Six rooms with private bathrooms. The Buchans suggest Idlewild, the master suite.
RATES	Year-round rates are $85-110 for a single or double. The cottage rents for $110 for two and $160 for four. There is a minimum stay during special event weekends. Cancellation requires seven days' notice, 14 days during special events.
CREDIT CARDS	American Express, Discover, MasterCard, Visa

Green Gables Inn, Walla Walla

BREAKFAST	Full breakfast is served on fine china with crystal and silver and includes hot entrées, seasonal fruit, hot pastries, yogurt, granola, cereals, assorted homemade jams, and beverages.
AMENITIES	Hot tea, cocoas, ciders, cookies and other treats served 24 hours a day in the dining room, freshly brewed coffee outside rooms in the morning, morning newspaper, classical music, mini-refrigerators and color TVs in all rooms, thick terry robes, candies, assorted bath amenities, Jacuzzi and fireplace in master suite, two fireplaces in common living area, central air conditioning, fresh flowers in season.
RESTRICTIONS	No smoking, no pets, children over 12 are welcome. Younger children are welcome in the carriage house cottage. April and Stan are the resident cocker spaniel and chocolate Lab. Calvin and Ray are the cats.
REVIEWED	*Northwest Best Places; Recommended Country Inn; Off the Beaten Path; The Pacific Northwest's Best Bed & Breakfasts; Bed, Breakfast and Bike Pacific Northwest*
MEMBER	Washington Bed & Breakfast Guide, Professional Association of Innkeepers International, Washington State Hotel & Motel Association, Blue mountain Motel Association
RATED	AAA 3 Diamonds
AWARDS	1990 winner of 2020 Award for Historical Architecture Restoration
KUDOS/COMMENTS	"The ultimate B&B experience!" "What a B&B should be in every respect."

STONE CREEK INN

720 Bryant Avenue, Walla Walla, WA 99362   509-529-8120
Patricia Johnson, Innkeeper   FAX 509-529-8120
EMAIL stonecrk@internetnw.net

LOCATION	One and three-tenths of a mile southeast of the Walla Walla city center and four blocks south of Pioneer Park where Division meets Bryant Avenue. Go east on Main/Isaacs, then south on Division Street to the inn.
OPEN	All year
DESCRIPTION	An elegant 1883 three-story Queen Anne Victorian mansion on 4 acres with a creek, tall trees, and original stone wall. The interior features 12-foot ceilings, five fireplaces, and crystal chandeliers. Listed on the National and State Historic Registers.
NO. OF ROOMS	Two rooms with private bathrooms and two rooms with one shared bathroom. Patricia recommends the Veranda Suite.
RATES	Year-round rates are $78-125 for a single or double with a private bathroom, $78-115 for a single or double with a shared bathroom, $125 for a suite, and $445-455 for the entire inn. There is a minimum stay during special events and cancellation requires seven days' notice, 14 days during special event weekends.
CREDIT CARDS	MasterCard, Visa
BREAKFAST	Full breakfast is served on china and crystal with linens and fresh flowers in the dining room and includes fresh fruit and juice, home-baked sweet rolls and muffins, egg and cheese dishes, waffles, and pancake specialties, with bacon and sausage.
AMENITIES	Terry robes and fresh flowers; private label bath amenities; evening turndown with truffles, wine, and appetizers or home-baked cookies and tea upon arrival; pool in summer, hot tub in winter; air-conditioned rooms; 4 acres of trees and gardens for strolling or gazing.
RESTRICTIONS	No smoking, no pets, children over 12 are welcome. Smoking is permitted on exterior porches and grounds. Beau is the resident sheltie. On any given morning you may see China pheasants, quail, and squirrels on the grounds.
REVIEWED	*Official Guide to American Historic Inns; Northwest Best Places; Lonely Planet; Fodor's*
KUDOS/COMMENTS	"Very hard-working hostess with great personality."

WENATCHEE

In the heart of apple country, Wenatchee celebrates its famous fruit with an Apple Blossom Festival during the first part of May. The Riverfront Loop Trail on the banks of the Columbia River makes for a pleasant evening stroll—or an easy bike ride for those who want to pedal the whole 11-mile loop, which traverses both sides of the river (and crosses two bridges) from Wenatchee to East Wenatchee. Ohme Gardens, three miles north on Route 97A, is a 600-foot-high promontory transformed into an Edenic retreat, with a fastidiously created natural alpine ecosystem patterned after high mountain country. Mission Ridge, 13 miles southwest on Squilchuck Road, offers some of the best powder snow in the region. On the third Sunday in April, the Ridge-to-River Pentathlon is an impressive sporting event.

THE CHERUB INN

410 North Miller, Wenatchee, WA 98801   *509-662-6011*

RIMROCK INN BED & BREAKFAST

1354 Pitcher Canyon Road, Wenatchee, WA 98801   *509-664-5113*
Douglas & Mary Cook, Innkeepers   *888-664-5113*
WEBSITE *www.cascadeloop.com/option3/rimrock*   FAX 509-664-5113

LOCATION	From the South Columbia River Bridge, proceed on Mission Street for 2.7 miles. Turn right on Pitcher Canyon Road and go 0.5 mile.
OPEN	All year
DESCRIPTION	A 1977 three-story gambrel lodge with a double-barn appearance and country decor, located below the rimrocks.
NO. OF ROOMS	Three rooms with private bathrooms. Try the Columbia Room.
RATES	Year-round rates are $70 for a single or double and $210 for the entire B&B. There is no minimum stay and cancellation requires 14 days' notice and a $10 charge.
CREDIT CARDS	MasterCard, Visa
BREAKFAST	Full breakfast is served in the dining room or on the deck and includes fresh fruit, home-baked breads and muffins, a hot entrée with breakfast meat, juice, coffee, and tea.
AMENITIES	Air conditioning; fresh-baked cookies; close to Wenatchee and Mission Ridge ski area.
RESTRICTIONS	No smoking, no pets, children over nine are welcome.
MEMBER	Wenatchee Hotel & Motel Association

WARM SPRINGS INN

1611 Love Lane, Wenatchee, WA 98801   *509 662-8365*
Dennis & Janice Whiting, Innkeepers   *800-543-3645*
EMAIL *warmsi@warmspringsinn.com*   *FAX 509-663-5997*
WEBSITE *www.warmspringsinn.com*

LOCATION	West of Wenatchee on Highway 2; exactly one mile from the intersection with School Street, turn left onto Lower Sunnyslope Road, then turn right onto Love Lane.
OPEN	All year
DESCRIPTION	A 1917 four-story Southern colonial estate decorated with traditional and country accents, on 10 acres along the bank of the Wenatchee River in the Wenatchee Valley.
NO. OF ROOMS	Four bedrooms with private bathrooms. Try the White River Room.
RATES	Year-round rates are $85-105 for a single or double. There is a minimum stay during holidays and festival weekends, and cancellation requires 10 days' notice.
CREDIT CARDS	American Express, MasterCard, Visa
BREAKFAST	Full breakfast is served in the dining room or guestrooms and includes juice, fresh fruit (from the valley), banana pancakes, sausage, coffee, and tea. Dinner and catered events are also available.
AMENITIES	Robes, hot tub overlooking the river, large deck for sunbathing or viewing wildlife, cookies, large meeting room overlooking the river, air conditioning, library, TV in rooms, three fireplaces on the main floor.
RESTRICTIONS	No smoking, no pets, children over 10 are welcome. Humphrey is the resident schnauzer.
REVIEWED	*Northwest Best Places; Sweetheart's Getaway Guide*
RATED	AAA 3 Diamonds

WESTPORT

For a small coastal town that regularly endures flood tides of tourists, Westport remains surprisingly friendly, scenic, and uncondominiumed. Bottom-fishing trips for halibut, lingcod, and rockfish are increasingly popular, and many charter operators now feature whale-watching cruises as well. Gray whales migrate off the coast March through May on their way toward Arctic feeding waters. Wet-suited surfers can be found year-round hoping to catch their own Big One along the jetty at Westhaven State Park, where there's a new concrete walkway cresting the dunes all the way to the historic Westport Lighthouse.

GLENACRES BED & BREAKFAST

222 North Montesano, Box 1246, Westport, WA 98595   *360-268-9391*
Carla Horne, Resident Owner

WHITE SALMON

Serious Gorge windsurfers will want to travel four miles west of the Hood River Bridge to "Swell City." Other draws to the area include the Ice Caves and Big Lava Bed, a 12,500-acre lava field filled with cracks, crevasses, rock piles, and unusual formations.

INN OF THE WHITE SALMON

172 West Jewett, Box 1549, White Salmon, WA 98672   *509-493-2335*
WEBSITE *www.gorge.net/lodging/iws*

LLAMA RANCH BED & BREAKFAST

1980 Highway 141, White Salmon, WA 98672   *509-395-2786*
Jerry Stone, Resident Owner   *800-800-LAMA*

YA' AT' EEH

PO Box 1400, White Salmon, WA 98672   509-493-3750
Fred Heany, Resident Owner

WINTHROP

Stroll through this Western-motif town and stop in at the Shafer Museum, housed
in pioneer Guy Waring's 1897 log cabin on the hill behind the main street.
Exhibits relate the area's early history and include old cars, a stagecoach, and
horse-drawn vehicles. It is said that Waring's Harvard classmate Owen Wister
came to visit in the 1880s and found some of the material for The Virginian here.
The valley offers fine white-water rafting, spectacular hiking in the North
Cascades, horseback riding, mountain biking, fishing, and cross-country or
helicopter skiing. An excellent blues festival in the summer brings in such talents
as John Mayall and the Bluesbreakers and Mick Taylor.

FARMHOUSE INN

PO Box 118, Winthrop, WA 98862   509-996-2148
WEBSITE www.methow.com/~devin/central/

WOODINVILLE

Woodinville's claim to fame is Chateau Ste. Michelle, the state's largest winery.
The grapes come from Eastern Washington, but experimental vineyards are on-
site, and tours of the operation, complete with tastings, run daily every half hour.
Just across the street from Ste. Michelle is the Columbia Winery, the state's oldest
premium-wine company. Columbia offers tours on weekends, and the tasting
room is open daily. Woodinville also carries a leg of the Sammamish River Trail, a
paved path that runs along the river from Bothell to Marymoor Park in Redmond.

BEAR CREEK INN

19520 NE 144th Place, Woodinville, WA 98072   425-881-2978

By the Creek Bed & Breakfast

20232 NE 148th Street, Woodinville, WA 98072   425-885-0639
Tom & Nancy Palazzo, Resident Owners

WOODLAND

Grandma's House Bed & Breakfast

4551 Lewis River Road, Woodland, WA 98674   360-225-7002
WEBSITE *www.telltalefinds.com*

YAKIMA

Irrigation has made this desert bloom with grapes, apples, mint, asparagus, and hops. The Wine Cellar is a fine place to sample local vintages and orient yourself for a more extended foray into the wine country. In town, the Front Street Historic District includes a 22-car train, which houses shops and restaurants, and the renovated Pacific Fruit Exchange Building, which holds a local farmer's market. A restored 1906 trolley provides summer-evening and weekend rides around Yakima. Work off the wine by hitting the Greenway Bike Path, which winds along the Yakima River. Start out in Sherman Park on Nob Hill and go to the Selah Gap. Look for bald eagles and blue herons, or pick out a fishing hole.

Birchfield Manor Country Inn

2018 Birchfield Road, Yakima, WA 98901   509-452-1960
Tim Newbury, Resident Innkeeper   800-375-3420
               FAX 509-452-2334

LOCATION	Take exit 34 from I-82 and go east two miles. Take a right (south) on Birchfield Road.
OPEN	All year
DESCRIPTION	Two adjacent prairie-style country inns, one constructed in 1910, the other in 1995, with English country decor and antiques.
NO. OF ROOMS	Eleven rooms with private bathrooms. Try room 5.

RATES	Year-round rates are $125-195 for a single or double. There is no minimum stay and cancellation requires seven days' notice.
CREDIT CARDS	American Express, Diners Club, MasterCard, Visa
BREAKFAST	Full breakfast is served in the dining room or guestrooms and includes fresh-ground coffee; tea; juice; a basket of homemade bread, muffins, and scones; house jams, and a hot entrée of the day such as frittata, savory turnover, or smoked salmon hash. Dinner and banquets for 15 or more are also available.
AMENITIES	Coffee, tea, cocoa, deluxe soaps, shampoos, conditioners, air conditioning, some handicapped access, meeting facility, separate cigar-friendly area, some rooms with private deck or patio, some rooms with gas fireplaces, two-person whirlpool tubs, personalized wine tours, tee times reserved at local golf courses.
RESTRICTIONS	No smoking in rooms, children over eight are welcome. There is a separate smoking area. Dawg is the dog and Mickey is the cat. Both are outdoor pets. Guest animals are welcome in certain rooms; in others, no animals are permitted in consideration of allergy sufferers.
MEMBER	Independent Innkeepers, Unique Northwest Country Inns
RATED	AAA 3 Diamonds

IRISH HOUSE BED & BREAKFAST

210 South 28th Avenue, Yakima, WA 98902　　　　509-453-5474
Gary Vance, Resident Innkeeper

MYSTERY MANOR

3109 South Wiley Road, Yakima, WA 98903　　　　509-966-9971
Charles & Tonya Cornelius, Innkeepers

LOCATION	Eight miles from stoplight at Main Street and Ahtanum, turn left on Wiley Road and go five blocks. The B&B is located across from an elementary school.
OPEN	All year
DESCRIPTION	An 1870 two-story barn-style lodge with beautiful grounds and an indoor swimming pool.
NO. OF ROOMS	One room with a private bathroom and three rooms with three shared bathrooms.
RATES	Year-round rates are $45-55 ($55-75 on the first Saturday of the month when the innkeepers do a mystery show) for a single or

double with a private bathroom and $35 ($35-55 on the first Saturday of the month) for a single or double with a shared bathroom.

CREDIT CARDS	No
BREAKFAST	Full breakfast with special meals available.
AMENITIES	Handicapped access; indoor pool; "Who done it?" mystery show the first Saturday of every month; massage therapist available; air conditioning
RESTRICTIONS	The resident dogs are Brut and Buffy, and Lucky the cat keeps them company.

A TOUCH OF EUROPE INN

220 North 16th Avenue, Yakima, WA 98902   509-454-9775
Chef Erika & James Cenci, Innkeepers   888-438-7073
German spoken
WEBSITE *winesnw.com/toucheuropeb&b.htm*

A Touch of Europe Inn, Yakima

LOCATION	Take exit 31 off I-82. Turn left (south) onto 16th Avenue. At the top of the hill, after crossing Lincoln, make a sharp right turn into the driveway at the end of the rock retaining wall lined with shrubs.
OPEN	All year
DESCRIPTION	An elegantly restored 1889 two-story Queen Anne Victorian inn with period decor, including carved mahogany and European furnishings.
NO. OF ROOMS	Three rooms with private bathrooms.
RATES	Year-round rates are $69-110 for a single or double. There is no minimum stay and cancellation requires seven days' notice.
CREDIT CARDS	American Express, MasterCard, Visa
BREAKFAST	Gourmet multicourse breakfast is served by candlelight in the dining room or the parlor and includes signature entrées. Three- to seven-course candlelight dinners are served with advance notice. "Chef Erika develops an exclusive, flavorful menu for prearranged, private, candlelight dinners. A true adventure in European dining—without the cost of airfare."
AMENITIES	Exquisite traditional high tea offered for small groups; fresh Yakima fruit basket; flowers and plants; robes; chocolate, tea, and soft drinks; community sitting room with desk; stationery; toiletries; hair dryers; library; phone in rooms.
RESTRICTIONS	No smoking, no pets, no children
REVIEWED	*The Best Places to Kiss in the Pacific Northwest; The Official Guide to American Historic Inns; Fodor's*

YELM

About 20 miles southeast of Olympia on the road to Mount Rainier, Yelm offers easy access to Mount Rainier National Park, Tacoma, and Olympia.

BLUEBERRY HILL FARM

18811 119th Avenue SE, Yelm, WA 98597   *360-458-4726*
Ron & Margaret Nixon, Innkeepers

LOCATION	From I-5, follow Pacific Avenue southeast to Yelm. Go straight on Bald Hill Road past the Four Corners BP station, turn left on 119th Avenue, and follow the signs.
OPEN	All year
DESCRIPTION	A 1990 three-story Swiss-German chalet on a working organic berry farm overlooking waterfalls and woods.
NO. OF ROOMS	Two rooms with private bathrooms and two rooms with one shared bathroom.
RATES	Year-round rates are $45-55 for a single or double with a private bathroom, $25 per person for a room with a shared bathroom, and $55 for the guest apartment. Breakfast is an additional $5 per person. There is no minimum stay.
CREDIT CARDS	No
BREAKFAST	Full breakfast is served in the dining room and includes bacon or sausage, farm eggs, homemade bread and Grandma's jam, or fresh blueberry pancakes with real maple syrup. Grandma's homemade soup is available every evening.
AMENITIES	Facilities for parties, seminars, weddings, and family groups; Grandma's delicious homemade berry jams to take home.
RESTRICTIONS	No smoking inside, no pets, children are welcome. Katie is the resident sheltie.

INDEX

313